1966 – Dawson – 5.00

THE
WORLD
OF
ICE

THE
WORLD
OF
ICE

JAMES · L · DYSON

ALFRED · A · KNOPF   NEW YORK
1 9 6 2

L. C. catalog card number: 62–8682

THIS IS A BORZOI BOOK,
PUBLISHED BY ALFRED A. KNOPF, INC.

PUBLISHED APRIL 23, 1962
SECOND PRINTING, DECEMBER 1962

ACKNOWLEDGMENTS

THE GREATEST debt owed by an author of a book such as this one is due the host of scientists who through the years have put into written form the knowledge on which it is based. Except for a few whose works appear in the bibliography, these people of necessity cannot be acknowledged and must be the unsung heroes of the book.

When one writes a book he is reminded of something he already knew—that the many from whom he would seek aid are more than willing to give it and will go to great length to provide it. Among those who have generously furnished information for this book are: Daniel B. Beard, Meredith F. Burrill, Dean S. Carder, Robert F. Dale, Wendell Phillips Dodge, Virginia P. Finley, Lawrence Koenig, Edward R. LaChapelle, Chester Langway, Jr., Preston P. Macy, Lawrence E. Nielsen, Daniel D. Streeter, Helon Taylor, C. E. Watson, and especially Troy Péwé, who supplied photographs as well as information.

Personnel, in addition to those already mentioned, from the following organizations furnished hard-to-get data or unpublished matter: Alaska Department of Fish and Game, British Glaciological Society, California Division of Highways, Pacific Gas and Electric Company, U.S. Army Quartermaster Research and Engineering Command, U.S. Army Cold Regions Research and Engineering Laboratory,

U.S. Board on Geographic Names, U.S. Forest Service, National Park Service, and U.S. Weather Bureau.

For photographs I am grateful to those persons and organizations to whom credit is given in the list of illustrations. To Charles C. Morrison, Jr., I am especially indebted for devoting much time and effort to the search for appropriate photographs, and for placing at my disposal the photographic files of World Data Center A for Glaciology at the American Geographical Society in New York.

Others who have furnished photographic material are: William E. Davies and Elizabeth Wellshear of the U.S. Geological Survey, Hugh Odishaw of the U.S. National Committee IGY, Colonel Louis DeGoes of the Air Force Cambridge Research Laboratories, Lieutenant J. P. Dalton of the Army Transportation Board, Max Bumpers of the Office of Navy Information, Philip M. Smith of the National Science Foundation, William D. Thornbury of Indiana University, and James H. Zumberge of the University of Michigan.

I am also indebted to Arthur Montgomery for many constructive suggestions and for encouragement while the writing was being done; to John Moss for helpful suggestions; to Helen Laubach for cheerfully and efficiently typing the manuscript, much of the time under the pressure of haste; to Harold Strauss, editor of Alfred A. Knopf, Inc., for an enjoyable and instructive association; and to Lafayette College for granting me a leave during which much of the writing could be done.

To Lolita Dyson I owe most—for counsel, encouragement, and constructive criticism from the inception of the idea to completion of the book.

JAMES L. DYSON

Easton, Pennsylvania
February 1962

CONTENTS

PLATES

THE

WORLD

OF

ICE

Introduction

SOMEWHERE on the west coast of Greenland in the spring of 1910—or it might have been 1909—a large iceberg broke off the end of a great glacier and slowly floated out to sea. It is probable, even likely, that the event was witnessed by no one. We neither know precisely where nor when it took place but it did occur; of that there can be no doubt. Where the berg went after that we cannot be certain, but for many months it drifted across northern seas—probably into Baffin Bay and over the Labrador Sea, then out into the North Atlantic. Just before midnight on April 14, 1912, on the edge of the Gulf Stream 400 miles south of Cape Race, Newfoundland, this berg, smaller than when it floated from its parent glacier but still of gigantic size, tore a 300-foot gash along the starboard bow of the "unsinkable" *Titanic*, the largest ship afloat. Within four hours this magnificent ship foundered, carrying 1,500 persons to their deaths in the worst peacetime sea disaster in history. The World of Ice had made itself felt—this time unfortunately in tragedy—and had demonstrated that it was a real force to be reckoned with.

The World of Ice in all its aspects continues to challenge man—on all continents as well as in the sea. Not until March 1958, when Dr. Vivian Fuchs led his British Commonwealth Trans-Antarctic Expedition into Scott Base after a trek of 2,100 icy miles, was the fifth largest continent on Earth completely crossed by man. In fact, much of the route covered by these pioneers had never even been seen before. Soundings made by the Fuchs party revealed the presence of a mountain range near the South Pole so deeply buried beneath the ice that not even a ripple on the surface of the ice sheet indicated its presence. And in the vast still-uncrossed eastern part of Antarctica there almost certainly are other large ice-buried ranges. Since the International Geophysical Year began in 1957, other expeditions have discovered a number of mountain ranges projecting through the ice of Antarctica. For untold thousands of years these great features of the Earth's countenance had stood sentinel-still, alternately bathed in summer light and winter night, unseen by human eyes. Scientists have made a wealth of other discoveries in Antarctica—that parts of the continent are hardly a continent at all because the land surface is far below sea level; that a large ice-covered sea in West Antarctica is four times as large as formerly believed; and that Antarctica has a world-wide but as yet little-understood effect on weather and climate.

Why did it take over 100 years after Antarctica was discovered to find this out? Despite the greatest assault on the unknown realms of science the world has ever known, we still know very little about the continent, not because of its remoteness, but because its secrets are guarded by an all-covering blanket of ice, in places more than two miles thick. So massive is this load of ice that should it melt, sea level the world over would rise high enough to submerge lands now occupied by much of the world's human population. There is enough ice in the Antarctic sheet and in the rest of the world's glaciers to form a layer 400 feet thick over the entire land surface of the globe—an icy world indeed!

At the opposite end of the world, ten years before the British trekked across Antarctica, a group of Russian scientists maintaining a research station on an ice floe drifting across the Arctic Ocean made equally startling discoveries. Day-to-day soundings as the floe drifted along revealed a large and previously unknown mountain range hidden on the bottom of the Arctic Basin. This great welt, named the Lomonosov Range by the Russians, stretches more than 1,500 miles across the Arctic Basin, connecting Greenland with the New Siberian Islands (Novosibirskiye Ostrova). In more recent years American drifting stations have discovered a huge plateau and other submarine structures in the Arctic Basin. Despite a wealth of information collected by the ice-drifting stations, we still know very little about the forms of life deep below the surface of the Arctic Ocean. The answers to many questions lie hidden in Arctic waters. Detailed study of the ocean depths is in itself a most prodigious undertaking, but to fathom the secrets of an ocean permanently covered with a sheet of ice as large as the United States is incredibly difficult and time-consuming. To get the answers here, as in Antarctica, we will have to reckon with the ice.

This is not all of the World of Ice. Permanent ice in tens of thousands of glaciers is scattered over the world's high mountain ranges. In vast areas throughout the northland—much of Canada, virtually all of gigantic Siberia, and other lands—the ground, within a few feet or in some places only a few inches below the surface, is filled with ice and permanently frozen. In it are entombed the well-preserved carcasses of extinct animals that roamed the Earth as far back as 30,000 or more years ago.

So, much of our world is permanently icy. But it wasn't always so. There is evidence that only about once every 250,000,-000 years have such icy times come. At least we know of only three such ice ages in the last 600,000,000 years—one in late Precambrian time, another in early Permian time, and the present one, which geologists tell us began more than half a million years ago.

Throughout the long, intervening periods, the Earth's climate was mild and uniform. The tropics frequently extended into high latitudes; reef-building corals spread through warm seas much farther north than they do today, sometimes to the latitude of Greenland and Alaska; palms, tree ferns, breadfruit trees, and other subtropical plants grew equally far north over a time span counted in many millions of years. During much of Earth's history even the Antarctic continent was free of ice. At times it was covered with dense forests. Ice and snow for most of this time were unknown.

Fortunately, many of Earth's most thrilling secrets are lightly held. Because of this we know that even during the present ice age there have been great climatic changes which for thousands of years have exercised profound control over much of the Earth's human population. Glaciers have come and gone, not once, but a number of times. We know that as late as 10,000 years ago a vast ice sheet covered practically the whole of Canada, northernmost New England, and the states bordering the Great Lakes; and at the same time another blanketed a large part of northern Europe.

Ever since the virgin forests were cleared to make room for the first New England fields, the farmers there have picked up and carried from the clearings millions upon millions of boulders and cobbles, dropped on the land by an immense sheet of ice. When the Pilgrims waded ashore on Cape Cod, the first dry land they touched was part of a great glacial deposit composed of rock and soil carried down from the highlands of New England by this same ice sheet. A few weeks after their first landing, these pioneers sailed across the bay to establish Plymouth on the bouldery mainland shore, but not until more than 200 years later did men realize that the oldest permanent community on the Atlantic coast north of Florida was standing on a glacial moraine.

We know, too, that about 1,000 years ago Erik the Red established a flourishing colony on Greenland and that it was maintained for several hundred years. We do not really know why it perished, but some of the sites of the ancient Norse homesteads are now emerging from beneath the shrinking ice which, in a colder period hundreds of years ago, had advanced over them.

As the Earth's human population grows ever larger and penetrates farther into the realms of ice in search of additional living space, the role of ice in world affairs will become ever more significant, especially because of its potential effect on the level of the sea and because of the world-wide influence of the Greenland and Antarctic ice sheets on weather and climate. Water supplied by melting mountain glaciers is vital for irrigation in many parts of the world—high mountain ranges are often bordered by arid and semiarid lands. In these and other places glaciers are responsible for disastrous floods. The quantity of fresh water locked up in glacier ice is far greater than the combined volume of all the lakes and rivers on Earth. Entombed within glaciers and the moraines they deposit are secrets of climatic changes which throughout the ages have guided the rise and fall of civilizations. And the causes of ice ages are still unknown.

It is vital that we learn more about these things—and they make a fascinating story. That is why I have written this book. And it is for the same reasons that men are maintaining lonely outposts on the bleak ice floes of the Polar Sea; that wherever there are glaciers—from Antarctica and Greenland to the Pamirs and Olympics—scientists are probing deeper into the mysteries of the ice and the snow which gives it birth.

1

Snowlines and Glaciers

THE BLANKET OF SNOW

SURELY I am not alone in my feeling of delight, mingled with awe, at the sight of the season's first snowflakes, for they recall to my mind, with their soft, white rush to the earth, all that I know and wonder about their origin and their effect on the world we live in. Perhaps no element of the weather provokes such contrasting emotions as snow—the child on his sled wildly careening downhill loves it passionately; the shovelers and clearers of highways curse it roundly. But regardless of our feeling about it, it follows from year to year a fairly regular pattern of distribution in time and place.

Late in August the blanket of snow begins to creep out from its summer hiding place in Greenland onto the ice floes of the Polar Sea and onto the Canadian Arctic islands, bringing to an end the brief summer of those lonely stations—Eureka, Isachsen, Resolute, and others. Quickly it sweeps across Ellesmere, Banks, Victoria, and Baffin Islands, and onto the Canadian mainland. With no slackening of pace it crosses the Arctic Circle and speeds southward down over the Northwest Territories and Hudson Bay to the northern limit of trees. From here on its rate of advance lessens, but by the first of December it will have covered practically the whole of Canada.

While the edge of this huge snow cover is streaking across Canada, smaller, isolated snow blankets begin to appear in the highlands far to the south—the mountains of central Quebec, the Adirondacks, the White Mountains, and many others. In some of the ranges of the Rockies these outposts appear on the summits and begin to move downward about the time the edge of the main snow blanket crosses the Arctic Circle, sometimes even earlier. Perhaps they have to make several starts before they become established for the season.

It is a curious fact that man has raised some of his structures to such heights that upon occasion they, too, bear a temporary snowcap. Tops of tall city buildings in middle latitudes are sometimes pelted by flying snowflakes that otherwise would be converted to drops of rain before they reach the streets far below. On November 3, 1958, while rain fell on the rest of New York City, two to three inches of snow fell on the Empire State Building. Were you, perhaps, among those hurrying through the rain in the streets, unaware that snow was falling anywhere within miles of the city, while the guards on the observation platform, 1,000 feet above, were making snowballs?

Southward from the Canadian border the forward edge of winter's expanding snow blanket meets with difficulty. Its advance is frequently broken by minor retreats, but by the first of January it usually will have merged with the smaller, isolated snow blankets in the mountains, and will have extended sometimes even into Texas and northern Georgia. Before the winter is done, the layer of snow may push its thin outer edge even farther south. Happily for the shivering Southerners, the snow during these extreme advances persists for only a short time.

But what really happens when this thin snow cover disappears from these forward drives? Its edge, called the *seasonal snowline,* merely retreats to a new position many miles to the north. Eventually it will retire to its normal late-winter stand— its main line of resistance—stretching from southern New England to the Pacific Coast. From this site it will continue to probe with exploring fingers and to make brief forays southward throughout the remainder of winter and early spring.

To get the best picture of this fluctuating snow cover we could book passage on a man-made satellite in late winter, when the Northern Hemisphere's blanket of snow is at a maximum, when the snow lies five or more feet deep on New England's ski slopes. A few circuits of the Earth would be sufficient to show us the snow cover as a white blanket draped over the top of the world. In North America, between the Atlantic Ocean in southern New England and the Pacific near the northwest corner of Washington, its irregular hem would show three huge folds extending far to the south. One of these would stretch down over the Appalachian Highlands, perhaps as far south as North Carolina and Tennessee. Another would spread over the Rockies and the plateaus of northern New Mexico and Arizona; and the third would extend the blanket down the Cascade Range and the Sierra Nevada into southern California.

Just as striking, but much more extensive, would be the snow cover over Europe and Asia. At the time of our space ride it might cover Scotland, the northern half of the European mainland, the Asian Soviet Republics (except those east of the Caspian Sea), North China and Korea, and Japan as far south as central Honshu.

In the Northern Hemisphere the seasonal snowline holds to a fairly constant position during the last half of winter. Thus for seventy or more days the snow cover extends to Chicago and Cleveland and, in the Appalachian Mountains, to West Virginia. New England ski resorts normally have from 100 to 160 days of continuous skiing. In northern Michigan the season may be equally long. A look down at the top of the world a week or two later would reveal that the edge of the snow in places had retreated as much as 200 miles northward, while in others it had made an equally great retreat to the south.

The snow blanket at the bottom of the world also shrinks and expands with the seasons. But in spreading out from Antarctica, its edge is rather indistinct, because it has really nowhere to go except across ice pack and open ocean. Only in Tasmania and the narrow southern tip of South America do large land surfaces extend far enough southward to meet the winter advance of the snow zone. The high backbone of the Andes, however, carries the winter snow cover northward, linking the many separate, perennial snowcaps of this lofty range into a narrow chain extending into the Equatorial Zone.

Another satellite trip in late April or early May would show us that the edge of the northern snow blanket had shrunk beyond the Canadian border and that its winter-worn edge had become quite ragged and broken up into fragments. Each spring these "islands of resistance," lingering behind in the mountains while the main body of snow withdraws many miles northward, occupy the same areas as the advancing snow outposts do in the fall. So in both spring and fall each of these mountain areas is surrounded by a very definite seasonal snowline.

Conspicuous snowlines often occur at much lower elevations in middle latitudes. Many of us have seen or have walked along a short-lived snowline on a hill near our homes. If the air temperature during a snowstorm is above the freezing point in the valleys and below it on the hills, the falling snow will accumulate only on the higher elevations, rimming them with a distinct snowline. The inhabitants of New York's long Finger Lake valleys many times see such a snowline several hundred feet up on the valley sides. Central Pennsylvania's innumerable wooded ridges occasionally display the same phenomenon. In fact, at some time or another almost every high hill in lands where snow falls has borne a short-lived snowline of this sort.

But the seasonal snowline lasts longer and is much more pronounced on the sides of mountains with high, precipitous slopes, such as the east face of the Sierra Nevada, which rears up 10,000 feet above the nearly snowless Owens Valley. It is no less conspicuous on the San Bernardino and several other high ranges, where it serves not only to help make southern California a land of contrasts, but also to provide copy for Chamber of Commerce advertisers who like to publish colored photographs of sun-drenched orange groves with snow-covered mountains in the background.

Throughout much of the year Scotland's great bald Ben Nevis has a snow-covered crown. A sharp snowline often appears

on the sides of the steep-walled Norwegian fiords. In spring and
fall Mount Washington's hoary summit lies like a jewel in the
dark New Hampshire forests.

Another place where a pronounced seasonal snowline appears is the high escarpment along the eastern edge of the
Catskill Mountains (Catskill Plateau). In the spring, for days
or even weeks after all signs of snow have disappeared from the
Hudson Valley, the upper part of this 2,000-foot wall may be
covered with snow. How many motorists, rushing along the New
York State Thruway at this season of the year, realize that if they
left this road at the Kingston or Saugerties Interchanges they
could, in ten or fifteen minutes, be in the middle of winter? A
three-mile trip up the road through Kaaterskill Clove, a deep
ravine cut by Kaaterskill Creek where it plunges down the escarpment, would put them on top of a rugged plateau locked in
winter's snowy grip—and only 2,000 feet above blooming for-
sythia and other signs of spring in the valley below. The short
detour would have carried them above the seasonal snowline into
climatic conditions which in the lowlands had withdrawn northward beyond the St. Lawrence Valley. This condition of "snow-
capped" mountains is duplicated each spring at many places in
the East as far south as northern Georgia.

In the higher parts of the Great Smokies, the East's most
massive mountain range, high altitude and heavy precipitation
combine to produce large quantities of snow—80 to 120 inches
annually around Clingman's Dome, the highest point in the
range. I shall never forget the incredulous looks given me on a
March day when, dressed and equipped for skiing, I boarded the
bus in Knoxville, Tennessee for the forty-mile ride to Gatlinburg,
the little resort town on the west edge of the Great Smokies. But
an hour later and 5,000 feet above the Tennessee Valley, I was
skiing on two feet of snow. While the seasonal snowline had fled
northward more than 500 miles in lowland areas, here in the
mountains it had moved upward only about 3,000 feet.

On the Fourth of July in some years one or two snowbanks
are still present on the steep upper slopes of Maine's Mount
Katahdin, but the only places in the eastern states where some
snow may linger on until midsummer, and rarely longer, are the
perpetually shaded, high ravines of the White Mountains. The

snowbank at the head of Tuckerman Ravine, nourished by avalanches from the steep headwall and by snow blown off the treeless upper slopes of Mount Washington, yields so reluctantly to summer temperatures that it usually persists well into July and sometimes August. Its passing marks the end of all snow in the eastern ranges.

While the snowbanks in the White Mountains are struggling against spring's rising temperatures, the main snow cover beats a rapid retreat northward across Canada. By the first of May it will have disappeared from the western prairies, a month later from northern Ontario and Quebec, and by the first of July will be clinging desperately to a few last footholds on the islands along the Arctic Ocean, before finally retiring onto the Greenland icecap.

In the last stages of this headlong rush across the tundra of Arctic Canada and Alaska, innumerable islands of bare ground begin to dot the snow-covered landscape, and finally the snow cover itself breaks up into a maze of little islands. Even before the snow disappears, lemmings, ground squirrels, and other small hibernating animals, having been snow-sealed into their winter homes since September, burrow up through the snow, many to fall prey to the hawks, owls, weasels, and other predators waiting for them to appear.

LANDS OF PERMANENT SNOW

As the snow leaves the eastern mountains by moving ever higher and higher, the same process is going on in the Cordillera of western North America—snow-capped mountains do not form a backdrop for southern California's orange groves all year long, Chambers of Commerce notwithstanding. But in a number of these western mountains—some in the Cascades and Olympics, many in Canada, and even more in Alaska—the rising rim of the snow cover at some time during late summer or fall reaches a place above which it will not retreat. This ultimate upper limit, really a zone, is the permanent snowline. It is known technically as the *regional snowline*, but geologists and glaciologists often refer to it simply as the snowline.

It is apparent, then, that the snowline is at the place where the snow, after being harassed for weeks or months by summer's rising temperatures, makes its final stand. From here the snow cover will descend again at summer's end, down from the mountains and down from the top of the world. The following summer, in its upward and northward retreat, the edge of the snow cover will again come to a halt at or near the place where it made its summer stand the year before. The position of the snowline, even though hidden by new snow during much of each year, will remain more or less fixed. It is always at or near sea level in the Antarctic, somewhat higher in the Arctic, and several miles high in Equatorial regions.

Above the snowline more snow falls on the land over a period of several years than disappears by melting and evaporation. Since some of this excess snow is transformed into ice and thus into glaciers, those regions of the world which lie above the snowline are the birthplace of glaciers.

THE SNOWLINE HAS ITS UPS AND DOWNS

Although the general slope of the snowline is downward from the Equator toward the Poles, this is not everywhere the case. There are places where the line slopes in the opposite direction— actually downward toward the Equator—for hundreds of miles. The elevation of the snowline may vary greatly along a single parallel of latitude or even from one side of a mountain to the other. This is because the height of the snowline at any one place Is controlled largely by summer temperatures and the amount of moisture and snowfall.

Because of an abundance of cloudy weather in summer and heavy snows dumped by moisture-laden winds from the Pacific rising over the mountains, the Olympic Mountains in the northwest corner of Washington have the lowest snowline in the United States south of Alaska—only 5,500 to 6,000 feet above sea level. In the drier but colder mountains of Glacier National Park, at the same latitude but several hundred miles inland, the snowline is twice as high.

On the mountains along the southeast coast of Alaska, one

of the wettest places on the entire Pacific Coast of North America, the snowline is 4,500 to 5,000 feet above sea level. One would expect that in the colder inland ranges, 200 to 300 miles farther north, the snowline would be lower. But in these inland ranges, from which the coastal mountains have cut off much of the moisture supply, the snowline is actually 2,000 feet higher— an even greater elevation than in the Olympics.

Nowhere in the world except in Antarctica does the snowline lie at sea level. But around the rim of this ice-covered continent the elevation of the snowline varies considerably from place to place. A number of ice-free areas near the head of McMurdo Sound (Latitude 78° south) attest to the fact that even this close to the Pole the snowline locally does not come down to sea level. Yet Little America, on the edge of the Ross Ice Shelf at about this same latitude, lies in a zone where snow accumulates all year round. Snowfall here is not great, probably little more than a foot a year, but very little of the snow which falls or blows in from elsewhere melts away. This was impressed upon those members of Operation Deepfreeze who found, when they revisited the site of Little America I in 1955, that only ten or twelve feet of the seventy-foot radio antennae protruded above the snow. These masts had been erected by the First Byrd Antarctic Expedition twenty-six years earlier.

In the high interior of Antarctica the annual fall of snow is even less. Because of the constant wind, accurate determinations of snowfall are almost impossible to make, but continuous measurements since the beginning of 1957, when the IGY South Pole Station was established, have revealed that the annual snow accumulation is only about six inches. Thus, in terms of water, total precipitation at the South Pole is no more abundant than in the sun-baked interior of Australia.

Despite this extremely meager yearly addition of snow, a small fraction of a foot in terms of ice, central Antarctica is buried beneath nearly two miles of ice, all of it from snow. How could such an apparently slow accumulation of snow have produced so much ice? A great length of time surely was required. Almost certainly the oldest ice in this vast sheet is many thousands of years old.

That the snowline nowhere descends as low as sea level in

the Arctic has been quite apparent to members of drifting stations on the ice floes. During the summer, men at these stations in the vicinity of the Pole have had to bore holes through the ice in order to drain off water from melting.

Over the Arctic Ocean the length of the melting season varies greatly from year to year. Air Force personnel on an ice island 135 miles from the Pole in the summer of 1952 reported that temperatures first rose above freezing on May 15 and that by the middle of August all the snow and one to two feet of the underlying ice had melted. In 1957 scientists on a drifting floe about midway between the Pole and Point Barrow, Alaska, reported that melting of the snow cover began in mid-June and that by July 8 most of the snow had disappeared. But a new snow cover which began to form after July 24 had reached a depth of about eight inches by the end of September.

Because the snowline in Greenland is everywhere at least a half mile high, a wide marginal zone of the ice sheet lies below the snowline and is subject to intensive melting during the summer. Yet enough of the island is encircled by the snowline to sustain there a sheet of ice which averages a mile in thickness and covers an area almost as large as that part of the United States east of the Mississippi.

In all the Arctic no land is as close to the North Pole as is Peary Land on the northern tip of Greenland. Still, here an area as large as the state of Maine is free of ice. Even the intense cold of the long winter is unable to overcome the low precipitation and produce an ice sheet. Members of the Danish Peary Land Expedition in 1948–9 reported that in winter there is so little snow that dog-sledging can be done only on the frozen rivers and fiords and on the adjacent sea ice. So dry is the climate that vegetation is able to exist only along rivers and where there are snowbanks. Precipitation at the elevation of the snowline, about 3,600 feet above sea level, is less than an inch annually. If Peary Land received as much snow as the White Mountains of New Hampshire, the snowline would undoubtedly be at or near sea level, and the entire area would be covered by a thick sheet of ice.

In sharp contrast with Antarctica and northern Greenland are the moister glacier regions, where snowfall is heavy and the snowline comparatively low. In most of these places mountain

ranges border relatively warm seas, the source of heavy precipitation that falls on the mountains largely in the form of snow.
One of the best examples is the string of coastal mountain
ranges between Cook Inlet, at the base of the Alaska Peninsula,
and the Columbia River. The northern section of this great
cordillera, the Chugach and St. Elias Mountains and adjacent
ranges in Canada, is the battleground along which the chill Polar
Front and warm, moist air from the Pacific are in almost constant
conflict. The mass of high mountains, the combination of warm
seas and prevailing onshore winds, and the Polar Front bring
down prodigious quantities of snow onto the mountains and hold
the snowline at a low elevation.

For 1,000 miles southward along the coast these conditions
remain essentially unchanged. Because of the equalizing effect
of the cool Japan Current, the snowline rises only about 1,000
feet from the Chugach to the Olympic Mountains.

Depth of the seasonal snowfall in many localities in this
vast stretch of coastal mountains is almost incredible. During
the nine years that snowfall records have been kept at Thompson
Pass, on the Richardson Highway in the coast mountains twenty-
six miles from the port of Valdez, Alaska, snowfall has averaged
fifty feet a year, and in the winter of 1952–3 a record-breaking
975 inches was recorded on the Pass. Actually, the fall may have
been even greater, for the road camp where the measurements
were made was staffed only from October to June, and there may
have been some snow before and after this period. And there
probably are other places in Alaska and British Columbia which
receive as much snow as Thompson Pass. Even so, the climate
along the coast at the foot of the mountains is mild. The lowest
temperatures on record are about the same as the lowest recorded in southern Georgia and northern Florida.

In Paradise Valley at the south side of Mount Rainier, a
mile above the sea and 9,000 feet below the summit of the peak,
the fall of snow also averages nearly fifty feet a year. During the
winter of 1955–6 a whopping 1,000 inches (83 feet, 4 inches) at
Paradise Ranger Station broke all records for the United States,
if not for the entire world. So Thompson Pass and Paradise are
fighting it out for the distinction of being the snowiest place
thus far known on the North American continent.

Of course, there never is anywhere near this depth on the

ground at one time, because snow begins to settle and compact as soon as it falls, and there are periods of melting throughout the winter. But there have been occasions when the maximum snow depth on the ground at Paradise was nearly thirty feet. Despite this fantastic amount of snow, the National Park Service, with the aid of Sno-Go snowplows, keeps the highway to Paradise open all winter for the benefit of skiers, but throughout most of the winter and spring the lodge and other buildings can be entered only by tunneling through the snow. Occasionally as late as the first of July this is the only way you can enter some of the tourist cabins and other small buildings.

When the snowpack is deepest, few people, except snow surveyors, venture very far into the uninhabited white wilderness of the Cascades and Sierra. For these rare individuals shelter cabins are scattered throughout the high areas. But how could one enter these buildings or even find them when they are buried under many feet of snow? The cabin builders long ago solved this problem by fitting each cabin with a "Santa Claus" entrance tower. This contraption is a roofed, chimneylike structure tall enough to extend above the deepest snowpack. Doors at various levels in the tower and ladders both inside and out enable the cabin to be used regardless of snow depth. A cabin equipped with one of these towers is a monstrosity in the summer but a haven of refuge to someone seeking shelter from winter's icy blasts. Here, deep under the snow with plenty of fuel and provisions stocked during the summer, is a quiet, snug place to wait out a blizzard.

The snow surveyors who use the shelter cabins have a most important task—to measure the water content of the mountain snow cover, so that the amount of run-off from each watershed during the melting season can be predicted. The farmer who depends upon this water to irrigate his crops must have advance notice of the amount of water he can expect while the snow cover, a major source of his supply, is melting off. The snow surveyor's data are also vital for forecasting potential flood danger.

Some of the snow courses along which surveys are made formerly required a trek of two or three days by men on skis. Now they are completed in a fraction of the time by use of snow tractors or helicopters. And even these modern means of travel are giving way to electronic devices capable of measuring the water content of snow and automatically transmitting this information by radio or radar to distant receiving stations. Thus the days of the shelter cabin and its Santa Claus tower appear to be numbered. They may soon pass into oblivion as man makes additional gains in his attempt to conquer the elements.

Not all mountains with unusually heavy snowfall possess snowlines and glaciers. There are places in the mountains of Oregon and northern California, several hundred miles south of the great Pacific Coast glacier belt, where the average annual snowfall is extraordinarily high and where, upon occasion, a single winter will see as much snow as glacier-clad Mount Rainier.

For many years the Pacific Gas and Electric Company operated a weather station at one of its storage reservoirs, known as Tamarack, in the Sierra Nevada about twenty miles south of Lake Tahoe. Although near-record snowfalls had been frequent at Tamarack, the operator of the station during the winter of 1906–7 knew, as storm after snowy storm passed over the mountains, that this was going to be a winter that would be talked about for a long time to come. When the last spring snow had been measured, the records showed that during the season seventy-three feet eight inches of snow had fallen, breaking the record for the United States—a record which stood unequaled for forty-nine years, until surpassed at Paradise Ranger Station in the winter of 1955–6.

Every winter since Tamarack was first occupied, it has been snowbound for weeks, sometimes as long as seven months. It is a safe bet, however, that life during these long periods of isolation was not monotonous for the operator of the weather station—he undoubtedly was kept busy at his job of measuring snow.

Tamarack has seen a number of winters much like the one of 1906–7. Although the weather station was closed down in 1948, it still holds the world's record for the greatest snowfall during a single calendar month—390 inches in January 1911. On the ninth of March in that same year the depth of snow on the ground was 454 inches, a greater depth than has ever been measured anywhere else in the world.

A few miles north of Lake Tahoe, in this same spectacular

snow belt, is famed Donner Pass, the highest point in a long narrow notch through which Highway U.S. 40 and the main line of the Southern Pacific Railroad snake their way across the crest of the Sierra Nevada.

In early November 1846 a wagon train of pioneers from Illinois, under the leadership of George Donner, was trapped by heavy snows just east of the pass. Week after week as blizzards piled the snow deeper and deeper, the food supply dwindled and finally gave out. The ordeal of these unfortunate people, fighting snow and cold and starvation, is one of the grimmest in the annals of American history. In their desperate struggle to keep themselves and their children alive they finally were reduced to eating the flesh of their own dead. In March, after several attempts, a rescue party finally reached this desolate snowbound group. It was a near-miracle that only thirty-six of the original seventy-nine members of the party had succumbed during the winter.

Today Donner Pass is a far cry from pioneer days. Although keeping the pass open during the winter is a continuous, grueling, and expensive battle, both U.S. 40 and the railroad are seldom closed to traffic for more than a few hours at a stretch. Yet travelers still have their troubles at times.

On the morning of January 13, 1952, the Southern Pacific's sleek streamliner, City of San Francisco, westbound from Chicago, pulled out of Truckee on the east side of Donner Pass and began the long climb to the summit, fourteen miles distant and 1,300 feet higher. Up through the swirling snow, around Horseshoe Bend, past Donner Lake, where thirty-six of George Donner's party had died, and into the protection of the four-mile string of tunnels and snowsheds leading over the crest, the streamliner slowly pushed its way. Then began the long descent down the west side of the range toward the Great Valley. One mile, two, three, its diesels roaring, the streamliner crawled along, against steadily increasing resistance from the drifting snow.

This was no ordinary storm. For nine more miles the diesels dragged the seventeen cars through the rapidly deepening snow. Then the streamliner buried its nose in a massive drift and shuddered to a stop, the diesels still roaring defiance at the storm through which they could move no farther. The City of San Francisco was stuck.

Before it spent itself, this storm had blocked the railroad and Highway 40, and for the first time since the introduction of modern snow-removal equipment all trans-Sierra routes were closed at the same time.

With several feet of snow on the ground and a blizzard raging, there was nothing for the crew and passengers of the streamliner to do except stay with the train and wait for rescue. On the sixteenth, rotary snowplows of the California Division of Highways broke through to the train, ending the four-day imprisonment of passengers and crew.

During its passage across the Sierra, this mighty storm dumped nine feet of snow on the range—the greatest four-day fall of snow ever recorded anywhere. As much as seven feet of snow fell in one twenty-four-hour period at the height of the storm.

Storms of such magnitude do not come every year to the northern Sierra, but seldom is there a winter in which the higher parts of the western slope do not receive thirty or more feet of snow. And yet there are no glaciers in these places. Even with the heavy snowfall, the snowline does not descend far enough to intersect the mountains. High temperatures and dryness in the summer months overcome the effects of heavy snowfall. If the cool, cloudy, wet summers of the Olympics extended this far south, there would be a great many glaciers here.

Southward across Washington and Oregon to Mount Shasta in northern California, the number of glacier-clad peaks decreases markedly. This is striking evidence of the rapid southward rise of the snowline, nearly 8,000 feet vertically in the 450 miles between Mount Olympus and Mount Shasta. From an elevation of 13,500 feet on Mount Shasta, the snowline rises to 16,000 or 17,000 feet in central Mexico, where it intersects that country's three highest volcanoes, with the unpronounceable Indian names, Citlaltepetl, Popocatepetl, and Iztaccihuatl.

The distinction of having the highest snowline in the world —21,000 feet or more above sea level—goes to the Andes Mountains, not where they cross the Equator, but in the very dry Horse Latitudes, 1,200 to 1,500 miles farther south. The closest approach to this height is on the Karakoram Range and other high ranges in the dry heart of Asia north of the Himalayas and the Hindu Kush. Even though the snowline in both the Himalayan and Karakoram Ranges lies between 18,000 and 20,000 feet, many peaks project so high above it—5,000 to 8,000 feet—that tremendous avalanches of snow, crashing down the upper slopes, pile up in the valley heads to nourish many hundreds of long valley glaciers.

LANDS OF SNOW INVIOLATE

Wherever they may be—in the mountains or on the plains—the lands which lie above the snowline are the only uninhabited regions of the Earth. Except for a relatively few recently established scientific stations, which can hardly be regarded as permanent settlements in the normal sense of the word, there isn't a single permanently occupied human habitation in all these lands. Yet they comprise almost ten per cent of the land area of the world. Man has pushed his living sphere into all other parts of the world, even across the deserts and up the slopes of active volcanoes. In all these places he has modified the face of the Earth and made it bow to his will—mostly by taking something away without replacement. He has spread his cities across the plains and over the hills and has tied them together with steel, asphalt, and concrete. With his plow and ax and his flocks and herds he has even attempted, rather successfully, to destroy the Earth's capacity to give him sustenance. So far, the world above the snowline has remained inviolate. It has not yet been subjugated, though man is trying his best to do it.

Regardless, however, of man's increasing power, resulting from the ever-widening horizons of science, for a long time to come he will be at Nature's mercy, for she holds the ice everywhere above us. It might be her whim to lower it slowly upon us, enlarging the size of the uninhabitable area and destroying many of man's puny works. Or she might raise it higher, as she seems to be doing now at this fleeting moment in her long life, giving man more of an opportunity to push forward his attack upon the land.

2

The Birth of a Glacier

❀❀❀❀❀❀
❀❀❀❀❀❀ THE WORLD'S GLACIERS, except for Antarctica, are infants as Earth features go. We know that some glaciers got their start 200 to 300 years ago, and that many others are 3,000 to 4,000 years old. Few, if any, are older than several hundred thousand years. And few, if any, are being born today, aside from places where unusual local conditions have combined to form an environment favorable for their creation.

How did all these glaciers get started? How is a glacier born? Has anyone ever witnessed the birth of a glacier? How much snow is needed to form a glacier? The only requirement is that there be excess snow remaining after each melting season, whether the seasonal snowfall amounts to six inches or sixty feet. If this condition exists for a number of years, glaciers will form. Where snowfall is light, 100 or more years may be required for enough snow to accumulate to form a glacier. Where snowfall is heavy and the yearly excess great, a mass of snow might be converted into a glacier within ten years. Once created, a glacier will survive as long as its source is above the snowline.

Two glaciers known definitely to have originated during the

past several decades are on a volcano. Paradoxical as it may
seem, they owe their birth to the destruction of the volcano, not
to its growth. Up until June 1912, on an uninhabited section of
the Alaska Peninsula, Mount Katmai was a large volcano. Flowing downward from its ice-clad summit were several glaciers,
some as long as six miles. Early in June 1912 a violent explosion
rocked the countryside, and several days of fiery eruption hid the
mountain and a large part of the surrounding land under a thick
pall of choking ash and dust. The first people to venture into the
area after the holocaust found that where the summit had been
there was a gaping crater with near-vertical walls, in places more
than 2,000 feet high. The cataclysm beheaded all the glaciers
which originated on the summit, cutting off practically their entire source of supply.

Parts of the newly created surface of the crater wall were
still above the snowline. Here, on shelves formed by landslides,
two small glaciers were born—when, no one can say definitely,
but according to geologists of the United States Geological Survey who have investigated them, probably between 1923 and
1930.

These two little glaciers continued to grow, while most other
glaciers were shrinking. Within thirty years they grew to be several hundred feet thick, and one reached a length of nearly a
mile. Among the world's glaciers, here are two of the youngest.

Before the time man began to record his observations and
thoughts, other glacier-clad volcanoes suffered a fate similar to
Katmai's. On the high walls surrounding Crater Lake in Oregon
is a record of the birth and death of many generations of glaciers.
It all began far back in the early part of the Pleistocene period,
500,000 or more years ago, when a number of volcanoes came
into being on the broad lava plateau, later to become the Cascade
Range. Some of these volcanoes continued to grow intermittently
throughout the centuries by spewing out lava, ash, and cinders.
Eventually they became great glacier-clad peaks, now so well
known by the names of Rainier, Shasta, Adams, Baker, Hood,
St. Helens, and others.

One of the volcanoes, later to be called Mount Mazama, began at a very tender age to have glaciers form on its surface.
According to Professor Howel Williams, who has spent years un-

raveling the mystery of Mount Mazama, the earliest glaciers of which we have a record were present when the summit of the mountain had an elevation of about 9,000 feet, a mile lower than Mount Rainier's present height and 2,000 to 3,000 feet below today's snowline. Thus we know that the climate then was cooler than it is now. For thousands of years the history of the mountain was one of alternate periods of eruption and glaciation. Outpouring of lava, hot gasses, and other volcanic materials would destroy the glaciers; later in a period of quiescence they would re-form on the newly created surface, and then for a while the mountain again would be crowned by ice and snow. Many times this sequence of events occurred. Finally the peak attained an elevation of 12,000 to 14,000 feet to become one of the largest volcanoes in the Cascade Range. Some of the glaciers flowing out from the ice fields mantling this magnificent peak were 1,000 feet thick and ten or more miles long and formed a system of ice streams much more extensive than the present one on Mount Rainier.

And then about 6,000 years ago, following a series of eruptions, the summit of the mountain collapsed or was blown to bits, creating a great crater five to six miles wide and 4,000 feet deep. This cataclysmic event, to be witnessed only by a few primitive men whose artifacts now lie buried beneath the ash and pumice ejected during the eruption, destroyed the top of Mount Mazama and all the glaciers on it. No new ice streams have formed on this mountain ruin because its highest parts are now far below the snowline.

Eyewitnesses of this interesting performance had not mastered the written word, so we have to rely upon the geologist for an account of what happened. The record has been inscribed indelibly by the hand of Nature on the encircling walls of the crater and in the features of the surrounding landscape. On the face of the cliffs overlooking the lake alternating layers of glacial deposits and volcanic debris show as clearly as though written in a book how glaciers lived, were destroyed by eruptions of the mountain, and lived again. And the record left by the last big ice streams—deep valleys carved in the side of the volcano and rock debris deposited at their ends, miles beyond the base of the peak—is the evidence which, more than any other, definitely establishes the former presence of Mount Mazama high above the surface of the lake.

Duplication of some of the events known to have occurred on Mount Mazama has actually been witnessed on Katmai. Scientists, visiting the mountain a number of times since the great eruption of 1912, have observed ash-covered remnants of beheaded glaciers, and although they cannot say for certain when the new glaciers were born, they have seen them in their incipient stage and have watched them grow larger and more active.

Here is the sequence of events as they must have happened in each glacier within Katmai's crater: Soon after the mountain's destruction, during a winter when the surface had cooled enough to allow snow to accumulate, a snowdrift formed on a shelf on the crater wall. In the following summer, because it was above the snowline, only part of this snowbank melted. This remnant was covered with additional snow during the next winter. Some of this snow melted and evaporated away. Repetition of this process, year after year, built up a very large and deep snowbank. A tunnel drilled into it, say, after ten or twelve years would have revealed a distinctly layered structure. A glaciologist would have been able to associate each of the various layers with the year in which it formed. Each annual stratum of *firn,* the name of compacted granular snow after it is more than one year old, would have been easily identifiable because of the thin dark film of "dirt" separating one layer from another. This material between layers is composed of ash and other fine volcanic debris blown during the summer months onto the surface of the snow.

As time passed, pressure from the weight of the firn made the mass more compact and dense and squeezed out some of the air. Water percolating downward from the melting of surface snow, plus small amounts of water from melting where the firn granules pressed against each other, refroze to further aid the change of firn into ice. After possibly ten years, when the firn had attained a depth of 150 to 200 feet, recrystallization, compaction, and refreezing in the lower part of the deposit converted it into ice. Glacier ice looks much like the dense firn immediately above it, but differs from it in being impermeable to air.

The ice, under its own weight and that of the firn on top of it, became plastic and began to flow—the sign that a glacier had been born. As each succeeding year added more weight in the form of an additional layer of firn, the front of the glacier crept slowly toward the lake which had formed in the bottom of the crater. The first layers of snow are probably still present as layers of ice at the bottom of the glacier.

Because the films of dust or dirt separating the annual layers of snow are not appreciably altered when snow changes to firn and finally to ice, they persist for many years. In crevasses these dark laminae give the glacier a layer-cake appearance by separating one layer of firn or ice from another. On the surface they are narrow streaks, so that the ice appears banded. As these layers move farther down the glacier they become contorted and may eventually be obliterated or obscured by other structures developing in the moving ice. Not all glaciers have a nearby supply of volcanic dust or ash for the marking of their annual layers, but dust is a ubiquitous material, and throughout the summer months enough of it falls on the firn fields of a majority of the world's mountain glaciers to form a visible film. Besides minute rock and mineral particles, these dust films may contain pollen, spores, insects, and bits of vegetation. These tiny particles hold weather and climate secrets of bygone years, and when studied under the microscope they may chronicle events of which man has no other record.

There is even dust on the apparently clean surface of the Greenland ice sheet. Scientists have cut samples of firn in which they have found the 1912 layer, recognized by the tiny embedded fragments of volcanic dust carried by the wind 2,000 miles across Canada from Katmai's great eruption.

Deep within the glaciers of the Canadian Rockies there no doubt are dirt bands containing many diminutive fragments of charred wood and bark sent into the air by heated updrafts from the large forest fires which occur so frequently there. Buried somewhere within almost all glaciers of the southern Canadian Rockies and those of Glacier National Park, Montana, there probably is a dirt layer bearing a record of the disastrous summer of 1910, when uncontrollable fires swept through vast areas in the virgin forests of Idaho, Montana, British Columbia, and Alberta, casting a pall of smoke over the entire Pacific Northwest.

Now that we have traced the brief history of the Katmai

glaciers, what about their future? Will they continue to grow as they have in the past? They are still enlarging from the excess of snow each year, and they will keep growing until the ice added each year is balanced by ice lost by melting and evaporation. From then on the size of the glaciers will remain constant as long as the climate does not change. If the climate becomes warmer, even imperceptibly so, the snowline will rise, and the glaciers will shrink until equilibrium is attained. If the snowline descends, the glaciers will again expand.

The birth and development of the Katmai glaciers become all the more interesting and significant when we realize that the history of these two ice bodies duplicates the birth and early history of almost all glaciers. And further, the beginnings of glaciers in the future—whether resulting from the growth or destruction of volcanoes, the rising of mountain ranges, or the lowering of the snowline—will follow the same pattern as the glacial events which have been taking place within Katmai's deep crater.

GLACIERS ARE CLASSIFIED

Anyone whose chief contacts with ice are on the skating pond or in the highball may be surprised to learn that some glaciers are much colder than others. In fact, the ice in some glaciers is always at the melting-point temperature. Such glaciers have been classified as "warm" or "temperate." Other glaciers, in which the temperature is always below the melting point, are termed "cold" or "polar." A glacier with its source far above the snowline in a high mountain range and its terminus in a milder climatic zone far below may be polar in its upper part and temperate in its lower. Because much has yet to be learned about the temperature deep within glaciers in many parts of the world, glaciologists are not in complete agreement on how to classify glaciers thermally.

On the basis of form, however, all glaciers can be placed in two main classes—*ice sheets* and *valley glaciers*. In the ice-sheet class are the Greenland and Antarctic sheets and a number of lesser ones, the largest on islands in or near the Arctic Ocean. Among these are Iceland, Svalbard (Spitsbergen), Franz Josef

Land, Novaya Zemlya, and several islands of the Canadian Archipelago. The ice sheet on Novaya Zemlya is 200 miles long, and six or seven of the other island ice sheets are larger than the state of Connecticut, but their size is insignificant compared with the ice on Greenland and Antarctica. There are small ice sheets on some of the mountains in lower latitudes, especially in Norway and southern Alaska. The smaller ice sheets, and sometimes those on Greenland and Antarctica, are termed *icecaps*.

All ice sheets, regardless of size, are nourished entirely by snow falling directly on them. Many ice sheets rest on plains or plateaus. For this reason the ice spreads outward in all directions —like batter on a griddle—pushed by pressure from the weight of the ice itself. If the ice is thick it can move for long distances up as well as down hill. The Antarctic sheet even flows over a number of mountain ranges. But the surface of an ice sheet in all cases slopes downward from its center to the edge, even though at places the land on which it rests may slope in the opposite direction.

The marginal part of an ice sheet, too thin to override mountains, may flow through and around them, leaving the highest peaks as rocky islands (*nunataks*) in a sea of ice. Some ranges may even block the flow of ice and prevent its further spread.

The ice of Greenland and Antarctica, blocked only partially by mountain ranges, escapes from the vast interior by sending long, narrow tongues through gaps in these barriers. These tongues of ice are *outlet glaciers*. They are not independent glaciers but depend upon the ice sheet for their existence and belong to the valley-glacier class. The outlet glaciers of some of the smaller ice sheets not bordered by mountains merely flow through valleys leading down from the plateaus on which the ice rests.

Several outlet glaciers in Antarctica, because they drain ice from a tremendous area, are the world's most colossal ice streams, some of them over 100 miles long and fifteen or more miles wide. Lambert Glacier, which discharges into Amery Ice Shelf on the side of the continent facing the Indian Ocean, is reported to be over 200 miles long.

Most valley glaciers do not drain from ice sheets, but have their sources above the snowline in the heads of high mountain valleys. It is not direct snowfall but rather avalanching of snow from steep slopes that furnishes the principal nourishment of these ice streams. And they are often called *mountain glaciers* to distinguish them from outlet glaciers. A mountain glacier fed by huge quantities of snow may flow down a valley for tens of miles to a point hundreds if not thousands of feet below the snowline. On the way it may be joined by several tributaries, the whole with a branching, treelike plan, conforming exactly to the pattern of the system of valleys through which it moves. Unlike ice sheets, all valley glaciers move only in one direction—down the valleys in which they are confined.

Some valley glaciers descend from the mountains onto plains, there to spread out, after the manner of an ice sheet, into broad flat masses known as *piedmont glaciers*. On the narrow coastal plain where the Alaska panhandle joins the main part of the state, several of these expanded glaciers have coalesced to form the Malaspina piedmont glacier, almost equal in area to the state of Rhode Island.

Piedmont glaciers are like ice sheets; in fact, they are ice sheets, but their mode of origin is exactly the reverse of other ice sheets. Little or no ice originates in a piedmont glacier. Ice is poured into it from valley glaciers, and it will exist only so long as this supply is maintained.

If the climate should become more favorable for glacier growth, some of the piedmont glaciers would expand and join with others to form large ice sheets. These might eventually become high enough to obtain their nourishment from direct snowfall and then engulf the mountains which gave them birth. The Greenland and Antarctic ice sheets may have got their start in this way.

Ice field, a term often used rather loosely, is sometimes applied to mountain icecaps.

Snow field, which has an even more vague meaning, generally refers to a large patch of snow which persists from year to year but never grows thick enough to change into ice and become a glacier. Sometimes the term is used to designate the firn area of mountain glaciers.

3

Ice Streams on the Move

❀❀❀❀❀❀
❀❀❀❀❀❀ IN THE SUMMER OF 1933 Park-naturalists M. E. Beatty and C. A. Harwell, while making a survey of Lyell Glacier high on the slopes of Mount Lyell in Yosemite National Park, were startled by a mountain sheep ram staring at them across the ice. They both were well aware that mountain sheep had been extinct for at least fifty years in the area where they were now looking at one. Then they realized that their discovery was not a living sheep but the well-preserved, mummified carcass of one. This fact was almost as astonishing as though the sheep had actually been alive. Even as they raced to examine their discovery, the finders began to speculate on how it came to be there. The animal certainly had met death many years before and had been preserved by entombment within the glacier. When it was found, two of its feet were still embedded in the ice, indicating that the body had only recently been exposed by melting. The ram seemed to be in a state of perfect preservation. The flesh and skin were dry and extremely hard. Beatty and Harwell did not attempt to taste the flesh, but it might have been no less palatable than the sun-dried meat commonly known as "jerky."

The animal's neck had been broken, but all other bones were intact. Presumably the sheep had fallen into a crevasse at the head of the glacier—or had been carried in by an avalanche— and subsequently encased in the ice. This inference is supported by clues yielded by the contents of the sheep's stomach, among which ten plant species were identified. The seeds of these plants were completely matured, showing that the animal was killed late in the summer, the only time of the year when crevasses at the head of the glacier are open.

Although no one knows exactly where the sheep met death or how far it was carried by the ice, it obviously was entombed for a period of at least fifty years, perhaps many more. The men calculated that at the rate it was moving, the glacier would have required 250 years to carry the sheep from the mountain wall at the head of the glacier, the most likely place for its death, to the point near the terminus where they found it. This interesting find, now in the museum at Yosemite, afforded the first opportunity to study the complete skeleton of a Sierra mountain sheep from the Yosemite region, because the species had been exterminated there before scientists had an opportunity to secure a specimen.

On many of the smaller mountain glaciers, like this one that yielded the mountain-sheep carcass, the ice strata, not having moved far enough to become too distorted, can be traced all the way from the firn area to the glacier terminus. Some of these little glaciers, one-half mile to a mile in length, have revealed as many as 400 annual layers, telling us at once the age of the ice in each layer and how long the ice has been in transit within the glacier.

An even more spectacular illustration of glacier motion than that afforded by Lyell Glacier is supplied by the Glacier des Bossons on the slopes of Mont Blanc near Chamonix. In August 1820 a party of climbers nearing the summit of the mountain was caught in a snow avalanche in the firn area of the glacier and whisked down the slope. The three front guides, Pierre Carrier, Pierre Balmat, and August Tairraz, hurtling downward and unable to free themselves, were swept into a deep crevasse and buried. After entombment within the ice for forty-three years, recognizable parts of the bodies and pieces of clothing and equipment appeared at the end of the glacier. During forty-three years within the ice they had moved a distance of nearly two miles, at a mean rate of about 240 feet a year.

At the time of the accident practically nothing was known about the rates of glacier motion, but around 1840 Professor J. D. Forbes, along with Louis Agassiz and John Tyndall, began to make systematic measurements of glacier motion in the European Alps. From these researches Forbes predicted that the guides would appear at the end of the Glacier des Bossons thirty-five to forty years after their burial in the firn. Time proved the accuracy of his prediction.

Agassiz and his contemporaries drove lines of stakes across glaciers to prove that although ice moves more slowly than water, ice motion at the surface of a glacier is much like the flow of water in a stream—fastest in the center and decreasing toward the sides. Each line of stakes, originally straight, was soon bowed in the down-glacier direction. This characteristic of glacier motion has been confirmed by similar experiments made many times since the days of Agassiz and Tyndall.

In recent years glaciologists have found, by drilling vertical holes into glaciers and measuring the bending of pipes left in the holes, that the deeper the ice below the surface, the slower it flows. Ice at the bottom, like that along the sides, moves slowest.

Although thickness is not the sole factor influencing the rate of glacier flow, as a valley glacier grows larger and thicker it usually flows faster. Ice within the largest glaciers in the European Alps, with lengths of eight to fifteen miles, moves nearly a foot a day. In some of the much larger Alaskan glaciers, the rate may be several feet daily. Some of the great outlet glaciers in the southern part of the Greenland ice sheet squeeze through the mountain gaps at more than 100 feet a day.

Occasionally a glacier which has been moving slowly may suddenly speed up and for a brief time move at an incredibly rapid rate. Many of you will recall that for several weeks late in the winter of 1936–7 Black Rapids Glacier, a long ice stream in the Alaska Range about 130 miles south of Fairbanks, made the headlines of several of the world's leading newspapers. *The New York Times* of February 12, 1937, proclaimed: "Glacier 'on loose again'; menaces an Alaska inn"; on February 16: "Mighty Black

Rapids in Alaska hurls tons of ice from face as it creeps down valley"; and on the first page of the February 23 issue: "Black Rapids Glacier sets a speed record; expert finds movement is 220 feet a day."

For a number of years until September 1936 ice within the lower reaches of Black Rapids Glacier moved too slowly to balance the effect of ice losses. Consequently, the glacier had been steadily growing shorter (receding) as more ice melted and evaporated each year than was added by snow changing into ice. But beginning in September 1936 and continuing into February 1937, the front of the glacier moved forward a distance of almost four miles, threatening to overrun the Richardson Highway, which at that time was Fairbanks's only land link with the outside world.

This spurt of the glacier might have gone unnoticed but for the fact that the Rapids Roadhouse, a hunting lodge on the Richardson Highway near the Black Rapids Glacier and directly in its path, was occupied during the winter of 1936–7 by the H. E. Revell family. For several weeks during the early part of the winter the Revells heard rumbling sounds coming from the direction of the glacier. Since the glacier was not visible from the lodge and because the sounds were accompanied by tremors, they were attributed to earthquakes. But on the third of December Mrs. Revell, while looking up the glacier valley with field glasses, was startled to see a huge jumbled mass of ice blocks about six miles distant. During the next few days as the Revells watched this wall of ice grow higher, they realized that the glacier was rapidly bearing down upon them. They could see that the blocks of ice "were jostled about and that many were gradually tilted until they toppled over and fell in a cloud of snow and small fragments, followed by a roar and by a jar that rattled the windows of the roadhouse." It was then that this obscure glacier, through a report sent by Mrs. Revell to the U.S. Weather Bureau station in Fairbanks, made the headlines and became known to millions of people.

For several more months the Revells watched this runaway stream of ice noisily closing the distance between itself and their home. Luckily the advance stopped about half a mile short of the road and the lodge. Had the glacier continued to push forward across the main valley, through which both the highway and the Delta River run, it would have triggered other spectacular events. First, the advancing mile-wide column of ice would have plunged into and across the river, effectively blocking the stream with a solid dam of ice 200 to 300 feet high. Next, this huge finger of ice would have poked itself at the highway. Slowly, irresistibly, with great blocks of ice breaking loose and crashing noisily down its steep front, it would have crept forward. The few trees bordering the road would have been crushed as though they were matches and ground to bits beneath the ice. Then the highway along a one- to two-mile front would have been overridden and obliterated. Water rising behind the dam of ice would have created a lake, inundating several additional miles of highway.

Had this happened, it would have been necessary to relocate the highway by moving it onto the steep mountain side. Such locations in the Alaska Range are at best rather precarious and extremely difficult to maintain because of the danger of landslides caused by spring thawing of the deeply frozen soil. Construction of a road across the glacier would have been impossible, at least while it was rapidly advancing, because of the shifting of blocks of ice on its surface.

During the six-month period of Black Rapids's great activity, the average daily advance of the ice front was 115 feet and at times undoubtedly exceeded 200 feet. Before the end of the year the advance slowed down, came to a halt, and the glacier again began to recede.

Although this forward dash of Black Rapids Glacier gained much publicity, it probably was a normal part of the glacier's history. A similar if less dramatic advance occurred just prior to 1912, and there are indications of still earlier ones. Increased snowfall over the large zone of accumulation for several years before the advances seems to be the most important factor in their initiation. For a time, snow and ice apparently accumulate faster than they can be drained off by the narrow glacier tongue. Finally, after the pressure of accumulated ice is built up enough to overcome the resistance, it spills out of the collecting basin and after a brief period of rapid flow reaches equilibrium again.

Earthquakes, which can cause avalanching of great quantities of snow from precipitous slopes, may have been partly responsible for Black Rapids's behavior.

The fronts of a number of other Alaskan glaciers are sufficiently close to highways to constitute a rather serious threat. Nine miles south of Black Rapids Glacier, the moraine-covered end of Castner Glacier lies only a few yards from the Richardson Highway. An advance of one mile would carry it across both the highway and the river.

When completed, the Copper River Highway will follow the deep gorge of the Copper River for seventy-five miles through the Chugach Mountains, connecting the interior with the port of Cordova. This newest major link in the Alaska highway chain follows the grade of the abandoned Copper River and Northwestern Railway, which was built early in the century to give the mines at Kennicott a port at Cordova. The railway grade has to swing first to one side of the valley, then to the other, to avoid the projecting fronts of Childs, Miles, and Allen Glaciers. These ice streams are now slowly shrinking, but all of them have experienced one or more advances in recent centuries. Childs Glacier in 1910 and 1911 moved forward 2,000 feet, coming within 1,500 feet of the Copper River railway bridge, which had just been completed at the cost of more than a million dollars. Had the glacier advanced to it, this imposing steel structure would have been crumpled and twisted beyond recognition and swallowed up by the advancing ice. And the mines could not have been operated, because there is no other route over which a railroad can be constructed between the mines and the coast.

Miles Glacier, on the opposite side of the valley, extended to the bridge site as late as 1885. For five and one-half miles along the front of Allen Glacier the highway, in following the old railroad grade, will lie on a mass of stagnant ice put here by one of the glacier's former advances and now protected from melting by a veneer of soil-covered moraine in which trees are growing.

Such advances may not occur again for many years; perhaps thousands of years will elapse before the glaciers again fill the Copper River valley as they did several thousand years in the past. In the meantime, people who travel the Copper River route, whether on the ground or in the air, will be able to view some of the most magnificent glacier scenery to be found anywhere on Earth.

In recent years mountains have not been much of a hindrance to the road builders, but mountains loaded with glaciers make a different story. Man can hurl his puny bulldozers against active mountain glaciers to no avail. A road cannot be constructed across an actively moving ice stream, nor can a tunnel be maintained through one; and no man-made structure is capable of withstanding the push of even a small glacier.

In the past several years unusual advances of other Alaskan glaciers have been observed and recorded. In the fall of 1956 Muldrow, one of the largest valley glaciers in Alaska, which drains ice from several of the great walled recesses on the north flank of Mount McKinley, suddenly became active after a long period of slow recession. Because of a greatly increased supply of ice, the terminal portion of the glacier thickened considerably, and the front moved forward nearly four miles in less than a year.

Even more spectacular glacier advances have occurred in the sky-scraping Karakoram Range in northernmost India and Kashmir. Professor Ardito Desio, Director of the Instituto Geologia Università, Milan, and leader of the expedition which made the first ascent of the world's second highest mountain, has reported rapid simultaneous advances of three tributary glaciers into the Kutiàh Valley, where they joined and continued to move forward as a single glacier for a distance just short of eight miles—all between March 21 and June 11, 1953. The ice front advanced at a mean rate of about fifteen feet an hour. One explanation for this phenomenal advance suggests that the disappearance of a large glacier from the Kutiàh Valley left its hanging tributaries without support. As a result, these smaller glaciers, with nothing to hold them back, began a rapid advance into the main valley, which was halted only after excess ice in the higher areas had been transferred to the lower. Whatever the reason for this advance—it might have been earthquake-caused avalanches—it was local, as evidenced by the fact that all other glaciers in the region were in a state of retreat.

During advances of such rapidity and short duration, the ice within the glacier obviously moves at essentially the same rate as the advancing glacier front. Despite these examples of "glaciers on the loose," we know that such rapid advances are exceptional and local and that ice within the majority of glaciers normally moves well under two feet a day.

HOW DOES A GLACIER MOVE?

How is it possible for a crystalline, solid mass of ice to wind its way down a long valley and transport tremendous volumes of ice to a point many miles away without appreciably changing its size, shape, and general appearance?

The ice at the surface of a glacier is relatively brittle, as attested by the cracks (*crevasses*) which develop in most glaciers. In few cases, however, do these crevasses extend to depths much greater than 200 feet. Below this depth the flow of the ice, though very slow, prevents their formation. This plastic behavior of ice in the deeper parts of glaciers has been demonstrated by the squeezing inward of walls of tunnels excavated in the ice. Thus there is a crust of relatively brittle ice at the surface of a glacier, beneath which is a zone of flow—the source of a glacier's mobility. When Black Rapids Glacier made its forward dash, the plastic ice flowed so rapidly that it caused the brittle surface ice to break up into a chaos of moving blocks.

To understand how a glacier moves (here we may be a little presumptive, for, despite many years of study, the exact nature of glacier motion is not fully understood) we have to begin with the snowflake itself. Every snowflake that falls is either a separate snow crystal or a cluster of crystals. Every one of these actually is a crystal of ice in which the atoms are arranged in exactly the same symmetrical pattern as in every other ice crystal. This atomic arrangement is just as orderly as in crystals of quartz or any other mineral. And ice, because it is a solid inorganic substance with a definite atomic structure, actually is a mineral.

As soon as the fallen snow crystals are buried and pushed more firmly together they begin to lose their feathery outlines and become more or less rounded in form. But the internal symmetrical arrangement of atoms does not change. When *melt water* (water resulting from the melting of snow and glacier ice), formed at the points of pressure between crystals, refreezes, it is added only to certain crystals. This results in the growth of some crystals at the expense of others, making the material coarser and more granular. Deepening of the snow and continued refreezing of melt water force out the air, making the material denser. Eventually, as it becomes a glacier it will be converted into a solid mass of interlocking ice crystals, many of which will continue to grow as long as they exist. Though single glacier crystals nearly a foot long have been found, few of them will ever attain a length greater than two inches. Since a glacier is an aggregate of mineral grains, it is a rock. How then can such a solid mass flow?

Although the ice crystals are tightly interlocked, the motion of the whole glacier depends largely upon them. The myriads of tiny atomic layers of which each crystal consists are capable of gliding over each other when subjected to steadily applied pressure, such as would result from the weight of the ice itself or from the pull of gravity against ice resting on a slope. It is only when most of the ice crystals are oriented so that their layers of atoms are approximately parallel to the surface of the glacier that ice flows most readily. It so happens that the pressure itself causes the ice crystals to rearrange themselves in this favorable direction. This process can be called recrystallization, since the atoms within the crystals have changed positions. If recrystallization did not occur, continued intercrystal gliding would greatly distort and elongate the crystals. But after miles of travel, the crystals at the end of a glacier, though larger than those farther up, have essentially the same equidimensional form. Even though the movement between any two adjacent atomic layers in a single crystal is small, the combined movement of billions and billions of them under continuously applied pressure is considerable, and is the principal process contributing to glacier flow —the plastic deformation of a solid substance.

In this respect ice is no different from any other rock. Deep below the Earth's surface where pressures are high, solid rock flows. Proof of this can be seen in folded and stretched rocks at many places at the surface where erosion has exposed them to view. And from what is known about them, these rocks flow just as does the ice within a glacier, though at infinitely slower rates.

So the study of glaciers reveals how rock deep within the Earth's crust has been deformed.

Ice within practically all glaciers, whether their fronts are stationary, advancing, or retreating, constantly moves forward. If the end of a glacier remains more or less stationary, it means that the forward motion of the ice itself is balanced by losses. If the rate of melting or evaporation should increase, the glacier would shrink, despite the forward motion of the ice within it. This is what happened to Black Rapids Glacier not long after its advancing spree ended.

Since ice is a solid substance, glacier motion in some degree takes place by the sliding of some parts of a glacier over others along fractures in the ice. This type of motion can be observed at the surfaces of most glaciers, but to what extent it takes place deep within the ice has not been determined.

Brittle surface ice, if badly crevassed and broken into blocks, is probably incapable in itself of forward motion; it must be shoved or carried by the active ice beneath. But it may break loose and slide off very steeply inclined glaciers in thundering avalanches, capable of moving a mile or more in a matter of minutes. Such avalanches are not uncommon in the Karakoram and other Asian ranges. In the Alps they have destroyed many chalets and a number of villages.

4

Ice Sculptures the Face of the Land

✿✿✿✿✿✿✿

✿✿✿✿✿✿✿ I F YOU walked across the lower part of Nisqually Glacier on Mount Rainier, you could not fail to be impressed by the great quantities of rocky debris strewn over the glacier. Much of the ice is completely obscured by it, and the valley at the end of the glacier is choked with a jumbled mass of it. All this mass of rock debris, whether on the glacier or piled at the end of it or washed out by melt-water streams beyond the ice, is known as *glacial drift*. That part of the drift being carried by the ice itself, or which has already been dumped at the end of the glacier, is called *till*, and because a glacier does not have the power to sort the material it carries, till is a heterogeneous mixture of rock fragments of all sorts and sizes, from huge boulders down to microscopic clay particles.

The ridges and mounds of till at the end of a glacier are known collectively as the *terminal moraine*. When a glacier front remains more or less stationary for a long time, its moraine develops into a distinct ridge, but if the front moves back and forth, the moraine will grow wider and may become very irregular. Whether it is a ridge or a band of mounds and piles of debris, a terminal moraine in most cases is a conspicuous landscape feature and can be recognized from a distance.

In contrast, drift carried away from a glacier by melt-water streams is sorted and spread out in a smooth sheet to become *stratified drift* or *outwash*. Near the glacier this layered material consists mainly of sand and gravel, but with increasing distance from the source it decreases in size, and finally nothing remains but silt and clay, which merge imperceptibly over the miles with other stream sediments derived from non-glacial sources.

At close range the terminal moraine of Nisqually Glacier does not make an especially pretty sight. And the glacier, here ignominiously incased in "dirt," is a far cry from the majestic, tumbled stream of ice with its eerie blue crevasses higher on the mountain. But the moraine is interesting, for by means of it the glacier tells much of the story of what it is doing.

Like Nisqually, the terminal portions of most valley glaciers contain large quantities of debris, and the methods by which this material is acquired and transported are the same in all glaciers. Rock debris on a valley floor is caught up in the ice and carried along in the bottom of the glacier. Rocks sliding from the mountainside onto the firn at the glacier's head soon become buried and are transported deep within the ice. Rocks falling onto the ice and scraped from the valley sides form dark marginal ridges on the glacier. Where these ridges meet at the junction of two glaciers they are carried forward as a single band known as a *medial moraine*. The surface of a large glacier fed by many tributaries may be striped by a number of these medial ridged bands, each representing a single tributary glacier.

While the volume of ice in the lower reaches of a glacier progressively diminishes because of melting and evaporation, the volume of its rocky load remains nearly the same or even grows. So at some point near the terminus of many glaciers there will be as much rock as ice, and beyond this point the glacier will be more rock than ice. Allen Glacier, across which the Copper River Railway was constructed, illustrates that some glaciers may extend under a thick cover of moraine for miles beyond their apparent ends. The ice beneath this protective covering, insulated from the sun's rays, will not melt as fast as the cleaner ice farther up the glacier. And when the glacier retreats, this rock-manteled ice may remain behind, completely separated from the glacier, to slowly stagnate over the years. So effective an insulator is soil and rock debris that a mass of ice, like that at Allen and a number of other Alaskan glaciers, may persist for hundreds of years.

A stream of ice shod with rocks acts as a huge rasp on the surface over which it moves. It grinds down the valley floor and pries pieces of fractured rock loose, which in turn are used as abrasives on the bedrock farther along. The smallest of these glacier tools, sand and silt, polish the rock over which they move; the larger pieces make scratches (*striations*) and grooves, and themselves become scratched and faceted by bedrock and other fragments they are rubbed against.

This grinding action of rock on rock produces much fine silt and "rock flour," the material which gives a milky appearance to glacier melt-water streams. Reflection of light from these fine rock particles suspended in the water creates the lovely shades of light blue and turquoise so characteristic of lakes into which glacier waters drain. No one who gazes down upon the powder blue waters of Lake Louise in Banff National Park, Alberta, can be unmindful of the part glaciers play in adding color effects to the mountain scene. Lefroy and Victoria Glaciers high on the Continental Divide beyond the head of the lake are the source of the color.

Glaciers are among Earth's greatest face-lifters; no landscape can long withstand their attack without being altered. Any glacier, regardless of its size, is a capable agent of erosion, but the thicker the ice, the more effective it is at cutting and grinding down the surface. A stream of ice 1,000 or more feet thick, and there are many like this, can scrape and pluck rock from both the sides and floor of its valley. Thus original, narrow, stream-made valleys are carved both wider and deeper when glaciers flow through them. The end product is a deep and often very impressive trench with a U-shaped cross section.

Where the bedrock in the floor of the valley is weakest, a glacier is able to bite more easily into the land, gouging out deep basins. When the ice disappears, these basins immediately fill

with water and become lakes. Other lakes may be dammed behind the terminal moraine dumped by the glacier across the
valley. Practically all lakes in the Alps, Rockies, and other ranges
in which glaciers formerly were more extensive were formed in
these two ways.

The towering cliffs and other scenic features which each
year draw droves of visitors to California's great Yosemite Valley
were fashioned some thousands of years ago when the valley
and all its tributaries were filled with streams of ice draining the
snow fields of the High Sierra. A valley with gently sloping forested sides was scraped out by the relentless grinding of the rock-
shod ice until it was converted into the deep trough we see today.

The great extent to which glaciers have deepened valleys is
not always apparent. The sheer walls hemming in Yosemite Valley terminate abruptly where they meet the valley floor, but for
many years it has been known that the valley floor is merely the
top of a deep fill of clay and sand, deposited in a lake which occupied the valley for a time after the last glacier disappeared,
and that the valley walls extend to a great depth below this level.
The thickness of this fill was determined in 1935 when scientists
of the California Institute of Technology carried on extensive
seismic tests in the valley. This they did by exploding charges of
dynamite at many places on the valley floor and measuring the
length of time for the vibrations to travel down through the old
lake sediments to the bedrock and back to the surface.

Each time a blast is set off, vibrations in the form of sound
waves carry the energy outward in all directions, through the
air as well as the ground. Those which travel downward through
soil and other unconsolidated materials to the rock floor underneath are reflected back toward the surface. Recording instruments synchronized with the explosion pick up these reflected
waves. Whether traveling downward or upward, these waves
pass through rock and various loose materials at known rates.
Because the length of time between explosion and receipt of the
reflected wave is thus a direct measure of the distance traveled,
the depth to bedrock can be computed with great accuracy. This
technique of sounding is the same as that employed in oil exploration, and enables man to "see" below the surface and locate
potential oil-bearing strata at depths of several miles.

Snowline, Olympic Mountains, Washington. As elsewhere, not sharply defined—a zone of scattered snowbanks and drifts. Above snowline all except steep or windswept surfaces are permanently covered with snow or glaciers. Glacier,

Paradise Inn, Mount Rainier National Park, in mid-winter. Snows at Paradise average almost fifty feet a season. Though some snowbanks remain well into July, Paradise is below snowline. Nearby Mount Rainier projects several thousand feet above snowline and so is birthplace of numerous glaciers.

"City of San Francisco," stopped by snow west of Donner Pass by big storm, January

The ice age in full swing. High peaks of Antarctica's Queen Maud Range are islands (nunataks) in sea of ice and snow. A large outlet glacier flows through range and off to right toward Ross Sea. Looking toward the high Polar Plateau.

Breeding ground of glaciers in Chugach Range, Alaska. Ice flows out from many cirques to fill high inter-mountain basin, one of main sources of huge tidewater Columbia Glacier. Some of these mountains are nunataks.

Snow and firn layers in wall of snow-bridged crevasse, Upper Seward Glacier, St. Elias Range, Alaska. Dark strata mark tops of annual sequences; five years' accumulation is visible; 100 to 200 feet below surface, snow has been converted into glacier ice.

Ice from several cirques on many-crested Mount Olympus spills over much-crevassed icefall to make two-mile-long Blue Glacier, one of several ice streams radiating from mountain.

Ice, born in high cirques of Cima di Rosso in Italian Alps, tumbles down to nourish Forno Glacier. Rocks in foreground fell from wall of cirque, partly hidden from view on left.

Seven-mile-long Harriman Glacier and its feeder tributaries, Chugach Range, Alaska.

Delta Glacier and its tributaries are typical branching valley glacier system. Ridges of medial moraine from tributaries stripe main glacier. Alaska Range, 100 miles southeast of Fairbanks.

Much-crevassed tidewater front of Surprise Glacier. Harriman Fiord, Chugach Mountains, Alaska.

Two sprawling glaciers nourished by masses of avalanching snow and ice on Nevado Huascaran (22,205 feet), Peru's highest peak, descend below snowline. Thatched roofs huts and nearby grain fields are about 11,000 feet above sea

After Commonwealth Glacier spills through a gap into Taylor Dry Valley near McMurdo Sound, Antarctica, it spreads out pancakelike into a piedmont glacier.

Western part of Malaspina piedmont ice sheet at foot of St. Elias Range. Agassiz Glacier is in center distance. Differential motion in ice of Seward Glacier, entering from right, contorts moraine bands on ice sheet.

Crevassed tongue of Glacier des Bossons in valley of Chamonix is fed by ice flowing from several cirques and from summit of Mont Blanc (skyline in center) three miles distant and two miles higher. The remains of three guides, lost in a crevasse below rock cliff just to left of Mont Blanc's summit in 1820, appeared near end of glacier forty-three years later.

M. E. Beatty examines mountain sheep carcass exposed by melting of Lyell Glacier in Yosemite National Park. When carcass was found, sheep had been extinct in Yosemite region for fifty years. This one was entombed within ice for at least that long, possibly as much as 200 or 300 years.

Mont Blanc. Glacier du Géant spills out of its hanging valley in impressive ice-fall to become Mer de Glace. Dark bands (ogives) arcing across glacier were crevasses, now filled with snow, broken ice, and dust, and squeezed shut.

Gilkey Glacier is formed by joining of several glaciers from Juneau Ice Field, southeastern Alaska. Dark bands below icefall in right distance distinguish ice from separate tributaries and show that center of each stream moves fastest.

Recessional moraines, made by Iliamna Glacier when its terminus lay on tidal flats of Tuxedni Bay, are among world's best developed. All these concentric moraine ridges have been broken by streams carrying outwash.

Aleutian Range, Alaska. So much snow falls on Iliamna Volcano that several ice streams draped over it unite to form seventeen-mile-long Iliamna Glacier. Irregular flow along its edges contorts moraine bands.

Vertical photo of Shoup Glacier in Chugach Range near Valdez, Alaska. Surface is much crevassed where glacier makes a 130° bend, but medial moraines are only slightly distorted as they round bend. Downstream toward bottom of photo.

The Yosemite tests revealed that at the head of the valley, in the vicinity of Camp Curry and the Ahwahnee Hotel, the bedrock floor lay at a depth of 1,800 feet below the surface. Farther down the valley near El Capitan the fill is 1,200 feet thick. Thus visitors to the valley see only a little more than half the height of the imposing walls which hold it in. If all the sediment were removed—a larger excavation project than man has ever attempted, but one that would be child's play for a glacier—a lake would again return to the valley, and the great granite cliffs of El Capitan and Glacier Point would tower almost 1,000 feet higher above its waters than they do above the valley floor today.

There are innumerable other deeply scoured glacial valleys, the true magnitude of which cannot be seen because they are partly filled with earth or water. When the former ice sheets spread southward over what is now upstate New York, the flow of ice was guided into long, shallow, north-sloping valleys. Concentration of flow in these valleys scoured them out until they were great deep rifts in the surface beneath the ice. These rifts are now occupied by the famous Finger Lakes. The floors of the valleys beneath Cayuga and Seneca Lakes, the two largest, lie several hundred feet below sea level, sure evidence that the valleys were scoured out by ice, since streams flowing to the sea are incapable of cutting their valleys far below sea level.

Although much of their magnificence is concealed by the sea water which has flooded them, *fiords* are among the most spectacular of glacier valleys. The best-known ones are along the Alaskan and Norwegian coasts, but the entire perimeter of Greenland is notched by them, and they are present in many other places, including Chile, New Zealand, British Columbia, Iceland, Scotland, Labrador, and the islands of Arctic Canada.

Many Norwegian fiords are more than fifty miles long. The longest of all, Sogne Fiord near Bergen, carries the sea 120 miles inland. Its sides rise several thousand feet above the water and in places extend to depths of nearly 4,000 feet below sea level. The nearby Hardanger Fiord is almost as long.

The Alaska panhandle is a maze of intersecting fiords—so many that it is difficult to determine the length of some of the individual fiords. The Portland Canal, a fiord on the British Columbia boundary, is 100 miles long and throughout practically

its entire length is less than two miles wide. Lynn Canal and its
extension to the south, Chatham Strait, is a single huge fiord extending from Skagway more than 250 miles to the open ocean.
Coastwise steamers can thread their way for hundreds of miles
through the fiords in southeast Alaska without once entering the
ocean.

The action of glaciers in gouging out previously existing
valleys is sometimes referred to as *overdeepening*, especially if
the ice creates basins in the valley floor or cuts it down below
sea level. When a glacier enters the sea it continues to erode the
surface on which it is flowing until it reaches a point where the
depth of water is nine tenths the thickness of the ice. Then the
glacier floats. Thus, since we know sea level was within 300 feet
of its present elevation when coastal Norway was being glacierized, the streams of ice which gouged out Sogne Fiord could
have been nearly 4,500 feet thick.

It might also be said that glaciers *oversteepen* the valleys
through which they flow, because they convert gently sloping
valley sides into vertical and near-vertical precipices. So recently
have most glacial valleys been carved out that the steep walls
have not yet had enough time to become stabilized by weathering. As a result, on the sides of many of these valleys huge masses
of rock hang poised precariously, ready to plunge down in fast-
moving landslides or rockfalls. These are sometimes triggered
by the prying action of frost in crevices, sometimes by earthquakes. A landslide is a local phenomenon, but when it crashes
into the water of a fiord or into a glacial lake, its effects may be
multiplied manyfold by the generation of huge waves capable of
tremendous destruction at distances of several miles from the
slide. In Norway's Innvik Fiord landslides have repeatedly
crashed into Loen Lake; in 1905 and again in 1936 the waves
they produced swept inland, destroying a number of homes and
killing more than 100 persons. On one occasion a lake steamer
was carried inland over a quarter-mile. People living in other
Norwegian fiords have had similar experiences.

Landslides occur more often in the fiords in Alaska's earthquake belt. At the narrowest part of the panhandle, about 100
miles south of Yakutat Bay and an equal distance west of Juneau,
the coast is indented by Lituya Bay, a fiord about seven miles long

and one to three miles wide. It constitutes the outlet to the sea for Crillon and Gilbert Inlets, two arms of a much larger but nearly glacier-filled fiord. Lituya is the only protected anchorage for many miles in either direction along the coast. Since it lies in the middle of a completely uninhabited section of the coast nearly 150 miles long, it is not the center of much boating ac- tivity. But fishermen in the Gulf of Alaska sometimes take refuge in the bay during periods of stormy weather.

On the night of July 9, 1958, the six persons on three fishing boats which had pulled into the bay because of predicted high winds certainly did not find the shelter they sought. Shortly after 10:00 p.m. the fishermen felt strong earthquake shocks, fol- lowed by an earsplitting crash. Almost immediately a ghastly sight met their eyes. A gigantic wave, several hundred feet high, emerged from Gilbert Inlet into the head of the bay and bore down upon them at better than 100 miles an hour. Before they had time to do much more than start their motors and make frantic attempts to head for the open sea or get their boats into a position which might give them some slight chance for survival, the wave, probably still 100 or more feet high, was upon them. In a few minutes two people were dead and their boat de- stroyed without a trace. Two others had had the nightmarish ex- perience of being flung—boat and all—by the wave a quarter- mile across the forest-covered spit at the mouth of the bay and into the sea beyond, where their boat was demolished in the crash. The two others, Howard Ulrich and his seven-year-old son, clung to their boat as it was carried up onto the wave crest and washed inland high above the tops of trees and then back into the violently churning, log-filled waters of the bay by the wave's backwash. Miraculously, Ulrich and his son came through this shattering experience uninjured and their boat remained afloat.

The giant wave in Lituya Bay was generated when 90,000,- 000 tons of rock, knocked loose by the quake which the fishermen experienced a few minutes before the wave struck them, slid into the deep water of Gilbert Inlet at the head of the bay. On the way down this rockfall sliced more than 1,000 feet off the end of Lituya Glacier. On the shore opposite the slide a surge of water rushed up the slope to the incredible height of 1,740 feet, strip- ping off all the trees in a virgin forest and the soil in which they grew. Although the wave diminished in height as it moved seaward, halfway down the bay the forest was completely removed to a height of more than 120 feet, and at the mouth of the bay, seven and one-half miles from the point where the wave was generated, trees, some with trunks three or more feet in diameter, were uprooted and removed from the shore strip as high as thirty-five feet above sea level. This wave accomplished the largest and quickest logging operation in history—in a time span of three or four minutes it stripped all the timber from an area of nearly four square miles, peeled the bark from the logs, and dumped most of them into the bay, where the churning action of the water sliced off all their branches.

A plane flight on the morning after the destruction revealed a three-mile-long log raft floating along the north shore of the bay. Small log rafts and single logs were scattered over the rest of the bay and over a strip of the sea extending five miles out from the bay entrance.

So astounding were the effects of the gigantic splash when the rockfall entered the water that, despite incontrovertible evidence that it happened, scientists could hardly believe that it did happen. This surge of water rose many times higher onto the shore than the wash from any earthquake sea wave (known popularly as a tidal wave) ever recorded. In order to determine if what happened was actually mechanically possible, scientists constructed a scale model of Lituya Bay on which to test existing theory and data on the hydraulics of waves.

Studies by government geologists have revealed that the giant wave of 1958 was nothing new for Lituya Bay. Other giant waves have rushed down the bay at intermittent intervals during the past 100 or more years. One in 1936, witnessed by four people, washed out trees along one section of shore to a height of 490 feet above sea level. Others have occurred in 1853 or 1854, about 1874, and probably also in 1899.

Although unobserved, waves are known to have occurred on these dates by the marks they have left along the shores. Years after a destructive wave has coursed through the bay the upper limit of its wash along the shore is a sharply defined *trimline* marked by old forest above and distinctly younger forest below. Before the 1958 wave destroyed practically all evidence of former giant waves, several distinct trimlines were present in the forest along the bay. Below the 1936 trimline the oldest trees were less than twenty-two years of age. In the forest just below the 1853–4 trimline the greatest tree age was under 105 years. Alders, willows, and cottonwoods which have begun to clothe Lituya's denuded shores since 1958 will eventually be displaced by the larger and longer-lived spruce, hemlock, and cedar. But for hundreds of years, unless obliterated by an even more tremendous wave, the trimline at the upper edge of this new forest will bear witness to the giant wave of July 9, 1958.

The fiords are still steep-sided—some, such as Gilbert and Crillon Inlets, are being made steeper by glaciers now—so landslides, some in Lituya Bay itself, others in Gilbert and Crillon Inlets, will undoubtedly continue to create giant waves. Such waves have been occurring on an average of about once every twenty-five years in Lituya Bay. Hence, as Don J. Miller of the U.S. Geological Survey says: ". . . the odds against one of these waves occurring on a single day spent in the bay are comfortably large (about 9,000 to 1)." On the other hand, the danger is greater for several years after a big earthquake, because the vibrations undoubtedly loosen other masses of rock both above and below the water, which may at any time break loose. When they do, the resulting waves are apt to be destructive, because in the narrow confines of a fiord the water, being unable to spread out, rises to extraordinary heights. Add to this condition the possibility that huge masses of ice, also capable of causing high waves, may break off the ends of the two glaciers, and it is obvious that Lituya in the future will continue to be the scene of dramatic natural events.

While a large ice stream cuts its valley deeper, its tributary glaciers do the same thing to their own valleys. Being smaller and less thick, however, these glaciers grind down the floors of their valleys at a much slower rate than the main glacier. So these tributary valleys are left hanging, once the ice is gone, far up the sides of the main valley, and are aptly termed *hanging valleys*. Their presence is disclosed by an icefall where the glacier flows out of them, down into the main valley. In mountain ranges from which glaciers have disappeared, hanging valleys are among the most distinctive land forms.

In mountains which have not been glaciated, hanging valleys are the exception rather than the rule. Streams typically will not create hanging valleys. In valleys which have never been glaciated the tributary valleys, no matter how small, and the main valley normally will join each other at about the same level. Deepening of the main valley increases the velocity of the tributary stream enough to enable it to keep pace with the downcutting of the main stream. A striking example of this process is furnished by Bright Angel Creek, a minor tributary of the Colorado River in the deepest part of the Grand Canyon. This little creek, with a length of only twelve miles, has carved out a canyon as deep as that of the Colorado.

Fortunately, Nature has already removed the ice from innumerable mountain valleys, exposing to view hanging valleys and other evidences of her sculpturing. Among the most versatile of the actors in the scenic drama in countless glacial valleys are the tumultuous waterfalls which leap from hanging valleys and drop their thundering ribbons of white to the placid waters in the valleys far below.

The most spectacular of Yosemite's cataracts is Upper Yosemite Fall, one of the highest free-leaping waterfalls in the world. Between the point where it springs out into space and where it crashes into the rocks below, the water drops 1,430 feet in a sheer fall—nearly 200 feet greater than the height of New York's Empire State Building—and this is only part of the total drop. The stream continues down a number of lesser cataracts to the bottom of Lower Yosemite Fall, nearly a half-mile below the lip of its hanging valley.

The best place from which to view this magnificent spectacle is Glacier Point on the south rim 3,000 feet above the valley floor and two miles directly opposite the falls. From here one has an unobstructed view, from top to bottom, of both the Upper and Lower Falls and the hanging valley from which they plummet. In few places can features resulting from profound glacial erosion be seen to better advantage.

While absorbing this scene, we need only let our minds carry us back 10,000 years or so, and again, standing on Glacier Point, we would be treated to another magnificent vista, but one completely dominated by ice. Before us would be a great river of ice filling the valley almost up to the point on which we were standing. Across the valley, trickling down from a small, much-crevassed hanging glacier, not quite long enough to flow into the main glacier, we would see the stream destined to become Upper Yosemite Fall. Ice would cover all save the rims of the great enclosing walls of granite. By turning our eyes eastward we could look up the two big ice streams in the Merced and Tenaya Valleys, which had joined to make the main Yosemite Glacier. So thick would they be that all the land between them except the tops of Half Dome and Cloud's Rest would be covered by the ice. In the far distance we could see sticking up through the vast sloping sea of ice only the highest peaks along the crest of the main divide. Today, comparable scenes await those who would travel to the Queen Maud Mountains and any of the other ice-engulfed ranges on the Antarctic Continent.

Yosemite is only one of an immense number of glaciated troughs adorned with hanging valleys. Such features are commonplace in all formerly glaciated mountain ranges, and today are in the making wherever there are great valley glacier systems.

In all mountain ranges where glaciers are or have been present, those places which have been ice-eroded for the longest time are the heads of the valleys. It is here that most glaciers originate. It is here that they exist for a long time before they expand enough to move down the valleys, and it is here that they make their last stand against a warming climate. Because of long occupation by glaciers, most of these valley heads have been converted into deep recesses. These amphitheaters, closed in by rock walls on three sides, are known as *cirques*.

Between the glacier and the headwall of the cirque, water from the melting ice penetrates fractures in the rock. Alternate freezing and thawing of the water pry rock fragments from the cirque wall. When the ice moves away from the wall it pulls out some of these fragments. Others fall into the opening between glacier and wall and eventually work their way down underneath the ice where, incorporated into the glacier, they are dragged along the cirque floor, deepening it by abrasion and by prying other rock fragments loose.

The gap between glacier and headwall, known as the

bergschrund, never gets more than a few yards wide because each winter it is filled by snow, some of which eventually becomes part of the glacier and moves slowly down the valley. Quarrying action at the bergschrund creates the headwall and keeps it steep and, of course, drives it back farther and farther into the mountain. Such enlargement of cirques on both sides of a mountain range will finally reduce the central part of the range to a sharp-crested, jagged ridge, the *arête.* The meeting of two opposing cirques makes a notch in the arête, known as a *col.*

From the highest parts of a range glaciers will ordinarily radiate outward in all directions. Thus, as the cirques surrounding such places are enlarged, their headwalls move toward a common point, where they will eventually create a sharp-pointed pyramidal peak, called a *horn.* Each face of the horn is the headwall of an encroaching cirque. The famed Matterhorn of the Swiss-Italian Alps is the best-known example of this type of mountain. It has given its name to thousands of peaks of similar origin all over the world, in every mountain range in which glaciers are present or from which they have recently disappeared.

The very nature of their origin makes horn peaks a challenge to mountain climbers. Many of the highest unclimbed peaks are horns, and only recently have a number of others been ascended for the first time. Everest—highest of them all—is a horn carved from a much larger mountain by the Khumbu, Rongbuk, East Rongbuk, and Kangshung Glaciers. The southwest face of Everest, 7,000 feet high and unclimbable, is a part of the headwall of the Western Cwm,* a huge cirque cut by the Khumbu Glacier from the Everest massif, the closely clustered group of high peaks culminating in Mount Everest. It is through this great ice-filled amphitheater that the successful climbing parties have gained access to the summit of the mountain.

Thus, as valley glaciers work over a mountain landscape, its features become sharper and more rugged, and the range will eventually be converted into a maze of jagged horn peaks and serrated arêtes, rising thousands of feet above deep glacier-

* Cwm, a Welsh term (pronounced "coom") equivalent to cirque, is used by the British.

gouged troughs. On the other hand, the features of a landscape buried under an ice sheet, instead of being sharpened are smoothed off as the rock-shod ice slides over them. Horn peaks and arêtes can hardly be created here. Moreover, if an ice sheet should invade and eventually cover a range previously subjected to mountain glaciation, the horns and arêtes would probably be smoothed and, if the ice sheet should persist long enough, worn down until little of their original character remains. Though the rate at which ice sheets erode is not known, it is less than that of large valley glaciers, because they do not flow as fast.

Based upon the amount of material now scattered over much of the northern United States and southern Canada in the form of moraines, experts believe that the recurrent ice sheet, in its occupation of Canada during several hundred thousand years, removed an average of not more than thirty feet of rock. In some places little more than the thin mantle of soil and weathered rock debris was carried away. Let us not, however, belittle the erosive capabilities of the former North American ice sheet. The removal of thirty feet of rock from 2,000,000 square miles is no small accomplishment.

Locally, however, as in the case of the Finger Lakes valleys, an ice sheet can cut deeply into the land. Beneath the ice in interior Antarctica, where buried mountain ranges are being smoothed off, there probably are places where subglacial valleys are aligned in the general direction of ice flow. These are being overdeepened by the more rapid flow of basal ice diverted into them, just as happened thousands of years ago in the Finger Lakes valleys. In coastal Antarctica, where ice is moving down the great outlet glaciers, future fiords are in the making.

The former North American ice sheet has given us many more examples of overdeepened valleys than the Finger Lakes. Early in the present century when engineers were laying out the route for the proposed Catskill Aqueduct—the ninety-mile-long conduit which brings water to New York City from reservoirs in the Catskill Mountains—one of many problems they faced was finding the most suitable place to cross beneath the Hudson River. In order to examine the type of rock and to determine how far below river level the tunnel would have to be driven to be in solid rock, bore holes were drilled at a number of possible crossing sites. At several locations along the narrow, fourteen-mile gorge where the river cuts through the Highlands between Newburgh and Peekskill, the drillers, from barges anchored in the river, started drilling into the mud and silt on the river bottom. Down, down, down, went the drills, 100, 200, 300 feet—nothing but clay, sand, gravel, and bouldery debris—until the drillers began to wonder if the valley had any rock bottom at all. After the exploration was completed, geologists knew that the flow of ice at the bottom of the former ice sheet, when it encountered the barrier of the Highlands, had been squeezed into the funnel of the river's gap south of Newburgh. Because of resulting faster flow and greater pressure in this notch, the ice gouged out the valley through the Highlands to depths varying between 750 and 950 feet below sea level. The valley has also been carved down below sea level, though not everywhere as deeply, all the way from the Highlands to the sea.

As a result of glacial action thousands of years ago, the two major lifelines of New York City, the Catskill Aqueduct and the parallel but newer Delaware Aqueduct, lie more than 1,000 feet below sea level where they cross the Hudson Valley near Storm King and Breakneck in the Highlands above West Point.

5

Mountain Glaciers
Are Nearly Everywhere

Except for Australia, mountain glaciers exist on all continents, even along the Equator in Africa and South America.

Go where you will, you will find no display of mountain glaciers comparable in magnitude and variety to that of the great crescent of mountain ranges bordering the Gulf of Alaska. Some of the ranges of this tremendous arc of mountains are loaded with ice, but the glaciers reach their crowning glory where the cloud-spearing St. Elias Mountains nearly choke off the neck of the Alaska panhandle by squeezing it against the sea. Clustered around Mount Logan and its neighbor Mount St. Elias, which rise higher above their bases than even the towering Himalayas, are some of the longest and largest mountain glaciers on Earth. Hubbard Glacier, nearly seventy-five miles in length, may be the longest of all. Logan Glacier, which shares its source with Hubbard, is nearly as long.

The mantle of interwoven ice fields and valley glaciers draped over this range and its westward extension, the Chugach Mountains, stretches for a distance of 250 miles. So great are the accumulations of ice that they completely blanket large areas on many of the mountain summits, even some of the highest. Tongues of ice flow downward through hundreds of valleys, converging and diverging, twisting and turning, and plunging out of hanging valleys in colossal frozen waterfalls. It is as though the country were held together by a tremendous spider-web of ice. Many of these ice streams descend into the head-water valleys of the Yukon River. On the south flank of the range some flow out onto the narrow coastal plain where they spread into broad, nearly flat piedmont glaciers. Many others push on to tidewater, meeting the sea in impressive icy cliffs 200 to 300 feet high.

Malaspina, one of two huge piedmont glaciers at the head of the panhandle, has a width of forty miles and extends all the way across the coastal plain, here twenty-eight miles wide. Near its center this great cake of ice is more than 2,000 feet thick. In the mantle of rock debris and soil covering its marginal zone, a forest of hemlock and Sitka spruce is growing. Some of the trees in this mile-wide strip of forest are seventy-five feet tall and 100 years old, growing on top of an estimated thickness of fifty to 150 feet of glacial ice.

It was across the maze of ice in these coastal ranges that surveyors had to establish the line of the International Boundary between Canada and Alaska. For 450 miles northward from the Stikine River the line crosses more ice than land. Occasional peaks, poking their rocky summits up through the ice, serve as the only stable features on which to anchor the boundary.

Every range in this great mass of mountains swinging around the Gulf of Alaska, including the high Alaska Range which lies behind the coastal mountains, contains large ice streams. Kahiltna Glacier on Mount McKinley's south flank is forty-five or more miles long. Black Rapids Glacier, with a length of twenty-seven miles and fed by eleven tributaries, each several miles long, is, in comparison with many others in southern Alaska, only a medium-sized glacier.

In this rugged land there are hundreds if not thousands of

small glaciers and many large ones which have not yet been named. Some have never been seen except from the air. Even so, the namers have been very active. Several of the glaciers, like Black Rapids, have been named for landscape features, and others for some characteristic of their own (Cascading and Crescent). Many bear names of people. Represented in these streams of ice are the names of explorers, scientists, members of European royalty, men who have financed expeditions, army officers—lieutenants as well as generals—miners, and sourdoughs. Along and near College Fiord, an arm of Prince William Sound, fifty miles east of Anchorage, the namers were not of the ordinary sort. Here are twenty-one glaciers bearing the names of United States colleges, with two former presidents of Harvard thrown in for good measure.

In 1794 Captain George Vancouver, sailing along the Gulf of Alaska coast, saw and described some of the tidewater glaciers in the vicinity of Glacier Bay. However, it wasn't until nearly 100 years later that extensive exploration and mapping of Alaskan glaciers got under way. Even before 1900, steamer excursions to some of the tidewater glaciers in the vicinity of Juneau had begun. Since then, several of these ice streams have become important tourist attractions. Mendenhall Glacier, one of the largest ice streams in the panhandle, is only four miles by road from the Juneau Airport. A block of ice carried from Juneau to New York by Pan American Airways gives Mendenhall Glacier the dubious distinction of having iced the cocktails of members of the Explorers Club at their annual dinner in 1951.

Another but much less well-known area of extensive and spectacular mountain glaciers lies at the extreme opposite end of the Americas, in the southern Andes between Chile and Argentina. Here a combination of climatic and land features similar to southeast Alaska—prevailing onshore winds blowing from warm seas against a mountain range in a fairly high latitude—nourishes many large ice fields and valley glaciers. Some of the longest glaciers flow down the east side of the range to the Argentine Lake District, which lies between the mountains and the pampas.

The little-known glaciers on the Chilean side of the range

occupy a rugged, uninhabited region chopped into countless little pieces by a maze of steep-sided interlocking fiords. Some of
the glaciers enter the sea, and the San Rafael Glacier, at 47°
south (equivalent to the latitude of northern Maine), is closer
to the Equator than any other tidewater glacier in the world.

In the Alps, which swing in a great crescent northward
from the French-Italian Riviera through Switzerland, around
northern Italy and into Austria, are the world's best-known and
most frequently visited glaciers. Between the Mont Blanc Range
on the French-Italian boundary and the Gross Glockner in Austria are more than 1,000 of them, ranging from those of insignificant size to the Great Aletsch Glacier, which is more than
seventeen miles long. The upper Rhone Valley separates the two
largest and most important glacier regions. These are the Bernese
Alps in Switzerland and the Mont Blanc Range–Pennine Alps in
Switzerland, France, and Italy. Here are such famed glacier-
carved peaks as the Matterhorn, Dent Blanche, Monte Rosa, and
the Dom—all in the Pennines—and the Jungfrau, Finsteraar-
horn, Aletschhorn, and Eiger in the Bernese Alps.

Civilized man had lived for a long time near the glaciers in
Norway and Iceland, but it was in the Alps that the scientific
study of glaciers really had its birth. Descriptions of glaciers and
attempts to explain their behavior were published during the
eighteenth century, but not until well after 1800 did real glacier
research begin. A number of tunnels have been excavated in
Swiss and French glaciers, one as early as 1891, by scientists so
that they could study the transformation of snow into ice. Permanent, well-equipped laboratories for the study of snow,
avalanches, and glaciers have been established near some of
the glaciers. Foremost among these important centers of glaciological research is the Jungfraujoch Research Institute high
in the Bernese Alps at the source of the Great Aletsch Glacier.
Here, in a setting of supreme mountain grandeur and surrounded by the material for their studies, some of the world's
leading glaciologists have carried on experiments on the behavior of snow, firn, and glacier ice under natural as well as artificially created conditions.

Five thousand miles east of the Alps is a lofty, isolated,
nearly barren region into which Afghanistan, the Soviet Union,

Sinkiang, India, and Pakistan all project, as though attempting to share whatever meager bounty it may have. Several of the world's highest mountain ranges, radiating from this piece of international real estate, form the jagged, ice-adorned crown of the Eurasian land mass—the topographical top of the world. At the center of this mass of mountains are the Pamir and Karakoram Ranges; extending westward is the Hindu Kush; northeastward, the Tien Shan; and eastward, like a titanic two-pronged claw clutching the high plateau of Tibet, are the Kunlun Shan and the Himalayas.

Tucked among the cirques and hanging valleys of these vast sprawling ranges are more mountain glaciers than in the whole of Alaska. Snowfall is heavy, especially in the Himalayan and Karakoram Ranges, against which the wet summer monsoons blow after their unhindered dash up the broad valley of the Indus from the Arabian Sea. Practically all snow falls in summer, since the winter monsoon blows in the opposite direction—from the cold, dry interior of the continent—and sucks up rather than dispenses moisture.

All the highest peaks—Everest, K2, Kanchenjunga, Makalu, Dhaulagiri, Manaslu—and hundreds of others are surrounded by glaciers. In the vicinity of Everest many of the ice streams are eight to fifteen miles long; 1,000 miles away, at the northwestern end of the Himalayas and in the adjacent Karakoram, there are larger ones. Still farther northwest—beyond the junction with the Hindu Kush—in the Pamirs lies the great Fedtchenko Glacier, fed by ice from twenty-five tributaries. A thickness of nearly 3,000 feet in its upper part and a forty-eight-mile length make it the largest valley glacier in Asia and one of the longest in the world.

THERE ARE MANY OTHERS

Europe's highest range, the Caucasus, squeezed in between the Black and Caspian Seas, shelters hundreds of glaciers. In size and distribution they bear a strong resemblance to those in the Alps.

There is nearly as much glacial ice in Norway and Sweden

as in the Alps and Caucasus combined, but it is mainly in the form of small icecaps, from which valley glaciers flow outward.

Several little glaciers lie hidden in the highest cirques of the Pyrenees.

Where the Prevailing Westerlies, laden with moisture from the Indian Ocean and Tasman Sea, blow against the Southern Alps of New Zealand, there is another notable area of mountain glaciers. Although none of the glaciers reaches the sea, this fiord area resembles on a small scale the coastal regions along the Gulf of Alaska and in southern Chile.

Valley glaciers are present in the Cascades and in nearly all the ranges of the Coast Mountains between Alaska's renowned glacier belt and northern Washington. Farther south they are present only on the big volcanoes. South of Mount Shasta none of the coastal mountains has enough elevation or snow to bear glaciers. But in the much higher Sierra Nevada, 200 miles inland, there are a number of diminutive glaciers, including the one on Mount Lyell which yielded the Sierra mountain sheep.

Within the Rocky Mountains the principal glacier areas lie along the Alberta-British Columbia boundary in and near Jasper, Banff, and Yoho National Parks, and in several of the ranges farther west. Some of these glaciers are among the most accessible in North America. Unique in this respect is Athabaska Glacier, one of several draining ice from the Columbia Ice Field in the southern part of Jasper National Park. A short side road leads from the Banff-Jasper Highway to the very edge of the glacier. Because much of the glacier is relatively free from crevasses, a regular schedule of snowmobile trips over its surface is operated throughout the summer. Probably nowhere else in North America is there a mountain glacier which can be traversed with so little effort.

In the Rockies south of the Forty-ninth Parallel all glaciers are confined to cirques, mainly on the north and east sides of mountains, since there isn't enough snow accumulation to push them down the valleys. Nonetheless, snow blown from mountaintops nourishes 200 to 300 of these small ice masses. The bulk of these glaciers is concentrated in two areas: the Wind River Range in Wyoming and the Lewis and Livingstone Ranges in Glacier National Park, Montana. Despite their small size, some of these glaciers have crevasses, ice caves, and cliffs as large and as spectacular as those on much bigger glaciers.

Because of their location in latitudes not usually associated with ice and snow, glaciers of the Equatorial Zone come under the category of oddities. On mountain summits high above the steaming jungles of New Guinea, where heavy precipitation and much cloudy weather bring the snowline down to 15,000 feet, there are several small glaciers.

On the other side of the Pacific, almost directly on the Equator in the Andes, several high volcanoes, at elevations of 19,000 to 20,000 feet, are crowned with glaciers. And in the Andean chain from its northern end in Venezuela south to the Tropic of Capricorn there are many hundreds if not thousands of glaciers.

The only other glaciers within the Equatorial Zone are near the Equator in East Africa on two huge volcanoes, Kenya and Kilimanjaro, and on several of the loftiest peaks of the Ruwenzori Range, a huge block of Earth's crust that has been thrust up thousands of feet above the Great Rift Valley. High altitude and heavy snowfall combine to produce glaciers on these mountains despite nearness to the Equator.

6

Glaciers
and Mountaineers

OUNTAINEERS have long had exper-
ience with glaciers. The people who climb high mountains are
forced by the steepness of the walls, the jaggedness of approach
ridges, and the ever-present menace of avalanching snow and
rock to follow the valleys all the way to their heads to get as high
on the mountain as possible before beginning the ascent of the
precipitous rock slopes. Since glaciers occupy the valleys, they
serve as routes of approach—sometimes the only ones—to the
inner recesses of the mountains. This holds especially true of the
ranges in southern Alaska and adjacent Canada, in the Himalayas, and in the Alps.

There is no way to approach the summit of Mount McKinley, North America's highest, except by way of its large glaciers,
Muldrow, Kahiltna, Ruth, and others.

The ice streams that flow down from the cirques surrounding Everest's rocky summit cone have felt the tread of every expedition that has ever assaulted the mountain. Time after time the British plodded up the Rongbuk and East Rongbuk Glaciers to the North Col, only to be defeated by altitude, weather, and other vicissitudes on the rocky summit pyramid. Victory was finally won on the opposite side of the mountain, where the Khumbu Glacier served as a pathway on which the climbers could ascend to an elevation of 22,000 feet before having to scale the ice-covered rocky cliffs. Many other glaciers on the flanks of the highest peaks in the Himalayas and the more remote ranges of central Asia have been traversed, in some cases many times, by mountaineers.

One cannot climb to the ice-covered crown of Western Europe, the summit of Mont Blanc, without traversing the high firn fields and one or more of the ice streams radiating from them— the Glacier du Géant and Glacier des Bossons in France, Glacier de la Brenva in Italy, and some of the minor glaciers on the upper flanks of this imposing mountain. Access to the glaciers here is easy. A great aerial cableway spans the Mont Blanc Range from Chamonix in France to Entrèves in Italy. In a few minutes skiers and climbers ride effortlessly up to the high firn fields and the higher peaks in the heart of the range. From here they have an almost unlimited choice of ski runs and climbs. Restaurants, snack shops, and bars at stations along the way carry the conveniences of civilization into the land of ice and snow. For the sight-seer here, the secrets of the glaciers are laid bare. For three miles the cableway hangs suspended high above the ice-filled Vallée Blanche and the Glacier du Géant. One can look down into gaping crevasses and see the annual layers of firn in the process of giving birth to glaciers large and small. On all sides one can see the ice at work sharpening countless horns, digging into cirque walls, and grinding away at the valleys. Tiny glaciers cling to shelves and notches on the highest peaks; icefalls pour from hanging cirques to build up larger glaciers; these in turn converge to form the Mer de Glace which winds its miles-long way far below the snowline toward the valley of Chamonix. Now, with the construction of the seven-mile Mont Blanc vehicular tunnel thousands of feet below the mountain summit and the cableway, there is no place on Earth where men have done so much to avoid glaciers and, at the same time, make them accessible.*

On some glaciers, especially where the valley floor has a gentle slope, there is smooth sailing. But where glaciers move down over steep declivities or pour out of hanging valleys, travel on their surfaces is apt to be hazardous indeed. At such places the brittle surface ice has to move faster and farther than the plastic ice beneath it. This it does by breaking into strips separated by crevasses which may extend almost across the entire width of the glacier. The plastic ice does not slide out from underneath its more rigid cover; it simply breaks it up and carries the strips along. Below an icefall, where the rate of flow slows down and the ice is compressed, these crevasses may be squeezed shut, but farther along they may open again. Because the central part of a glacier moves faster than the sides, which are held back by friction against the valley walls, additional crevasses open up between these zones of differential movement. And along the sides short marginal crevasses may form. These initially intersect the edge of the glacier at an angle of about 45°, opening up-glacier, but may be rotated later, by faster flow toward the glacier center, until they are at right angles to the ice margin. The intersection of several sets of crevasses, transverse, longitudinal, and marginal, and additional ones which develop from other stresses within the ice, converts the surface of the glacier into a jumble of blocks and pinnacles (*seracs*).

Melting of the ice and motion of the glacier cause the blocks to shift position and some of the seracs to topple. At any one instant there may be little or no apparent motion in the glacier, but in the span of several days—perhaps in several hours —the surface of the ice can undergo startling changes. Routes made by climbers through crevassed and broken areas on one day may be obliterated by the next. The great icefall on the Khumbu Glacier, through which several Mount Everest climbing expeditions have carried tons of supplies, serves as a good illus-

* In 1961 a French Army jet, flying too low, severed the traction cable of the aerial cableway, plunging six persons to their deaths on the glacier in Vallée Blanche.

tration. During the 1951 reconnaissance of the route by which the mountain was finally conquered, the icefall was particularly active. Eric Shipton, leader of the reconnaissance, had this to say about it:

A broad crevasse had opened across our former route, and it took us an hour and a half and a lot of very hard work to find a way across it. This check, though a salutary warning against over-confidence, was not serious, and it was not until we were over the crevasse that the real trouble began. Here, about one hundred yards from the Serac, we found that a tremendous change had taken place. Over a wide area the cliffs and towers that had been there before had been shattered as though by an earthquake, and now lay in a tumbled ruin. This had evidently been caused by a sudden movement of the main mass of the glacier which had occurred sometime during the last fortnight. It was impossible to avoid the sober reflection that if we had persisted with the establishment of a line of communication through the ice-fall and if a party had happened to be in the area at the time, it was doubtful whether any of them would have survived. Moreover, the same thing might happen on other parts of the ice-fall.

With regard to our immediate problem, however, we hoped that the collapse of the ice had left the new surface with a solid foundation, though it was so broken and alarming in appearance. Very gingerly, prodding with our ice-axes at every step, with 100 feet of rope between each man, we ventured across the shattered area. The whole thing felt very unsound, but it was difficult to tell whether the instability was localized around the place one was treading or whether it applied to the area as a whole. Hillary was ahead, chopping his way through the ice blocks, when one of these, a small one, fell into a void below. There was a prolonged roar and the surface on which we stood began to shudder violently. I thought it was about to collapse, and the Sherpas, somewhat irrationally perhaps, flung themselves to the ground. In spite of this alarming experience, it was not so much the shattered area that worried us as the part beyond, where the cliffs and seracs were riven by innumerable new cracks which seemed to threaten a further collapse. We retreated to the sound ice below and attempted to find a less dangerous route. Any extensive movement to the left would have brought us under fire from the hanging glaciers in that direction. We explored the ground to the right, but here we found that the area of devastation was far more extensive. It was overhung, moreover, by a line of extremely unstable seracs.*

* By permission from Eric Shipton: *The Mount Everest Reconnaissance Expedition 1951* (London: Hodder and Stoughton; 1952).

The Everest Reconnaissance Party obviously had a very rough time of it in negotiating the icefall; but had the Khumbu been moving anywhere nearly as fast as Black Rapids Glacier, Shipton would have had to report that the route was impassable and that Everest was unassailable from this direction, with the result that the great peak might still be unconquered. As it turned out, the icefall, according to Hillary, was incomparably worse during the 1953 ascent than when the Shipton party was on it in 1951.

Because of slower motion toward the edges of glaciers, these parts may not be as badly crevassed as the centers. Thus it is sometimes possible to skirt crevassed zones by following a route near the edge of the ice, but as we can infer from Shipton's statement, and as all mountaineers know, use of such a route might be suicidal because of snow and ice avalanching from the steep valley sides. This forces climbers toward the center, often into the roughest part of the glacier.

Higher up where the ice is covered with snow and firn the going may be much easier, but even here one must be constantly on the alert. Many people have been injured and some have perished by breaking through weak snowbridges into deep crevasses.

In the late winter and early spring of 1898, several thousand prospectors, hoping to strike it rich in the newly discovered gold fields of the interior, landed at the port of Valdez near the head of the Gulf of Alaska. The only known passable route across the mountains into the interior lay over the Valdez-Klutina Pass. But the pass and the valleys on both sides were filled with more than twenty miles of ice—the Valdez Glacier to the south of the pass, the Klutina to the north. Ordinarily, a long grueling trek across such a forbidding thing as a glacier, in a region essentially unexplored at the time, would have caused most people who had spent their lives in Pittsburgh, Chicago, and other urban areas to hesitate and perhaps to decide to terminate their adventure there and then. But the hazards of this route to the interior were no deterrent to gold-hungry prospectors. Goaded on by the prospect of riches at the end of the trail, they struck out confidently from Valdez toward the terminus of the glacier four miles to the east, some carrying their provisions and gear on their backs, others pushing or pulling heavily laden sledges. Some of the more fortunate had teams of dogs, and a few even horses or mules.

Trouble was not long in coming. The place where they first set foot on the glacier, its steep crevassed terminus, was a warning of worse things to come. After this obstacle was surmounted, often after spills into crevasses and with considerable cursing and much sweating, the gently sloping surface of the glacier provided a fairly easy route. But at two or three places where the glacier apparently flows over steps in the valley floor, there are other steep crevassed sections. Tent towns sprang up at the foot of these more difficult parts of the trail. At times a tent town would be occupied by as many as 300 or 400 people, each awaiting his turn to follow the narrow, hazardous trail across the barrier. Just below the summit pass, the last major obstacle, a steep snow slope, reached after fifteen weary miles on the ice, reared up 1,000 feet high to discourage the fainthearted from pressing onward. So steep and long was this slope that sledges had to be pulled up it by block and tackle. There were large tent towns both at the bottom and the top of this slope. After attaining the pass, the prospectors could look down across six more miles of ice, but they could find some cheer in the knowledge that it was all downhill.

The full impact of the hardships these people had to endure comes only with the realization that most of the prospectors who followed this route required a month or more to transport their equipment and year's supply of food across these twenty-some miles of glacier trail. A man had to move his outfit in relays, as there was too much for a single load. Men spent much time pulling one another and their animals out of crevasses. In the late spring they had to wade through waist-deep slush from melting snow and ice—so bad that movement for a number of weeks was limited to night, when lower temperatures hardened the snow. Snowslides from the oversteepened valley sides were a constant threat, and many persons saw all their worldly goods, and their hopes along with them, buried irretrievably under snowslides. Many dogs and horses and some of the men were lost in slides and crevasses.

There are people everywhere who can fashion success out

of adversity. For a time, firewood was sold in the vicinity of the summit pass for a dollar a pound. For those glacier travelers who had no oilstoves, wood was almost as valuable as gold. They needed a lot of it for cooking and for heating their tents during the weeks that they were on the ice. The alternative to buying wood on the glacier was to cut a cord of it in the woods near Valdez and transport it, along with all their other provisions and gear, up the hazardous glacier trail.

The route to the Promised Land may be rough and fraught with almost unendurable hardships, but if hope is high and the expected rewards are great, many will follow it. The urge is strong and much the same, whether the goal be gold, knowledge, or the lure of unexplored lands and unconquered summits. Although the men who undergo the vicissitudes inherent in these quests are of many breeds, they all have some things in common —stamina, courage, the will to win, and enduring faith.

Despite the hardship and suffering, more than 4,000 prospectors used the Valdez-Klutina Glacier route in the spring of 1898. At one time an estimated 2,500 of them—a slowly moving string of human ants—were strung out over the glacier trail. It will probably be a long time before any of Alaska's modern highways experience so great a traffic congestion.

Several other glaciers in southeastern Alaska served as routes during the gold rush, but none approached the Valdez-Klutina in volume of traffic. By midsummer the influx had stopped, and many who had entered the interior earlier were already hiking back out on the glacier trail, anxious to flee the country which had taken all their worldly belongings and given them in return nothing better than suffering and frustration. The gold rush had been a short-run drama, but the glacier had played a most important role in it. The opening of a new trail in 1899 into the interior through the narrow canyon of the Lowe River, now followed by the Richardson Highway, practically put an end to travel on the glacier trail. Only a handful followed it from then on.

For a period of about fifteen years beginning in 1912, the pack trains which supplied the Ramsey-Rutherford Gold Mine used a trail which traversed the lower five miles of Valdez Glacier. But apparently no one followed the entire glacier route of the 1898 prospectors between 1900 and the summer of 1959, when Dr. Lawrence E. Nielsen led an expedition over it. Nielsen's group, however, was able to make the trip with considerably less discomfort than the seekers of fortune sixty-one years before. Each member of Nielsen's party, plus his food and equipment, was flown individually, because that is all the Super Cub could carry in one load from Valdez to the firn-covered ice near the summit pass. From here they followed the route down to the end of the Klutina Glacier, back to base camp at the pass, then down the Valdez Glacier to Valdez town. During the two weeks spent in the area they climbed six peaks, several of them first ascents, and explored some of the tributary glaciers. The '98-ers most certainly would have regarded such antics as sheer madness. But what wouldn't they have given for a plane ride across the mountains?

On the trip down the Klutina Glacier, members of the Nielsen party were thrilled to find hundreds of the prospectors' relics strung out along two or more miles of the old trail. There were snowshoes, parts of tents and dog sledges, pieces of partly burned wood, duffel bags, and even a woman's shoe. Some of the relics, abandoned or lost on the firn area, were coming out of the ice onto the surface after being buried in the glacier for sixty-one years. Shortly after starting down the Valdez Glacier, one of the party picked up a loaded pistol cartridge; soon they were finding all kinds of objects—shovels, canteens, shoes, oil-stoves, utensils, and many others. Amid their excitement the members of the expedition realized that they had found the site of the big tent town which had been located at the foot of the long steep slope below the summit pass—but now it was more than a mile farther down the valley. Had it been near the center of the glacier rather than along its edge, where friction against the valley sides slows the movement of the ice, it probably would have moved farther.

Among the relics there were numerous bones of dogs and a nearly complete horse's skeleton—mute evidence of the struggle in which men pushed themselves to the brink of exhaustion and their animals beyond it.

MOUNTAINEERS TAKE TO THE AIR

When Allen Carpé and Theodore Koven were landed from a
small ski-equipped plane high on the Muldrow Glacier on Mount
McKinley in 1932, a new era in mountaineering began. Now
there was another use to which the glaciers would be put. Planes
could transport men and supplies high onto the glaciers—even
into the cirques themselves—thus eliminating arduous treks of
many miles, back-packing supplies and equipment to the mountains, and then additional miles up long, crevassed glaciers.

This was not the first time that planes had used glaciers for
landing places. Landings had been made on the Jungfraujoch in
1919 and in 1928, and in 1921 Durafour had put his plane down
on the firn at about 14,500 feet near the summit of Mont Blanc.
But these were stunt landings undertaken mainly for the sake
of adventure.

A more serious use of glaciers for landing places was made
in 1929 when the First Byrd Antarctic Expedition landed its
planes on the ice sheet. Since then the airplane has been indis-
pensable in the exploration and scientific investigation of that
icebound continent.

But landing a plane on the nearly level snow surfaces that
cover vast reaches of both the Antarctic and Greenland ice
sheets is not quite the same as putting one down on a mountain glacier. Pilots who do this risky job have to fight the menace
of tricky winds—sudden updrafts and downdrafts and other un-
predictable vagaries of the air—which without warning can fling
a plane to destruction against encircling rock walls or drop it
as suddenly onto jagged glacier surfaces. After running a gaunt-
let of hazards such as this, a pilot may put his plane down on
a tiny sloping firn surface on the brink of a yawning crevasse.
Taking off is an equally exciting experience. But there are a
number of pilots for whom this sort of thing is routine, especially in Alaska, where the bush pilots had a lot of experience
landing on snowbanks in remote areas long before called upon
by mountaineers and scientists to undertake the higher, more
hazardous glacier landings and take-offs.

In many cases the spot on which a pilot puts his plane

down, no matter how precarious it may be, has been investigated from the air and perhaps also from the ground; and it probably is the most suitable place available. In 1950 Fredy Wissel of St. Moritz and Hermann Geiger of Sion began to put to serious use this new technique of landing at near-impossible spots high in the Alps. As a result of this pioneer effort, Alpine huts and hydroelectric installations are supplied and high-tension lines checked by airplane. Supplies are also flown in to mountain villages cut off by avalanches.

But the greatest risks are taken when pilots fly mercy missions to rescue people too sick or injured to be removed in any other way. Hermann Geiger has rescued by plane hundreds of injured skiers and mountaineers from one end of the Alps to the other. To do this he has even landed his Super Cub on little glacierettes clinging to steep cirque walls. For a while, his landing and take-off above 14,000 feet on Monte Rosa was the highest ever made by aircraft.

Altitude records of all kinds have a habit of being short-lived. In June 1959 Terris Moore, in conjunction with a U.S. Army Project for investigating the capability of aircraft for various uses in high mountain terrain, landed his Super Cub ski-plane on the ice-crowned summit of Mount Sanford in Alaska's Wrangell Range at an altitude of 16,200 feet, leading the way for two Army twin-rotor helicopters, which landed soon after.

Eleven months after airplanes had descended onto Sanford's summit snow, Linc Luckett made two helicopter landings at 17,400 feet on Mount McKinley to remove two injured climbers. At the same time bush pilot Don Sheldon, veteran of many mountain glacier landings, put his light plane down on McKinley's firn at 14,200 feet and removed a climber overcome by illness. This was a very daring rescue, especially so because he was guided in making his landing largely by instructions telephoned from Boston by Bradford Washburn, who probably knows more than any other man about McKinley's terrain and who himself pioneered in the use of aircraft in the exploration and study of Alaskan and Yukon glaciers.

Glaciers will continue to serve as highways to the high peaks and will be used more and more as landing fields for planes supporting both mountaineering and scientific expeditions. There is little justification for wearily carrying quantities of supplies and equipment great distances over rugged terrain, when the same thing can be done in a small fraction of the time by planes. And the sport of landing light planes high on mountain glaciers surely will become a venture in its own right. Terris Moore's landings on Mount Sanford were done partly in the interests of science, but he has called such landings the ". . . least spoiled sport, and the most sublime of them all."

Others have agreed with Moore, for now regular glacier landings have become a thriving tourist business in the Alps. Today at Sitten in Valais you can choose any of thirty standard sight-seeing air excursions from the airport, which include landings on the Rhone Glacier and a number of others in the vicinity of the Matterhorn, and even on the firn of Switzerland's highest mountain, Monte Rosa.

For a number of years supplies for mountaineering expeditions have been parachuted onto firn- and snow-covered glaciers. More recently men have landed on glaciers by this means. Men have even parachuted onto the firn atop Mont Blanc, but unless such stunts are undertaken by experienced mountaineers someone else may have to risk his life in a climb or a hazardous plane landing to rescue irresponsible people from an environment in which they could not long survive.

7

Where the Water Comes From

THROUGH countless streams, water from the glaciers finds its way into many of the largest rivers. Little rivulets from the glaciers of the high peaks in the Ruwenzori help to give the Nile—Earth's longest river—its start. Some of the water in the Amazon, mighty torrent of the tropics and Earth's largest river, is born amid the snow and ice of the high Andes. Much greater in volume and of more significance is the glacier water in the Indus, the Brahmaputra, and the sacred Ganges, all nurtured by the great ice streams in the Hindu Kush, the Karakoram, and the Himalayas. After the Indus leaves the mountains, it flows for 700 miles across the Indian Desert, returning to the sea the life-giving water which many years earlier was carried by the monsoon in the opposite direction across this parched land and dumped, as glacier-forming snow, on the high ranges of its upper reaches.

Many rivers emerge practically full-grown from glaciers. In Alaska alone there are hundreds: the Matanuska, the Chitina, and a number of tributaries of the Copper, to mention but a few. Melt water from glaciers in the mountains of British Columbia is a large factor in making the Columbia the third largest river in the United States.

The Rhone and the Po, the Rhine and the Danube feel the effect of the glaciers in the Alps. Because of their glaciers, along with their high elevation and heavy precipitation, the Alps are one of the largest potential sources of hydroelectric power in all of Europe. Each summer after the snow at lower elevations has disappeared, great quantities of water released by the melting glaciers continue to feed the streams. The glaciers also constitute a vast reserve supply of water as insurance against the years when diminished snowfall and drier conditions may come again to the region, as they did before and during the Middle Ages. Should such a period recur, the glaciers, even though receding, might continue to supply water to the streams for many years, perhaps even throughout a very long, warm, dry period.

Since several of the larger Alpine glaciers are the sources of water used for the generation of electricity, they have been very intensively studied. Their thickness, rate of motion, and the amount of water yielded by melting have been determined with great accuracy over a period of years. Each year the advance or retreat of the fronts of a large number of glaciers is carefully observed. There are questions to be answered. How long a warm, dry period can the glaciers survive? Are the glaciers shrinking or are they expanding? And at what rate?

With their ever-increasing need for electricity and the ever-present possibility that the ice may advance into their villages and across their lines of communication, is it any wonder that the Swiss and their near neighbors maintain a close watch on the glaciers? The destiny of these people is tied closely to the behavior of streams of ice.

Not only in the Alps, but in other densely populated regions, glaciers are kept under close surveillance because of the effect which their variations might have upon the uses of their water—irrigation, municipal supply, hydroelectric power, and others. The city of Boulder, Colorado has the distinction of owning its own glacier, a small one, Arapaho, but nonetheless a constant source of pure, cold water for the city.

Nisqually Glacier on Mount Rainier is one of the most carefully observed glaciers in the United States, since it and several nearby ice streams are the principal source of the Nisqually River, on which the city of Tacoma is dependent for hydroelectric power. Every five years geologists make a detailed map of the lower two miles of the glacier in order to determine changes in the volume of the ice. This mapping project was initiated in 1931 because of a long period of world-wide glacier recession, greatly accelerated after 1920, which had caused an alarming shrinkage of Nisqually Glacier.

During the past forty years many small glaciers in the Rockies, Cascades, and other mountain ranges have disappeared. Numerous streams which formerly continued to flow with significant volume after the last snow had melted away in the spring now are greatly reduced in size or even disappear during the dry part of the summer.

Many communities in the western states and Canadian Provinces, dependent upon glacier-fed streams for their water supply, are experiencing unprecedented expansion, a trend destined to continue for years to come. It is almost certain that these communities are basing their future water-supply forecasts on stream-flow measurements made during the past several decades, a time of accelerated glacier shrinkage. The runoff from glaciers during this period has been high, because it has included water from both current precipitation and from melting of ice that came from snow in earlier times, in some cases as long as several hundred years ago. The predictions could create a false sense of security and lead to severe future water shortages, not only if the glaciers should melt away, but also if a reversal in the climatic trend should cause them to stop shrinking and thus lock up the snow in their icy reservoirs.

Even the increased glacier-melting of the present time seems not to be sufficient to satisfy civilization's insatiable demand. Man is attempting to extract from glaciers more water than they yield by natural melting.

For many years Chinese peasants in some of the western provinces reputedly have been "blackening" glaciers by spread-

ing thin films of *loess,* the wind-blown silt so common in parts
of China, over the ice in order to hasten melting and thus gain
more water for crop irrigation. More recently the Russians
have found by experimenting on glaciers in the Tien Shan that a
thin layer of coal dust, spread over the ice surface at the rate of
about thirteen tons to the square mile, greatly accelerated melting by increasing the absorption of solar radiation, and that it
is possible by such methods to increase the annual runoff in
mountain rivers by more than fifty per cent. Such tactics, however, must be employed with some care, lest we use up our icy
principal as well as the interest and eliminate a dependable
source of water. Many years might be required for a glacier destroyed in this way to form again. And it might never regain its
former size.

   Although it appears that by conversion of sea water to fresh
the water-supply problem in coastal areas may someday be less
acute, it would pay us to remember that the wise use of the
method of producing water by blackening glaciers might pre-
clude the need here and there for the construction of expensive
dams, all of which sooner or later are made useless by filling of
the reservoir with sediment. Actually, there probably won't be
much danger of eliminating glaciers by the blackening method
until the problem of how to transport huge quantities of blackening material is solved. But this may be no real deterrent to the
Chinese government, with limitless masses of man power at its
command.

TOO MUCH WATER

The hardy people of Iceland, who have had to contend with both
glaciers and volcanoes ever since the island was first settled, are
aware of what happens when a large part of a glacier is suddenly converted into water. In this harsh land a number of active volcanoes are covered with glaciers. Eruptions have given
rise to devastating floods. Dr. Sigurdur Thorarinsson in his paper, "The Thousand Years Struggle Against Ice and Fire," * de-

   * *Museum of Natural History, Department of Geology and Geography, Miscellaneous Papers,* No. 14 (Reykjavik; 1956).

scribes one of these "glacier bursts" caused by the volcano Katla in 1918, which had a maximum discharge of water estimated at three times that at the mouth of the Amazon River. This flood wiped out all traces of life on a wide plain which had been settled for hundreds of years.

Beneath the western part of Vatnajökull, Iceland's largest icecap, there is a permanent center of volcanic heat which continuously melts the ice from below, forming a huge subglacier reservoir. On an average of once every ten years the bulk of this water is released as a flood which breaks out from under the edge of one of the principal outlet glaciers.

Wherever there are glaciers, with the exception of frigid Antarctica, there are floods of another sort. These are from ice-dammed lakes gushing out intermittently from along the margins of the ice. When a glacier recedes beyond the mouth of a tributary valley in which it has created a lake by blocking a stream, the water in the lake bursts forth in a torrent, a flood ensues, and the lake is quickly drained. If the glacier should then advance again, it might seal off the tributary valley, re-creating the lake. Subsequent recession would again liberate the lake water, causing another flood. Some glaciers have been behaving in this manner for many years.

Not only is damage done by the rushing waters of the floods, but the lakes themselves may inundate valuable land. One of Argentina's largest glaciers, the Moreno, which drains an extensive ice field on the crest of the Andes, has been advancing for many years across the valley of Lago Rico. In 1939 the inhabitants of the valley watched helplessly as the lake, blocked by the tongue of ice, rose twenty-one feet above normal. Eventually this dammed-up water escaped by breaking through crevasses and enlarging them into a channel or by floating the ice and escaping beneath it. In 1942 continued advance of the glacier again blocked the valley and raised the lake—this time nearly fifty-six feet—inundating many thousands of acres of farming and grazing land.

The breaking out of a glacier-dammed lake in the Andes in 1934 caused a flash flood on Argentina's Mendoza River which took a number of lives and destroyed seven railway bridges and nearly eight miles of track on the Transandine Railway.

Elsewhere in the Andes other ice-dammed lakes occur from time to time, and in all cases their relatively short lives are terminated by floods. In the Peruvian Andes the severe floods from the bursting of glacial lakes are known as *huaycos*.

Numerous ice-dammed lakes are present along the margins of Vatnajökull's largest outlet glaciers. The water of these lakes rises until it is deep enough to float the ice barrier holding it in. As soon as the critical depth is reached, the ice barrier floats and the lake drains underneath it in a rushing torrent. Iceland's largest glacial lake, which formerly emptied approximately every four years, now bursts out from behind its ice dam about every two years, because the glacier confining it has been getting thinner. The water in the lake does not have to rise as high in order to float the ice; hence less time is required to fill the lake.

Among the many glacier-dammed lakes reported from Alaska, Lake George, about forty air-miles from Anchorage, is the most famous—and probably the largest in the world. Knik Glacier, a twenty-five-mile stream of ice with its source on the highest part of the Chugach Mountains, terminates several miles downstream from the mouth of a large tributary valley, effectively sealing it off with a dam of ice nearly seven miles wide. Lake George lies in the tributary valley behind this ice barrier. Each year during spring and early summer, rains and melting snow and ice swell the lake until it is about fourteen miles long and from two to four wide. Then the overflow begins along the channel between the edge of the glacier and the valley side, first as a trickle and then in a few hours as a roaring torrent. This stream, bordered for five miles by hard rock of the mountain on one side and the glacier on the other, quickly deepens its channel by cutting into the ice. Great chunks of undermined ice crash down into the swirling water, shattering into myriads of fragments. Some of the chunks of ice are carried by the Knik River twenty-five miles to tidewater.

Lake George's flood sometimes washes out sections of the Anchorage-Palmer Highway, which crosses the Knik River seventeen miles from the end of the glacier, and the Alaska Railway, seven miles farther downstream.

The overflow usually begins in late July or early August.

After about a week the lake is drained and the flood is done. Motion of the glacier during the winter slowly squeezes shut the outlet channel, and by April the stage is set for re-creation of the lake and another late-summer outburst. Few people have visited Lake George, and fewer still have been there when its raging flood was pouring noisily along the front of Knik Glacier, but millions of people all over the world have witnessed this awe-inspiring spectacle in Walt Disney's great motion picture, *White Wilderness*.

For a distance of 870 miles between Anchorage and the Portland Canal at the southern tip of the Alaska panhandle, only two highways pierce the coast ranges to link interior Alaska and Yukon with tidewater. Another, the Copper River Highway, only about one-third completed, will be continually threatened by glaciers in a position to advance upon it should climatic changes, earthquakes, or some other phenomenon set them to advancing.

Roads cannot be constructed over the coastal mountains because all passes are filled with ice. The only routes available for future highways are in three or four valleys which rivers have cut through the mountains. The two which seem destined to be followed by roads in the near future are the Stikine and Taku. A road through the Taku Valley would connect a large isolated section of northern British Columbia to the sea at Juneau. The lower part of this valley, however, is flooded annually by the breaking out of Tulsequah Lake, impounded behind Tulsequah Glacier, which lies just inside the British Columbia boundary but drains ice from the Juneau Ice Field in Alaska. The valley of the Stikine is also periodically flooded by the bursting of an ice-dammed lake.

A tremendous road-building program is about to get under way in Alaska. In a few years hundreds of miles of highways will be laid across areas which are now virgin wilderness, to tap forest and mineral wealth and to open up vast sections to agriculture. Some of these roads will be pushed up valleys to the glacier tongues themselves. Others will be constructed alongside glaciers. And still more miles of roads will be built along and across streams which drain glaciers and carry the flood waters of ice-dammed lakes.

The Alaskans will have to continue to live with their glaciers and floods. Ice-dammed lakes will form where none now exists. So the planning done for the new highways, and the settlements which will surely follow them, must be marked by foresight and by an understanding of the forces of Nature displayed so vigorously there. Otherwise lives will surely be lost, damage to property will be continuous and great, and highway maintenance costs will be staggering.

Sometimes during the height of the melting season, very heavy, warm rains may fall on a glacier. Then the normal melting, the heavy rain, and the accelerated melting caused by the rain, each capable of making a heavy flow, combine to produce a flood, in some cases as violent as those from the breaking out of glacier lakes. Several floods of this type have left their mark on Mount Rainier. In 1947 Kautz Creek below Kautz Glacier went on a rampage after heavy, warm rains had fallen on the glacier. When the ensuing flood was over, not a trace remained of the lowermost mile of the glacier.

The sudden release of tremendous volumes of water during glacier bursts makes the resulting floods unique. There is no warning in the form of a slow rise of the stream. The first sign of the flood is the flood itself, a wall of rushing water moving at high velocity down the valley. The energy of such a fast-moving mass of water is incredible. Almost everything in its path is swept up and carried away. One of the huaycos in the Cordillera Blanca in Peru placed a boulder fifteen feet in diameter on the side of a valley eighty feet above the stream bed and buried the lower part of the valley under a blanket of rock debris 140 feet thick.

Since glacier bursts have taken lives, have destroyed towns, hydroelectric installations, and transportation lines, and have ruined agricultural land, various kinds of attempts have been made to reduce the damage they do. In a number of cases watchers have been posted to send out warnings when a flood was imminent. The floods from Lake George and the lake at Tulsequah Glacier occur about the same time each summer, so they take no one by surprise. But it has been necessary during the danger season to station men with heavy equipment at the railway and highway bridges on the Knik River in order to remove floating debris caught in the structures. On one occasion when Moreno Glacier in Argentina raised the level of Lago Rico, several 500-kilogram bombs were dropped from government aircraft in an unsuccessful attempt to break up the ice dam.

For hundreds of years, especially from the fifteenth to nineteenth centuries, floods from glacier-dammed lakes have plagued the inhabitants of glacier valleys in the Alps. And it is there that the most elaborate projects for the control of such outbursts have been made. The repeated flood from Marjelen Lake, dammed by the Great Aletsch Glacier, has been eliminated by diversion of its waters through a tunnel driven through an adjacent mountain into another valley. Now, before the lake rises to the critical level, its waters drain off slowly and harmlessly through the tunnel.

The Norwegian government is also carrying on extensive studies of glacier-dammed lakes and is making plans to construct diversion tunnels at one of the lakes at the Svartisen Ice Field in the northern part of the country, in order to prevent flood damage. It is probable that before long similar measures may be used to control floods from some of the glacier-dammed lakes in Alaska.

FLOODS OF ANOTHER DAY

Men who have witnessed these modern floods have written descriptions of them and their effects. But long before man learned to record his thoughts, even on slabs of clay, there were bigger and better glacier bursts than modern man has ever seen. Some of the largest lakes the world has ever known were formed by the retreating ice sheets which at one time covered much of North America and Europe. Deep valleys now containing streams far too small to have cut them, and in some cases no running water at all, mark the channels fashioned by some of these ancient deluges.

When glaciers filled the valleys of the Northern Rockies and spread southward and westward to the edge of the vast Columbia Plateau, repeated floods in the form of great sheets of melt water poured across the plateau. Some geologists believe

that the bulk of the water came from the periodic breaking out
of a vast lake, Lake Missoula, dammed in by the glaciers in western Montana. All agree that the flood was glacial melt water. It
debouched onto the Columbia Plateau in the vicinity of the present site of Spokane, Washington. It fanned out toward the southwest, inundating thousands of square miles and converting hundreds of small valleys into deep trenches known now as *coulees*.
This impressive system of trenches, among which the Grand
Coulee is the best known, gives the name Channeled Scablands to
the region. The rampaging waters were then funneled into the
gorge of the lower Columbia River for passage through the Cascade Mountains in a single powerful stream to the sea.

If this flood could be repeated today, it would pour over the
city of Spokane. It would sweep away Grand Coulee and Bonneville Dams and the Hanford Works of the Atomic Energy Com-
mission, would strip away the soil from millions of acres of
agricultural land and spread many feet of sand and gravel over
other millions of acres, and then, pouring down through the
lower gorge of the Columbia, would wipe out Vancouver and
Portland.

Today the arid and semi-arid Channeled Scablands, some
of them too dry for agricultural use, are being subjected to another flood. This one, in the form of water for irrigation, has its
source in the glaciers and ice fields of the Canadian Rockies,
shrunken remnants of those which poured out the spectacular
flood of earlier times. The Grand Coulee with its now-dry waterfalls and plunge pools—marks of the foaming torrent which
once flashed through it—is the site of a peaceful reservoir. Its
water, source of irrigation for millions of acres of desert land,
is pumped up from Roosevelt Lake, the 125-mile-long body of
water held back by Grand Coulee Dam.

8

The Ice Age in Full Swing

THE BIG ICE SHEETS

THE 1,600-mile-long Greenland sheet has a maximum width of 600 miles, and much of this vast area lies above the snowline. Although there are some visible surface features such as broad depressions, swells, and even valleys, most of the interior is a monotonous plain. Near the edge of the sheet the ice is deflected around hills which project through it to form nunataks. Where the ice is thicker it overrides these obstructions, but their presence is indicated by undulations on the glacier surface. Farther inland where the ice is 3,000 or more feet thick, irregularities on the buried land surface are for the most part undetectable on the surface of the ice.

One by one the thin layers of snow, spread over the immense expanse above the encircling snowline, are covered and compacted by later layers and converted into firn. As the firn becomes ice, it moves farther and farther downward and outward toward the edge of the sheet. Eventually ice from the very center of the sheet must reach the edge. Some of this ice may travel 300 to 400 miles along a route and over a period of time which are as yet unknown.

At several places the edge of the sheet pushes beyond the coast out into the sea. Along the shore of Melville Bay, on the west coast near the big U.S. Air Force base at Thule, ice forms the shoreline for a distance of nearly 250 miles.

Around much of Greenland, however, there is an ice-free border. At Thule it is twelve miles wide and at Godthaab, the island's capital, its width is seventy miles. In several places this marginal zone is well over 100 miles wide. Within this bare area are many small detached glaciers, icecaps as well as valley glaciers.

As the inland ice pushes outward against the barrier of coastal mountains—and much of Greenland's perimeter is mountainous—inexorable pressure of the mass behind it concentrates the flow into valleys where the outlet glaciers carry it through the mountains. Thus ice which is moving with inconceivable slowness in the interior quickens its pace as it approaches these exits.

Flowing down through the mountains and then on to tidewater, these ice tongues scour out the fiords through which they flow and transport rock debris into the sea. Neither of these accomplishments, however, is much in evidence. These ice streams, unlike valley glaciers in the mountains, carry most of their load along the bottom, very little on top. And this material is deposited out of sight beneath the water of the fiords. Very little debris slides or falls onto the largest outlet glaciers because they practically engulf the mountains through which they pass.

The most visible activity of these glaciers—and really spectacular—is the delivery of ice to the sea. This they do on a grand scale. Where the edge of the Greenland ice sheet rests in the sea, a great deal of ice calves * directly from it, but most of the bergs are produced by the fast-moving outlet glaciers. No one knows how much ice debouches into the seas along Greenland's coast, but some estimates run as high as 125 cubic miles a year—enough to make a sizable crop of icebergs. Rink Glacier on the west coast has dumped an estimated 500,000,000 tons

* The breaking of chunks of ice from a glacier where it rests in a body of water is known as *calving*.

of ice into the sea in a time span of a few minutes—and it re-peats this feat about once every two weeks. Many of the bergs calved from these glaciers are several hundred yards long, some a mile or more, and they tower as much as 300 feet above the water. An estimated 10,000 to 15,000 large bergs break loose an-nually along the shores of Greenland.

The largest bergs are calved when the front part of an out-let glacier enters water deep enough to float it. Then the end of the glacier is raised by the buoyancy of the water and is literally torn loose, often along large crevasses. Other bergs, usually smaller, are calved when the ice in the lower part of the glacier front is melted by sea water, undermining the upper part which eventually drops off for lack of support. Bergs created in this way often plunge beneath the water with a mighty roar, to reappear a moment later in a great upward surge, sometimes with a roll like a giant porpoise. Then after a few ponderous but diminishing bobs up and down, they reach equilibrium and slowly float away.

After reaching the open sea, east-coast bergs are caught in the south-moving East Greenland Current. This current car-ries them around Cape Farewell, the southern tip of the island, to meet the West Greenland Current, which takes them into Davis Strait, where many of them finally disappear. Most west-coast bergs move initially northward on this same current, some of them for several hundred miles, into Baffin Bay where they swing westward toward the shore of Baffin Island. Then, caught up by the cold Labrador Current flowing down from the Arctic Ocean, they move southward along the east coast of Labrador. Those which do not become grounded in shallow water to slowly rot away eventually drift south of Newfoundland and across the busy North Atlantic shipping lanes. The number of these farthest travelers varies greatly from year to year. Sometimes there are more than 1,000. There have been years when fewer than twenty were reported.

After breaking from their parent glacier, some of these bergs may travel for three years and cover 2,500 miles. Many of them are large enough when they enter the shipping lanes to constitute a serious menace to ships, especially since the zone south of Newfoundland is characterized by frequent and heavy

fog. It was the *Titanic* disaster on the edge of the Gulf Stream
in 1912, caused by a berg just like many that ride the North
Atlantic shipping lanes today, that led to establishment of the
International Ice Patrol, supported by fourteen nations and conducted by the U.S. Coast Guard. By means of ships and planes,
the patrol follows wandering bergs, warning other ships to detour south of the danger zone.

Although most bergs which reach the Gulf Stream melt
rapidly in the warm water and soon disappear, some have been
carried much farther south. Bergs have reached Bermuda
and the Azores, and in June 1934 one was sighted in the middle of the North Atlantic Ocean at Latitude 31° north (the
latitude of Jacksonville, Florida), 2,000 miles due south of the
southern tip of Greenland. It is a good thing these farthest travelers are quite small and capable only of knocking a few chips of
paint from a ship's hull or at best making a small dent.

Fortunately, few ships collide with icebergs. From the
Titanic disaster until 1959, the only loss of life from such a
mishap occurred during World War II when a merchant ship
sank after colliding with a berg in the North Atlantic. This
ship had had no warning because during the war years the ice
patrol had been temporarily discontinued. Submarines were a
far greater menace than bergs.

But the fate of the Danish passenger-cargo ship, *Hans
Hedtoft,* on January 30, 1959, is a grim reminder that, despite
radar and other modern aids to navigation, the danger of icebergs has been far from eliminated. The *Hans Hedtoft* was an
ultramodern vessel built especially for winter use in northern
waters. Her hull had a double steel bottom, was armored bow
and stern, and contained seven watertight compartments. She
was equipped with radar and the most modern electronic aids
for navigation. Her builders, like those who had designed and
built the *Titanic,* regarded her as essentially unsinkable. On the
outward leg of her maiden voyage from Copenhagen to Godthaab, Greenland, all had been well. When she sailed from
Godthaab on January 29 for the return run to Copenhagen,
there was little reason to believe that this part of her voyage
would be more eventful than the first. But the next morning—
the day the Coast Guard started its annual ice patrol—soon

after rounding Cape Farewell at the southern tip of Greenland, the vessel collided in heavy seas with an iceberg and radioed that she was sinking.

For several days a search was carried on by the West German trawler, *Johannes Kreuss,* which reached the scene of the disaster an hour after the last radio message was received, and by several other vessels, including the Coast Guard cutter *Campbell,* and by planes. But not a trace of the *Hedtoft* or any of its ninety-five passengers and crew was found. Among the passengers, ironically enough, was Augo Lynge, a Greenland member of the Danish Parliament, who had vigorously opposed construction of the ship because he regarded the use of passenger vessels to Greenland too dangerous in January, February, and March. Also aboard ship were thirteen crates of irreplaceable national archives, including documents dating back to 1780, being taken to Denmark for safekeeping.

Even though the *Hans Hedtoft* went down far outside the area in which the ice patrol normally operates, this ship's master, Captain P. L. Rasmussen, was a veteran of many years' sailing in the Arctic and one of his country's most respected Polar seamen. Furthermore, the tragedy occurred in waters where bergs are known to be abundant at all times. Yet this ship is no more!

Collisions between ships are not uncommon. An iceberg is just another ship, but one which has no pilot. Icebergs cannot be readily detected by radar, for ice apparently is not a very efficient radar reflector. With hundreds or even thousands of these unmanned ships of ice roaming the North Atlantic, is it any wonder that ship captains are glad to heed the ice patrol's warnings? Many of these bergs are far larger than the biggest ocean liners. The berg that destroyed the 45,000-ton *Titanic* was estimated to have a displacement of 200,000 tons. And there are some more enormous than this. In an encounter with such a berg, the ship almost certainly would come out second best.

The Antarctic ice sheet also contributes ice to the sea. Bergs calve off along much of the coast because the ice sheet itself comprises a large part of the continent's coastline. There are also many huge outlet glaciers. The Beardmore, Leverett, and Robert Scott Glaciers, draining into Ross Sea, are each over

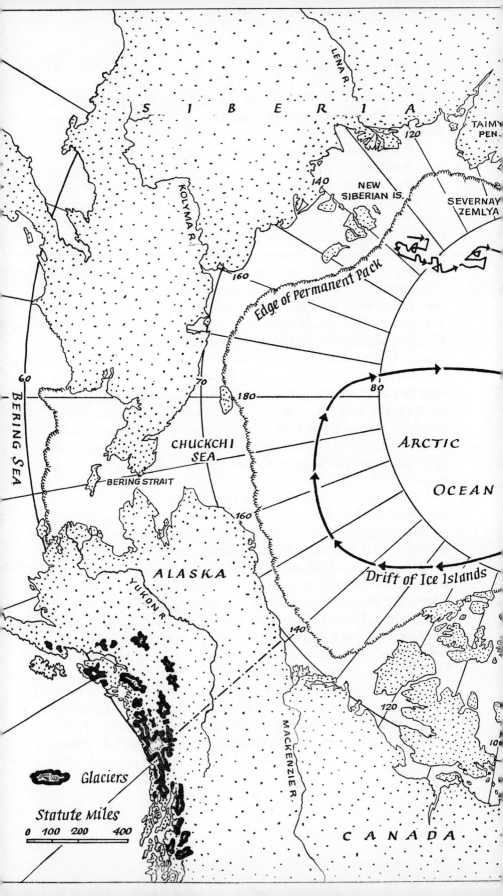

The Arctic

100 miles long. But none of these glaciers contributes a single iceberg directly to the sea. As they enter the sea they merge into and help to nourish a great floating sheet of ice as large as the state of California and known as the Ross Ice Shelf. Tremendously deep firn over its surface is proof that glaciers are not responsible for all the ice in it. Apparently, as the glacier ice pushes farther and farther into the sea, it thins by melting at the bottom, but the loss is partly compensated for by addition of firn on top. By the time this moving ice reaches the outer edge of the shelf, several hundred miles from shore, there may be little remaining glacier ice in it. All the ice shelves scattered around the rim of the continent are similar to the Ross Shelf, although some of the others contain a higher proportion of glacier ice.

IGY scientists determined from seismic soundings and drilling that the Ross Shelf in the vicinity of Little America Station, which is located on it, varies in thickness from about 790 to 1,050 feet and is floating on more than 1,000 feet of water. The edge of the shelf, which stretches across the entire 500-mile width of the Ross Sea, rises as a cliff from 100 to 150 feet above the water. Nearer the Queen Maud Mountains, where most of its ice has been contributed directly by outlet glaciers, the shelf is thicker and consequently its surface is at a higher elevation. The edge of the shelf moves seaward about five feet a year, a sure indication that glacier ice is being added to it constantly.

From time to time sections of the shelf break loose and float out to sea in the form of huge tabular icebergs. At the time they break loose some of these bergs have lengths of fifty to 100 miles and contain more ice than any of the world's largest valley glaciers. An Antarctic berg measuring sixty by 208 miles —larger than the state of Massachusetts—was reported by the Navy icebreaker U.S.S. *Glacier* in 1956. Because of their tremendous size, some of the Antarctic bergs probably float around the southern seas for ten or more years. Although many bergs float into the South Atlantic to the latitude of Buenos Aires, no ice patrol checks on their progress because they never drift close to the world's busy shipping lanes.

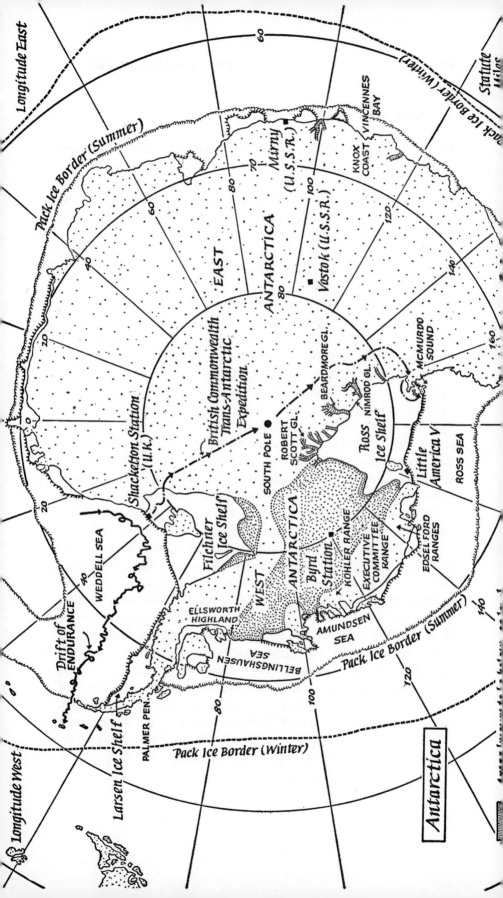

Antarctica

CREVASSES

In the immense interior plains of Greenland and Antarctica there are extensive areas in which crevasses are scarce. Ice motion is so imperceptibly slow and so uniform in rate that they just can't develop. Where the ice passes over uneven surfaces or is deflected around mountains, or where its flow is funneled into outlet glaciers, crevasses are apt to form on a grand scale. In the imposing crevassed zone where the Antarctic ice sheet flows down from the Rockefeller Plateau to the Ross Ice Shelf there are crevasses several miles long and nearly 100 feet wide.

Many crevasses when covered by a bridge of drifted snow can be crossed in safety, especially if the members of a party are wearing skis and are roped together. Snow bridges may even be strong enough to support dog sledges carrying heavy loads. But in recent decades dog-sledging has been giving way to the use of motorized vehicles. This is especially true of major over-ice expeditions in both Greenland and Antarctica. Dog-sledging, however, is not about to become a thing of the past. Dog teams were even used by the British Commonwealth Trans-Antarctic Expedition, led by Dr. Vivian E. Fuchs, to scout the route ahead of the vehicles and to make side trips. But the usefulness of these animals ended when the expedition reached the Pole, because the remainder of the route had already been explored and marked, and the dogs, slower than the vehicles, would have retarded the advance. So the dogs were flown out to the base at McMurdo Sound. This, it seems, is what is in store for sledge dogs more and more as time goes by. Men, dogs, and equipment will be flown from an advance base to a locality on the ice where local exploration or scientific projects are to be done. When their work has been completed the dogs will be flown out or to another assignment where they are needed.

The rolling stock of the big motorized over-ice expeditions may include sno-cats, U.S. Army weasels, and various kinds of tractors with big cargo sleds capable of transporting many tons. Few indeed are the snow bridges which can support such weight. When the adjacent ice is snow-covered there may be no visible sign of the buried crevasses to persons traveling on the glacier surface, but these fractures must in some way be detected in advance of the approach of the vehicles.

Crevasse detection can be done from the air, but communicating the exact location of individual crevasses to a ground party by an aircraft is a difficult task, and aircraft are not always available or able to do the job. The thing which has probably contributed more to the safety of over-ice travel with heavy vehicles than any other piece of equipment is the electrical crevasse detector. Since its prowess was demonstrated in Greenland in 1955, it has become standard equipment for a number of exploring parties on the big ice sheets. It was first used in the Antarctic in 1956 by the Army-Navy Trail Party which established the 600-mile tractor route from Little America Station to the site of the United States IGY Byrd Station in the heart of West Antarctica.

The detector is carried by the lead vehicle of a party, usually a weasel because of its light weight. In addition to a recording device, the detector consists of electrodes in dishpan-like mounts, attached to a frame which is pushed along the surface thirty to forty feet in front of the vehicle. An electrical current fed into one set of electrodes passes through the snow and ice to the other set. Fluctuations in this current, occasioned by the different densities of snow and firn, are continuously recorded on the warning device in the cab of the vehicle. When the frame bearing the electrodes is pushed out onto the less dense snow bridging a crevasse, the current abruptly weakens and immediately buzzers and flashing lights in the cabin warn of the danger. The device has functioned satisfactorily at speeds up to twenty miles per hour, though at such rates the weasel driver may find himself in a crevasse almost as soon as the lights begin to flash.

In some of the big over-ice trail-construction operations during the IGY, crevassed areas along projected routes of travel could not be avoided. In such cases snow bridges were dynamited into the crevasses, additional snow was bulldozed in, the fill was compacted and graded, and then the heavy tractors and cargo sleds could cross in safety.

In both Greenland and Antarctica a number of vehicles and men have broken through snow bridges and plunged into crevasses. In some cases the men were rescued; in a number of cases they lost their lives. Some of the vehicles which have broken through snow bridges and fallen into crevasses have dropped as much as seventy-five feet before becoming wedged, and men have been reported to have fallen 150 feet into these wedge-shaped openings. In the extreme cold of Greenland and Antarctica the brittle surface zone on the ice sheets apparently is thicker than on glaciers in temperate zones. This may be the reason for deeper crevasses on the colder glaciers. On Alaskan glaciers, for example, crevasses exceeding 100 feet in depth are rare.

The hazards of over-ice travel are still great but the crevasse detector and careful aerial reconnaissance have materially reduced them.

HOW OLD IS THE ICE?

No one yet knows where the ice which originates in the great central heart of East Antarctica reaches the coast. Some of it travels at least 1,000 miles, perhaps a great deal farther. Even if it were moving at an average rate of a foot a day, the trip would require 15,000 to 20,000 years. The rate, however, may be much slower, since some of the outlet glaciers, which undoubtedly flow much faster than ice in the vast interior, move little more than a foot a day. Is it possible that some of the most ancient ice in Antarctica is a million or more years old? Perhaps! But at the moment all we can do is conjecture. Someday, after scientists process the voluminous data they collected during the 1957–8 International Geophysical Year, and make additional observations, we will know the answer. Already the ice sheets are beginning to give up their age secrets.

An important objective of glaciological work on the Greenland and Antarctic ice sheets is the sampling of ice at great depth below the surface. During the IGY most of this was done by means of rotary core drills, actually pipes with a cutting edge on one end, similar to those used to obtain rock cores. The drill, rotated by power supplied by a gasoline motor, forces its way downward, enclosing and trapping an ever-lengthening core of firn or ice in the pipe. The sections of core, periodically broken free and pulled to the surface, can be fitted together to make a continuous section through the firn and ice from the surface to the point of deepest drill penetration. Complete cores more than 1,000 feet long have been taken from the ice sheets in both Greenland and Antarctica and from the Ross Ice Shelf. More recently the Army has been testing a thermal drill which it hopes will be capable of drilling through more than two miles of ice. This drill, also a pipelike device, removes a core from the glacier but does so by melting rather than cutting. The electrically heated drill melts into the ice at a speed of about six inches per minute. Melt water is sucked into a tank in the upper part of the drill where it is stored until the drill is removed from the hole—after each ten feet of core has been trapped in it. The designers of this drill are confident that it will be able to drill through 12,000 feet of ice to bedrock at Byrd Station in Antarctica. Some of the cores, after a preliminary examination in the field, are packed in dry ice and shipped to laboratories for detailed examination.

Some of the first cores taken in Antarctica were shipped in the Navy's icebreaker, *Glacier*, to Boston, and then transported in refrigerated trucks to the U.S. Army's Snow, Ice and Permafrost Research Establishment (SIPRE) * near Chicago, 10,000 miles from their starting point. The hundreds of motorists who passed these trucks thought—if they thought about it at all— that here were just more hard-to-pass trucks with more beer, furniture, or television sets, never dreaming that they were carrying age-old ice from the bottom of the world.

Fortunately, in Greenland annual ice strata hundreds if not thousands of years old are recognizable. This is especially true where summer temperatures are high enough to melt the surface snow and firn. After refreezing and burial under more snow, these former icy crusts become visible layers with a texture quite different from that of unmelted firn. SIPRE scientists found that ice from a Greenland core at a depth of 165 feet represented snow that fell during the American Civil War.

* In 1961 SIPRE was replaced by the U.S. Army Cold Regions Research and Engineering Laboratory (CRREL) with headquarters at Hanover, New Hampshire.

Somewhere down below this is an ice layer from snow that fell on Greenland while Washington's men suffered through the winter at Valley Forge.

Over much of interior Greenland and practically all of Antarctica there are no dust films, and because the temperature is always below the melting point, in some cases far below, there are no melt crusts to mark annual layers. In such places glaciologists are hard put to make age determinations of the ice, especially if there are no known key horizons such as the 1912 layer in northern Greenland * which can be used for correlation.

To find out more about the change of snow into firn and eventually into ice and to determine age relationships, deep pits have been excavated in the firn at scientific stations and bases in both Antarctica and Greenland. In the walls of these pits scientists can study the changing features of the firn as it increases in density and undergoes other changes with increasing depth below the surface. In interior Antarctica, where continuous low temperatures do not allow easily recognizable melt features to form, it was found that summer and winter snow layers are different in appearance. Winter layers are relatively thick and the snow as a rule is fine-grained and closely packed; summer snow is coarser, loosely packed, and thin-layered.

The recent discovery of very thin icy crusts on the high, cold, interior plateau of Antarctica, where temperatures are always far below 32°F., has been rather perplexing. Some scientists believe that these form from the freezing of supercooled rain or mist when it hits the surface or from melting caused by direct radiation from the sun.

The chief Soviet glaciologist, P. A. Shumskii, has advanced an interesting theory for the formation of these crusts. He believes they may be formed by the sun's rays penetrating along the vertical axis of suitably oriented snow crystals and melting them from the inside in a sort of "greenhouse" effect. If this theory should be proved correct, there is a possibility that accurate age determination can be made, because such crusts could not form in the absence of the sun during the long Antarctic night.

* See p. 27.

Some of the most satisfactory pits, as far as identification of annual layers is concerned, have been dug at the sites of former camps or bases where materials and equipment abandoned on known dates can serve as reference points with which to check the age of the strata in the pit walls. A twenty-three-foot pit dug in the summer of 1958 on the Ross Ice Shelf at the site of Admiral Byrd's 1939 camp, Little America III, exposed his ill-fated snow cruiser, a huge, buslike vehicle which he had hoped could be driven into the heart of the continent, but which, disappointingly, bogged down and became useless almost as soon as it was unloaded from the ship. The vehicle was found resting on the 1939–40 summer snow layer. Layers in the pit wall showed that ten years were required to bury the cruiser, and that in the succeeding eight years another twelve feet of snow were deposited on top of it. Each of the eighteen annual layers is identifiable in the walls of the pit; some are separated by ice crusts, and the top of the 1947–8 layer is marked by chips of paint which fell onto the snow from the hull of the cruiser.

Many of you can recall the great interest created by the snow cruiser during its 1,000-mile trip from Chicago, where it was built, to the point of embarkation at Boston. Because of its nineteen-foot width—as wide as some of the highways over which it passed—it blocked traffic wherever it went, and in eastern Massachusetts created the greatest traffic jam in the history of the state, tens of thousands of cars strung out in a nearly endless line behind it. Thousands of people lined the highways in an effort to get a glimpse of the behemoth machine that was going to carry man in comfort across the icy wastes of Antarctica, perhaps even to the Pole itself. Now it lies in the bottom of a snow pit near the edge of the Ross Ice Shelf where scientists are studying the changes which take place in aging layers of snow and firn. But this giant vehicle has not yet made its last trip. Someday the part of the shelf in which it rests will break loose and go floating away in the form of a huge tabular iceberg. If by that time the cruiser has not been exhumed and removed, it will float away in the berg, perhaps to wander for several years in the seas surrounding the continent. Eventually the berg will break up and melt away and the cruiser will sink to its final resting place at the bottom of the Southern Sea.

Scientists can figure out the amount of water in ice and firn strata. Hence the annual precipitation for each year as far back as the ice strata are recognizable—and someday probably to the greatest depth of core recovery—can be calculated.

This information on water content has also been used to determine the approximate age of core ice from great depths, where annual strata are difficult or impossible to recognize. Studies at Little America V show us that there the average annual water accumulation is a little over eight inches. By applying this yardstick to a core from a hole drilled to the bottom of the ice shelf, it was found that strata at a depth of 170 feet, where the firn is changing to ice, were deposited at the beginning of the nineteenth century and that the entire thickness of the shelf represents about 1,225 years of accumulated snow, provided of course that the annual precipitation has remained constant for that length of time. Three films of what appears to be volcanic ash were found far down in the core. They probably chronicle a time during the Middle Ages when Mount Erebus, which still emits smoke and steam on the other side of Ross Sea, 450 miles away, suffered periods of more violent eruption.

But there is another, more accurate means of identifying annual strata deep within an ice sheet, which is only now coming into full use. In all water that falls as precipitation—either in the form of water or ice—practically all the oxygen has an atomic weight of 16, but mixed with it is a very small amount of the heavier isotope, oxygen–18. Fortunately, the ratio of O^{18} to O^{16} depends upon temperature: the lower the temperature, the smaller the amount of O^{18} in the water or ice. Thus in Antarctica and Greenland summer snow has a higher O^{18}/O^{16} ratio than winter snow.

So in those parts of the ice sheets where surface melting and downward percolation of the water have not destroyed the original oxygen-isotope ratios by mixing, they are still present within the ice that has formed from the snow. If cores of ice from deep inside a glacier are transported to the laboratory, the O^{18}/O^{16} ratios of summer and winter layers can be measured in a mass spectrometer. In this way annual strata and the age of the ice can be identified and computed. Dr. Samuel Epstein of the California Institute of Technology has identified annual layers in a Greenland core from a depth of well over 1,000 feet.

Careful studies of ice and firn strata can tell us a great deal about the Earth's climatic history. Scientists believe the ice may reveal vital information about major shifts in wind circulation and paths followed by storms, enabling us to understand present climatic changes and perhaps aiding us to predict those of the future.

The annual layers in the Greenland and Antarctic ice sheets have become the depositories for the products of atomic fission. The age of snow which fell on the ice prior to 1954 can be estimated by means of its tritium (heavy hydrogen) content. SIPRE scientists have found, however, that since then tritium from hydrogen bomb explosions has disturbed the snow's natural tritium balance. So it is not possible by this means to determine the age of snow that fell since 1954. Careful studies of these fission products in the snow and firn may lead, however, to valuable information about the circulation of the Earth's atmosphere since the advent of nuclear fallout, beginning with explosions of the atomic bomb in 1945.

When the drill penetrates more than several hundred feet, recovery of cores becomes increasingly difficult. As the ice is brought to the surface, release of the tremendous pressure under which it has been confined causes the cores to expand and shatter.

Escaping gas—really air trapped in the ice at the time of its formation and compressed by weight of added layers—also causes damage to the cores. Since these gases can be chemically analyzed, scientists are tremendously interested in them, for through them we may be able to understand the composition of the atmosphere at the time the ice formed. Are the smokestacks of our factories and the exhaust pipes of our automobiles seriously increasing the amount of carbon dioxide in the atmosphere? What natural changes, if any, has the atmosphere undergone throughout the past millenniums?

From evidence in our museums, art galleries, and libraries, and in a number of unfrequented attics, we can learn how our ancestors lived, even the more primitive ones who knew nothing of the written word. We know what they wore and what they ate. But neither our museums nor our laboratories preserve samples of the air they breathed. Did Columbus and Erik the Red and Charlemagne breathe the same kind of air we do? What about its content of pollen, spores, bacteria, and carbon dioxide? It now appears that in Greenland and Antarctica, our great iceboxes of climatic history, we are going to get the answers.

THE ICE IS THICK

Among the vast quantities of supplies carried by the big expeditions to Greenland and Antarctica in recent years, one of the most important items has been dynamite. Some of it has been used for blasting snow into crevasses, some for construction, and some for other purposes. Most of it, however, has been exploded on the surface of the ice sheets to make miniature earthquakes in order to find out the thickness of the ice.

No one knows the amount of ice in these two big sheets in which more fresh water is stored than in all the lakes of the world combined. Not until many more thickness determinations are made, many of them in the vast reaches of Antarctica on which man has never trod, will we have the measure of the Earth's supply of water. Despite the many depth soundings made during and since the International Geophysical Year, we have only begun to scratch the surface. This, then, is a reason for the dynamite explosions which have been echoing across the icy wastes near the top and bottom of the world. The methods used are the same as those by which the depth of Yosemite Valley was obtained. The explosive waves pass down through the ice and bounce back from the rock floor beneath it.

Scientists are also using the force of gravity as a means for calculating the thickness of the big ice sheets. A small compact instrument, a gravimeter, set up at any point on the surface of an ice sheet will measure the gravitational attraction of the land mass beneath the ice. Since this attraction diminishes proportionally as distance between instrument and land surface increases, the thickness of ice can be learned. Though this method is quicker and less cumbersome than the seismic, the gravimeter has to be calibrated occasionally with the results obtained by seismic means.

Studies made by scientists in Antarctica during the International Geophysical Year have caused them to revise upward by more than forty per cent their estimates of the amount of glacier ice in the world—now believed to be at least 4,500,000 cubic miles. As more and more soundings are made in both Greenland and Antarctica, there could be further upward revision, although beneath the ice in the vast interior of East Antarctica there may be some undetected mountain ranges and plateaus whose summits rise close to the surface. The only places remaining in the world where mountain ranges might yet be discovered are in the great ocean abyss and beneath the immense reaches of ice in Antarctica. And there is room in both places for some rather large ones.

Between November 1957 and March 1958 the British Commonwealth Trans-Antarctic Expedition made thousands of soundings on its 2,100-mile trek across the continent. Between the Weddell Sea and the Pole in a section never before traversed by ground travel, soundings revealed a rise in the land surface beneath the ice to within 1,500 feet of the surface, apparently the crest of a mountain range rising about 7,000 feet above its base. No one has ever seen it, but someday its contours may be explored in detail by seismic and gravity sounding and by other geophysical means.

Along the entire length of their route, which essentially followed the dividing line between East and West Antarctica, the Trans-Antarctic Expedition found that the land surface beneath the ice is everywhere above sea level. When they arrived at the South Pole, the midpoint on their traverse across the continent, they found that United States scientists manning the station there had already determined that they were living on top of 8,300 feet of ice resting on a land surface 900 feet above sea level.

But the situation is quite different over other large areas of the continent. At Byrd Station in West Antarctica, 300 miles from the nearest known shoreline, U.S. scientists were treated to quite a surprise when their seismic sounding revealed that the station, one mile above the sea, rested on ice two miles thick. In other words, the land surface here is a mile below sea level.

Along 1,700 miles of tractor and sledge traverses radiating from Byrd Station across West Antarctica, soundings indicated that most of the land surface is below sea level. Beneath the ice a deep trench, far below sea level, connects the Ross Sea with the Amundsen and Bellingshausen Seas. Much of Ellsworth Highland and Marie Byrd Land, named when nothing was known about the thickness of ice in West Antarctica, lie over this trench and would not be land at all but an inland sea if the ice were removed. And the string of coastal mountains—the Edsel Ford, Executive Committee, and Kohler Ranges, stretching for 1,000 miles eastward from the Ross Sea—would be an island lying 400 to 500 miles from the mainland. At one place near Byrd Station an ice thickness of 14,000 feet was measured. On the opposite side of the continent in the sector claimed by Australia, the Russians found that the ice thickness in the vicinity of their station, Pionerskaya, 250 miles inland from the coast, was 10,000 to 12,000 feet. Here, as at Byrd Station, the land surface is several thousand feet below sea level.

It is possible that West Antarctica is a group of islands, and that the Palmer Peninsula, reaching out nearly 1,000 miles toward South America, is part of an island separated from East Antarctica by a trench connecting the Ross and Weddell Seas. A fourth or more of the entire continent may be below sea level.

British, French, and U.S. Army expeditions found that the Greenland ice at places in the interior is two miles thick and that practically all of the island inside the marginal mountains is a large basin, several very large sections of which are below sea level. Estimates hold that almost half of the area on which the ice sheet rests lies below the level of the sea.

9

Ice Breaks the Back of the Continent

THE saucer-shaped land surface beneath the Greenland ice sheet and the large areas below sea level, both there and in Antarctica, are evidence that the load of ice is heavier than the Earth's crust can bear without bending downward.

Another clue to this overloading can be found at the continental margins. The edge of every continent is a steeply inclined slope (the *continental slope*), which along most coasts falls away to the ocean basins at depths of 10,000 to 12,000 feet. At its top this slope joins the much gentler sloping upper surface of the continent. The junction of these two slopes, however, is everywhere under water, at a depth that averages between 400 and 500 feet. Thus, despite the great height of two to three miles to which the edges of the continents rise above the ocean basins, their margins are flooded by the sea. These submerged parts of the continents are the *continental shelves*.

Their width varies greatly. In places along the Arctic coast of Siberia and on the north edge of Australia the shelf is 400 or more miles wide. The North Sea and the English Channel lie on the shelf; so do the Yellow and East China Seas. Off the coast of New Jersey and Long Island its width is nearly 120 miles. Off Miami Beach it is only five miles wide.

Along some coasts, including New England, the sea has spread inward across the entire continental shelf. Between New York and Central America the sea covers only the outer part of the shelf, leaving a coastal plain on its inner side.

The world-wide, nearly uniform elevation of the continental edges bespeaks a relationship among all continents and between each continent and the surrounding oceanic deeps. It implies that all the continents are composed of essentially the same geologic materials and that the rock upon which they rest is also essentially everywhere of the same composition, though differing greatly from that of the continents. The continents are composed of relatively light rock; this is the reason they stick up so much higher than the ocean basins, which are underlain by rock of greater density. Geologists and geophysicists, from studies of gravity variations and the behavior of earthquake waves passing through both continental and oceanic rock, have known of this relationship for a long time.

But just where do ice sheets fit into this picture? To find an answer, we must take another look at the margin of the Antarctic continent. We know even less about the continental shelf and slope than of the icy interior. But soundings indicate definitely that the shelf is generally much deeper than around other continents. Its outer edge over long distances is 1,200 to 1,800 feet below sea level. The shelf off much of Greenland, too, has abnormally great depth. This would appear, then, to be additional evidence that the ice sheets on Greenland and Antarctica are pressing the continents down for hundreds of feet. On the other hand, some geologists believe that the shelves around Greenland and Antarctica were cut down to their low elevation by glaciers when the ice was more extensive. And this may be so, but ice sheets in their marginal zones seem to be capable of cutting deeply into the land only where the flow is concentrated in narrow channels, as it is in outlet glaciers.

Continents are known to rise and fall without the aid of ice sheets, but it can hardly be mere coincidence that puts the lowest continental shelves around the only two lands bearing heavy loads of ice. Neither Greenland nor Antarctica, however, are at their maximum depression; both have probably been rising for some time because their ice sheets are thinner than they used to be. Glacial scratches and ice-transported boulders on exposed mountains in Antarctica show that the thinning has amounted to 1,000 feet or more. But parts of Antarctica are so far below sea level that they almost certainly would still be below the sea, even if all the ice melted away and the crust rose to the level where equilibrium were restored.

In any event, man will continue to probe the thickness of the Greenland and Antarctic ice sheets in the hope that by so doing he will learn a great deal more than the thickness of the ice. He will hope to learn much about the strength and nature of the crust and the effect of loads upon it, and he certainly will learn to what extent sea level will be affected if these ice masses should melt away or expand again.

WHAT LIES BENEATH THE ICE?

Is it probable that extensive deposits of mineral resources will be found under the ice sheets of Greenland and Antarctica? The Geological Survey of Greenland, established in 1946, has conducted a number of studies along the narrow, exposed rim of the island. Its work in the future may reveal important mineral deposits. Beds of low-grade coal crop out in the marginal area and extend for unknown distances beneath the ice. Many ore minerals, including radioactive ones, have been found in small amounts, and for years Greenland has been the sole source of the world's supply of cryolite, a rather rare mineral used in the electrolytic process for the production of aluminum. It is concentrated in a single deposit near Ivigtut on the west coast not far from Cape Farewell. Appropriately, the name of this mineral comes from two Greek words meaning ice-stone. It was given this name, not because of its occurrence in Greenland, but because it is translucent and white and has much the appearance of ice. Perhaps Nature was endeavoring by protective coloration to safeguard one of her possessions!

The only other currently operated mineral project in Greenland is a small lead mine. Greenland is also one of the few places in the world where iron occurs in the pure state. There isn't much of this native iron, but Greenlanders have used it as metal for their tools and weapons.

How many other unusual mineral deposits lie hidden under the ice? No one dares to predict. But the great diversity of geologic structures and rock types around the edge of this big island indicate that there almost certainly are mineral deposits of some magnitude hidden somewhere beneath its icy blanket. Certain it is that in North America, geologically closely related to Greenland, no section as large as Greenland is without rich mineral resources.

Antarctica is even larger, and yet we know less about this ice-bound continent than we do about Greenland, but geologists have found a great variety of geologic structures and rocks. There are extensive series of sedimentary rocks thousands of feet thick containing beds of coal. Most of it is low grade, but some anthracite has been found. Huge sheetlike intrusions of basalt and other igneous rocks cut across these strata. Some of this rock has been extruded onto the surface in the form of lava flows. Great masses of granite are exposed in some of the ranges.

Over large areas in East Antarctica the sedimentary rocks are essentially horizontal. Those in West Antarctica have been compressed into folds; many have been metamorphosed by heat and pressure into slates and marbles. Part of the continent is broken into great blocks separated by faults. Some of the blocks, including the narrow 2,000-mile strip between East and West Antarctica which extends from the Ross to the Weddell Sea, and the one stretching across East Antarctica, have sunk; others, exemplified by the Queen Maud Range, have been pushed up thousands of feet. Other faults divide these major blocks into many smaller ones. Some geologists believe that the two depressed blocks connecting the Ross with the Weddell and Amundsen Seas are similar in origin and structure to the Rift Valley of East Africa, which stretches as a great groove 4,000 miles from Lake Nyassa to Suez.

Within Antarctic rocks are many minerals which, if present in greater quantity, might form exploitable ore deposits. Yet no such concentrations have been discovered. But far less than one per cent of the continent's area has been examined. All the geologic knowledge we have has been collected from widely scattered points on its rim and from a few of the mountaintops projecting through the ice. It is likely that there are large mineral reserves somewhere on the continent far below the ice. Would the fabulous iron ores of the Lake Superior region have been found if the exploration of North America had been limited to a marginal zone less than fifty miles wide?

We really don't know what lies beneath Antarctica's icy cover. As far as mineral resources are concerned, there may be little or there may be much. The continent's vastness and the varied assemblage of known rocks and structures points to the possibility of much.

Up to the present time the seismograph and gravity meter have been used mainly to find the thickness of the ice. And they will continue to serve this purpose, but increasingly in the future they will be utilized to find out what is below the ice. Both of these devices and also the magnetometer, an instrument for measuring magnetic intensity, are capable of recording data from which we can learn something about the character of rocks far below the surface. When a charge of explosive is set off on the surface it is the waves reflected from the bedrock which tell us the thickness of the ice. But some of the waves penetrate the rock below the ice. When passing from one kind of rock into another these waves are bent (refracted), so that they pass laterally through the rock, later to emerge and return to the surface. From these refracted waves, geophysicists and geologists can determine the type of material through which they passed. Thus someday we may know something about the geology of the mountain ranges which Dr. Fuchs discovered only 1,500 to 2,000 feet below the Antarctic Polar Plateau, even though we shall never see the landscape which they make.

We can already drill through ice as thick as that overlying these ranges and bring up undamaged samples of ice for detailed study. Will we be able to drill through the ice and into oil-bearing strata below? As oil reserves in other parts of the world diminish there may come a time when substantial effort will be made to find petroleum in Antarctica. Its extraction, except possibly where the ice is thickest, would not be an insurmountable problem for the engineers. Mining would be a greater problem, but it is likely that someday mines will be extended down through the ice and into ore deposits below.

For a long time to come, man will need increasing supplies of natural resources. An abundance of power created by nuclear energy or perhaps directly by the sun will make practicable the extraction of mineral products from ores of far lower grade than can be used under present conditions. It may be that for this reason the subglacial resources of Antarctica might never have to be tapped, even though they should prove to be of vast extent. Time, of course, will tell, but when and if the need for resources known to be in Antarctica comes, man will make the attempt. He will, as he has always done, go to great lengths to make money and, eventually, to assure his survival.

WHAT ABOUT SETTLEMENTS?

Will permanent settlements ever be established on the Antarctic ice sheet? It seems fairly obvious that there will be permanent scientific stations. Many important secrets of the world and its weather and climate are hidden here. If it becomes apparent that weather and climate of much of the world are in part controlled by the Antarctic, man will set up permanent weather stations as a step toward his goal of predicting world-wide weather and climatic changes. If he is ever to gain control over the weather, he will have to know much more about Antarctica. The United States, the Soviet Union, and other nations which operated stations on the ice during the International Geophysical Year are continuing these operations, and it looks as though they are here to stay.

The time is fast approaching when Antarctica will be connected to the world's tourist routes. American tourists—and those from other countries, too—are looking for newer and more distant places and will soon be turning their eyes to Antarctica. From the comfort and comparative safety of his plane or boat

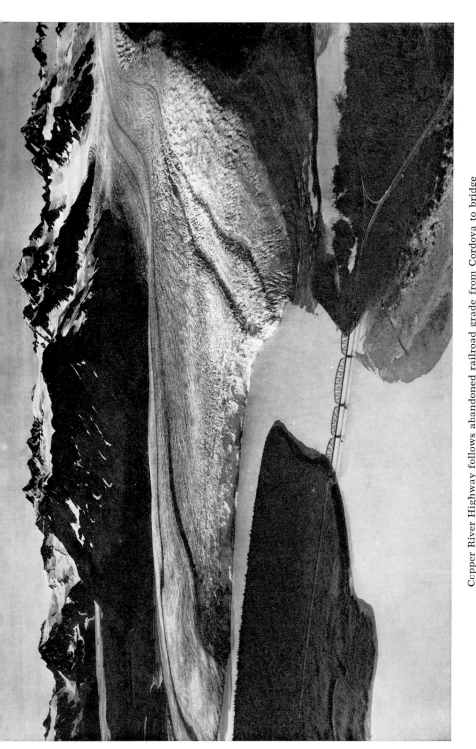

Copper River Highway follows abandoned railroad grade from Cordova to bridge at Childs Glacier. Soon road will be extended north (right). Glacier is half mile from bridge. In 1911 it reached trees just above north end of bridge, only one-

147

In Copper River Valley, Allen Glacier spreads out in piedmont ice sheet. Glacier's abandoned moraine parallels glacier front and pushes Copper River across valley. Melt water, dammed between moraine and debris-covered glacier, forms a lake. The railway grade lies on outwash and on stagnant ice in moraine. Allen

Medial moraine system on Barnard Glacier in St. Elias Mountains—one of most beautiful ever photographed. On main glacier there is a moraine for every tributary, and moraines on tributaries show that they, too, have tributaries.

Dikes protect port of Valdez from burial in outwash of Valdez Glacier. As more and more outwash is brought down, dikes will have to be raised higher and higher. The glacier was route followed by several thousand prospectors into

The Alaska Railroad is less than a mile from Spencer Glacier between Seward and Anchorage. A few miles from here, railroad goes through long tunnel to

Skiers crossing a crevasse on a thin snow bridge. A glacier on slopes of the Breithorn, Swiss Alps.

A "glacier table" on Mer de Glace. Boulder has protected ice beneath it from sun's rays. Eventually it will slide off its pedestal, which will then quickly melt away. Vertical structures in ice are foliations developed by flow and shearing within glacier.

"Dirt cone" on a glacier
ice surface, where locall
tected from sun by film
bris, forms a cone whil
rest melts to lower levels. F
the dirt has been scraped

Glacial grooves and stri
on bedrock. Glacier r
from right to left, gri
down upstream side of
obstruction and plucking
from downstream side.

(XXIV) (FOLLOWING PAGE) El Capitan (cliff on left) towers 3,500 feet in nearly
wall of granite above floor of great glacier-gouged Yosemite Valley. In e
stage, valley was even deeper; its flat floor is the top of a fill of sand and g
deposited by streams after ice disappeared. Just beyond El Capitan, fill is
1,000 feet thick. Bridal Veil Fall plummets 620 feet from its hanging v
formed because its small glacier could not cut into the granite as fast as
ice stream in main valley.

Glacial sculpturing—past and present. By grinding out countless grooves and striations, one over the other, and by plucking rocks loose for thousands of years, a mighty ice stream created Harriman Fiord. Surprise and Cataract Glaciers are continuing work of their larger parent.

Hanging valleys—filled. Marquette and Beloit Glaciers cascade over steep icefalls to the water of Blackstone Bay. Horn peaks on skyline are nearly buried in ice. Kenai Mountains, Alaska.

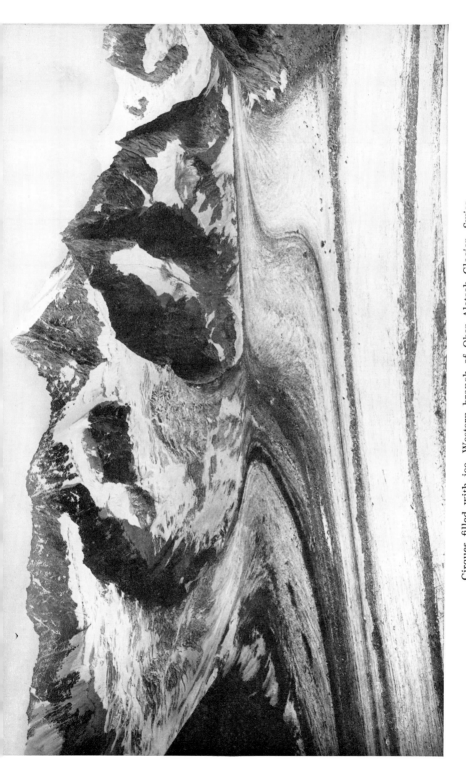

Cirques filled with ice. Western branch of Ober Aletsch Glacier, Swiss Alps. A crevasse where a glacier pulls away from the cirque wall, called the bergschrund, is well developed in cirque on left.

Cirque—empty. Walls nearly 4,000 feet high enclose spectacular Iceberg Cirque in Glacier National Park, Montana. Up to 1920 a glacier with a 200-foot ice cliff lay at far end of mile-wide lake. Ten thousand years ago ice was more than 2,000 feet thick.

Hanging valleys—empty. Ten thousand years ago ice cascaded from hanging valleys in Glacier National Park, Montana, just as Marquette and Beloit Glaciers do today. Magnificent horn peaks accentuate glacial land.

Horn peaks and hanging valleys—low view. Waterfalls drop over lips of two hanging valleys. One on right falls into a lower hanging valley which is tributary to main valley. St. Mary Lake fills glacier-gouged basin. Glacier National Park, Montana.

Horn peaks—high view. Remnants of intense glacial sculpturing along main divide of Lewis Range, Glacier National Park, Montana. A small glacier still plucks away at horn left of center.

The Garden Wall, an arête in Glacier National Park, is one of the finest master-pieces of glacial sculpture in America. For seven miles this knife-edge wall sepa-

the tourist will view scenes of grandeur discovered and explored only a short time before by men, many of whom, under conditions of the utmost hardship, drove themselves to and beyond the limit of their endurance. And, as is always the case, where the tourist goes there will be facilities to care for him. Such establishments will appear first at the most accessible spots on the rim of the continent and later even on the ice of the interior. Night clubs may arrive before we know it; golf courses will pose a greater problem. Already a planeload of sightseeing U.S. Congressmen has made a trip to Antarctica. No land is too distant for the sightseer.

In Greenland, tunnels and large storage chambers have been excavated in the ice and are being maintained. In 1960 the U.S. Army Engineers made excavations in the surface of the Greenland ice sheet near Thule and then built a town in them. The streets, one of them 1,000 feet long, were roofed with arched corrugated steel. After completion, the entire town with its sunken streets and thirty-some prefabricated buildings—including dormitories, laboratories, gymnasium, recreation center, and nuclear power plant—was covered with a five-foot layer of snow. Like the several Little Americas and the snow cruiser in far-off Antarctica, this new town—Camp Century it has been named—is now being buried under additional annual layers of snow.

In 1961 Byrd Station in West Antarctica also went "underground." This move was undertaken because the buildings of the old station, constructed in 1956, had been gradually collapsing under loads of accumulating snow. How long these establishments can be maintained is one of the problems that time will have to solve. In addition to learning much about the properties of ice and snow, their occupants will undoubtedly learn a great deal about living within an icecap. Some of the men responsible for Camp Century feel that large cities can be built inside ice sheets, and that in this way survival during an atomic war could be assured. There would be some real problems involved in this kind of undertaking—the method of selecting the occupants of these hidden cities, how and when to move to the shelter, and so on. Perhaps the designers were thinking more about these places being impregnable sites for military installations!

In any event, most of us hope that the nuclear problem can be solved before mankind has to resort to a subglacial life in order to have a future.

Admiral Byrd long ago suggested Antarctica as a storehouse for surplus food, to be used when and where the need for it arose. The continent certainly could hold a lot of food, but there it would probably stay—we can't distribute the great surpluses we have now.

Antarctica, packed with secrets vital to the welfare of all the world, has been a symbol since inception of the IGY of international harmony and co-operation. Scientists of many nations have been working side by side with a mutual respect that transcends feelings of distrust, frequently in evidence when politicians and diplomats get together, no matter how hard many of them try to iron out political and ideological differences.

Perhaps the politicians should be given a vacation as far as the administrative control of Antarctica is concerned, and a tribunal of scientists given an opportunity to operate the continent as an international science research center and natural laboratory. In this way Antarctica could serve as a symbol of man's ability to get along with his fellow man and as an example for civil governments to emulate in their dealings with each other, especially in this era when new nations are being born amid violent feelings of nationalism.

Until recently it seemed that Antarctica was going the way of so many other lands after their "discovery" by Caucasian man. Today seven nations—Australia, France, New Zealand, Norway, Chile, Argentina, Great Britain—claim eighty per cent of Antarctica. The United States has never recognized any of the claims; neither has it made any claim of its own, although by virtue of having made the earliest and most extensive explorations, it appears to have the most valid foundation for a claim. But over the years of our vast operations in Antarctica we never did; and, no matter how some of our citizens feel about the matter now, it is too late to change our mind.

Some of the current claims are huge, and several of them overlap. All, like pieces of pie, converge at the Pole. For such a magnificent piece of Earthly real estate to be chopped up into segments just doesn't seem fitting.

The twelve-nation treaty ratified by the nations that participated in the IGY is a sign that, despite the claims, there is widespread feeling that Antarctica could become truly international. At least it is the place where man will have his last chance to make the experiment; there is no other land on Earth over which some nation does not hold sovereignty. The treaty includes provision for the right of inspection of each country's installations and operations, which for a long time has been one of the stumbling blocks impeding disarmament negotiations.

In any event, Antarctica is going to be inhabited—sparsely, certainly—but it is coming. Scientists and explorers and the people who assist them are there now; the tourists will follow, and others will not be far behind.

❀❀❀❀❀❀

10

❀❀❀❀❀❀

Ice of the Sea

THE POLAR PACK

❀❀❀❀❀❀
—————
❀❀❀❀❀❀ GREENLAND's load of ice is the largest in
the Northern Hemisphere, but it is not the most extensive. The
honors go to the thin layer of sea ice crusting the Arctic Ocean
and adjacent seas. This floating, much-fractured slab of ice,
formed by freezing of sea water, is known as *pack ice*, or the
ice pack. When smallest, in August, it covers an area four times
that of the Greenland ice sheet. At this time it spreads out in all
directions from the center of the Polar Sea, nearly reaching Point
Barrow, Alaska and several places along the Arctic shore of
Siberia. It pushes hard against Greenland, Ellesmere, and other
Canadian islands, holding these northern shores in an icy grip
which is never relaxed. Because of this never-slackening hold on
the upper rim of North America, the "Northwest Passage" for
surface ships is an "inside passage" lying far to the south
through the maze of straits, channels, and sounds which braid
northern Canada into a hodgepodge of islands. Someday an icebreaker will be built which is strong enough to force a sea route

around the top of North America, but no surface ship now afloat is capable of crashing its way through the pack between the Norwegian Sea and Alaska.

North of the Norwegian and Barents Seas the warm waters of the Gulf Stream chew into the Arctic Ocean's frozen mantle, driving back its edge hundreds of miles Poleward beyond Svalbard and Franz Josef Land; thus the Pole is off-center in the pack. A large section of the pack between the Pole and Alaska is farther from both land and open water than the Pole is. The center of this area, in the vicinity of Latitude 84° north and Longitude 175° west and 400 miles from the North Pole, is known as the "Pole of Inaccessibility" because it is the most difficult point on the Polar pack to reach by over-ice travel. This designation, however, is losing its significance as air and submarine traffic increases in Arctic regions.

A steady flow of water is poured into the nearly enclosed Arctic Basin by the Gulf Stream and to a lesser extent by the large Siberian and Canadian rivers and by the Pacific. This inflow is balanced by an outflow in the opposite direction, the cold East Greenland Current, which leaves the Arctic Basin between Greenland and Svalbard and continues along the East Greenland coast, passing into the North Atlantic through Denmark Strait. The icy waters of this strong current retard melting of the pack and carry its edge southward in a narrow tongue for several hundred miles along the east coast of Greenland.

Like the blanket of snow, the Polar pack expands and contracts with the seasons. In the fall and throughout the winter the pack thickens several feet by addition of new ice to its undersurface. It also slowly spreads outward by freezing of the sea surface around its edges. By October or November the pack will have squeezed down through the Chukchi Sea to Bering Strait. At the same time that the pack is expanding, land-fast sea ice, forming an ever-widening fringe along northern shores, will be creeping out across the water to meet the pack.

In March the expanded pack and the land-fast ice, with which it has merged, form a very irregular, but continuous, sheet of sea ice double the size of the permanent pack. It cements together all the islands of the Canadian Arctic Archipelago, covers Baffin Bay and Davis Strait, and forms a wide

band along the coast of Labrador southward to and into the Gulf
of St. Lawrence. At this time of year the entire Siberian coast
from the White Sea to Bering Strait is tightly sealed by the sea's
icy crust.

The Arctic ice pack is not a smooth, unbroken sheet. Under
the influence of winds and ocean currents it continually cracks
and breaks up, summer and winter, into *floes*. Cracks wide
enough to be navigable are known as *leads*. They may be miles
long and, in the marginal zone of the pack, may be several miles
wide. Because adjacent floes may move at different rates and in
different directions, irregular, lakelike open spaces, known as
polynyas, develop between them. In summer ice-free areas are
common all over the pack. In August 1958 the atomic submarine *Skate* surfaced in a polynya only forty miles from the Pole,
and two years later the *Seadragon* found open water dead centered on the Pole itself. Although open waters in the ice pack
are a boon to submariners, they are a real barrier to over-ice
travel. That is why Peary selected the deepest part of winter for
his trek from Cape Columbia to the Pole. In winter, cracks,
leads, and polynyas freeze over almost as soon as they start to
form and may be covered with six inches or more of ice in
twenty-four hours.

When the ice pulls apart at one place it must squeeze together at another. Two floes may move away from each other for
a time, then move back, grinding together with inexorable force,
crushing their edges, and piling up the cakes into jagged *pressure ridges* ten or more feet high.

The ice pack is a myriad of floes, all continuously in motion. When they are all drifting in the same direction and at the
same rate, the Arctic landscape is marked by calm. But at other
times, especially during storms, the ice can display a terrifying
violence. In his book, *The Friendly Arctic*, Vilhjalmur Stefansson has vividly described what can happen when floes come together. In a matter of minutes slabs of ice may be forced up
until they stand fifty feet high before they break off and crash
to the floe surface. The grinding together of floes is accompanied
by a deafening din of crashing, scraping, and screeching. Persons camped on floes are constantly faced with the possibility
of having the campsite rent by a crack or destroyed by the tele-

scoping of the floe as another one crunches into it. Stefansson tells of camping on a floe which was telescoped nearly a mile during a particularly stormy night; ice which before the storm had been relatively smooth had been converted into a "chaos of ridges."

The thickness of ice in the pack varies considerably, but probably averages eight to twelve feet in winter and five to ten feet in summer. Under pressure ridges and places where slabs of ice have been piled up, the base of the ice may extend to sixty or more feet below the water line.

Although the wind is responsible for much movement of ice within the pack, ocean currents are a greater force in driving the pack. Tremendous quantities of pack ice, after circling around the Arctic Ocean on these currents for several years, are carried out into the Atlantic by the East Greenland Current. In addition, the pack is thinned two to three feet each summer by surface melting. These two processes are compensated for by renewed freezing each winter at the bottom and along the edges of the pack. Thus none of the pack can be very old. The Russians have determined the age of ice within a number of floes to be from two to nine years old. There may be other floes with older ice.

The drift of ice-bound ships and floe-stations indicates that pack ice originating north of Siberia eventually drifts across the eastern Arctic Basin and into the North Atlantic between Greenland and Svalbard. Pack ice on the North American side, caught in a great clockwise circular course from which there is no ready escape route, remains longer in the Polar Sea and is generally older than ice on the Eurasian side.

In the early days of Arctic sea exploration, carried on mainly by people looking for new lands, ship captains, navigating the ice-filled waters in the marginal zone of the pack, constantly were faced with the possibility of having their craft freeze fast to the pack. In 1879 this fate befell the *Jeannette* in the Chukchi Sea north of Bering Strait. Under the command of Lieutenant George DeLong of the U.S. Navy, this ship had pushed into the pack near Wrangell Island, then thought to be a continent extending far to the north, on a voyage its captain hoped would lead to the Pole itself. But the ice never released its grip on the *Jeannette,* and after a two-year eastward drift in the pack she was finally crushed by the ice and abandoned in the vicinity of the New Siberian Islands, about 700 miles from the point where her drift had begun. The members of the crew trudged across the ice to the desolate coast of Siberia, but several of them, including DeLong, died from cold and starvation before they could reach civilization. Four years later a number of articles from this ship were found on an ice floe off southern Greenland.

It was this long ride of the remains of the *Jeannette,* apparently across the Polar Sea and perhaps over the Pole itself, that convinced the great Norwegian scientist-explorer, Fridtjof Nansen, that the Pole might be reached by allowing a ship to become caught in the pack near the point where the *Jeannette* had been abandoned and drifting on it across the Polar Sea to open water off the Greenland coast. Nansen had earlier suspected the existence of this current because of the finding on the Greenland coast of an implement traceable to Alaskan Eskimos and by the presence of abundant driftwood from tree species common in northern Siberia.

In September 1893 Nansen's ship *Fram,* built to withstand the crushing pressure of the floes, was run into the ice off the New Siberian Islands in Latitude 78°50′ north, not far from the place where the *Jeannette* had come to grief. For three years the ship drifted with the pack, reaching its highest Latitude, 85°55′ north—the farthest north ever reached by a surface ship—in November 1895 and finally emerging into the open sea off the north coast of Svalbard in August 1896. So successfully had the *Fram* taken all the battering that the Arctic pack could give that the hull design of all modern U.S. icebreakers built during and since World War II has followed the lines of this famous ship.

Six months after the *Fram's* great drift began, when it was apparent to Nansen that the ship would never reach the Pole, he left Captain Otto Sverdrup in command of the ship and set out across the ice for the Pole with Lieutenant Frederik Johansen as his companion. They had twenty-eight dogs to pull the sledges carrying their provisions and the two kayaks with which they intended to cross open leads. Since there would be no hope of finding the drifting ship on their return, Nansen determined that he and Johansen on their own would somehow get to Europe by way of Svalbard.

For twenty-six days after leaving the ship they traveled north, while the badly broken ice over which they traveled constantly drifted south. Finally on April 8, 1895, in Latitude 86°13' north—closer to the Pole than man had ever been, but still a good 225 miles short of their goal—they had to give up their quest and reluctantly turn southward.

Then began one of the most heroic ordeals of suffering and courageous battling against the elements recorded in the annals of Polar exploration. Five months from the time they left the *Fram*, and down to their last dog, they reached Franz Josef Land. Here, in a hut they built with stones, earth, and walrus hides, they spent the winter—nearly nine months of bitter cold, darkness, and loneliness. In the spring they again set out toward the south. About a month later, still in the Franz Josef Archipelago, these two ragged, grimy, heavily bearded, and unrecognizable men came face to face with Frederick Jackson, leader of a mapping and exploring expedition to Franz Josef Land. Neither Nansen nor Jackson had known that the other was anywhere near the part of the world in which their miraculous meeting took place.

In August, at the same time Otto Sverdrup was bringing the *Fram* through the last ice floes and into the Norwegian Sea between Greenland and Svalbard, Nansen and Johansen, aboard Jackson's relief ship, were starting back to Norway and home. Although Nansen never reached the Pole he did prove that his ideas about the general drift of the Arctic pack were correct, and the expedition made a wealth of scientific investigations and cast new light on the geography, meteorology, and oceanography of the unknown North.

In 1937–40 the Russian icebreaker *Sedov* drifted along a route essentially parallel to the route of the *Fram*. In the interval between these drifts, several vessels made shorter drifts in various parts of the Arctic.

Plane landings and take-offs far from shore on the Arctic sea ice have been commonplace for many years, but prior to 1927 this dual feat had never been accomplished. In that year

George Hubert Wilkins and his pilot, Carl Ben Eielson, be-came pioneers in a new phase of aviation history when they made two ice landings and take-offs with their ski-equipped plane in the course of a flight which took them across more than 500 miles of the ice-covered Arctic Ocean. A third landing was made seventy miles from shore when the plane ran out of gas.

Wilkins and Eielson were not the first to take off from the Arctic pack. Two years earlier, on May 21, 1925, a Dornier fly-ing boat, the N–25, had taken off from the ice only 120 miles from the Pole. This plane, however, with another like it, the N–24, had been landed on an open lead during the attempt of an expedition consisting of Roald Amundsen, Lincoln Ellsworth, and four others to fly two planes from Svalbard to the Pole. The N–24 was wrecked in landing, but the other plane was dragged onto the ice and saved from being crushed between two floes. After laboriously hacking out a 1,500-foot runway on the ice, and after repeated unsuccessful attempts to take off, the ex-pedition finally became airborne in the N–25 and returned to Svalbard twenty-four days after it had come down on the open lead.

Bernt Balchen in the early 1920's had visualized the Arctic as a great air crossroads of the future, but the possibility of us-ing planes to land expeditions on ice floes was first suggested by Nansen and his countryman, Harald U. Sverdrup, in 1926. They envisaged landing an expedition near the Pole on a floe which would drift with the current, as the *Fram* had done, down between Greenland and Svalbard into the North Atlantic.

This was done in 1937 by the four-man Russian North Pole Drift Expedition, under the leadership of Ivan Papanin, which drifted for nine months from the vicinity of the Pole almost to the 70th Parallel off the east coast of Greenland. This drift sta-tion, with its nine tons of supplies and equipment, was estab-lished by landings made by four four-engine aircraft on a large ice floe. At the time of the landings the floe was about ten feet thick.

During the latter stages of its drift, the station was con-stantly menaced by cracking of the ice and the breaking up of the floe. At times the ice cracked right through the camp, and some of the supplies and equipment drifted off on the new floes.

When the station was evacuated, the floe on which it rested was less than 100 feet wide. This expedition, which contributed much knowledge about a previously unexplored part of the Arctic, marked the beginning of the era of scientific probing into Arctic secrets by expeditions floating on the ice.

The Russians have also placed several very large scientific stations on other floes, and all of them, including the 1937–8 expedition, were established by heavily loaded, four-engine aircraft which made landings on unprepared sea ice. Since 1937 Russian scientists have been making observations from ice-floe drift stations on the North American as well as the Eurasian side of the Arctic Basin and over the North Pole. Some of these installations have been equipped with motorized vehicles and with aircraft for making observational flights to surrounding areas. It is difficult to get the jump on Soviet scientists in any phase of Arctic research.

The Americans got off to a much later start in placing scientific stations on drifting floes. The Tenth Rescue Squadron of the U.S. Air Force maintained a drifting station on a floe for two weeks in 1950, but the first full-scale scientific ice-floe station was not set up until April 5, 1957, when Drifting Station Alpha was established on a floe about 700 miles north of Point Barrow, Alaska. Its personnel and matériel were transported by planes of the Alaskan Air Command.

During 1957 all went well with the station, but what happened to it in 1958 illustrates well the hazards of life on an ice floe. Beginning in April, the men at the station watched their floe getting smaller and smaller as first one section of the ten-foot-thick floe, then another, cracked off and slowly floated away. In May the entire camp, including all personnel and twenty-one buildings, was moved to another floe, and a new runway was constructed. Cracks soon developed through this runway, so a third one had to be prepared.

Finally, with a tremendous roar, a crack ripped right through the camp and across the runway. A fraction of an inch wide at first, the crack slowly widened until both the camp and the runway were divided between two floes. Especially disconcerting was the fact that the camp and the longest section of the runway were now on separate floes. Since the future of the station at that point didn't appear very bright, the decision was made to abandon it. Accordingly, on November 4, nearly a year and a half after it had been established, and when the station was 300 miles from the Pole, its twenty scientists and airmen were removed by an Air Force rescue plane which had flown 800 miles from Thule, Greenland. Landing and take-off were made on the abbreviated runway with the aid of flares to light the Arctic night which had closed in several weeks earlier. At the time Station Alpha was established, the floe had an area of several square miles. When the station was abandoned, the floe measured only about 1,000 feet on a side.

Exactly four years before Alpha's evacuation, Russia's Station SP–3 was rent by a crack that passed beneath some of the tents and within several minutes had split the camp by a lead of open water 150 feet wide. On several other occasions, both before and after Alpha's demise, other Soviet stations had similar experiences. Despite the propensity which floes have for breaking up, several of them have been occupied by scientific stations for more than a year, and one carried Russia's Station SP–4 for three years along a route which spanned the entire Arctic Basin and passed almost directly over the Pole.

THE ANTARCTIC

The ice floes on Antarctic waters are similar to their counterparts in the Arctic Ocean. The two antipodal ice packs, however, are somewhat unlike in character because of differences between the distribution of land and water in the two regions. In one case the sea ice has a cold, nearly enclosed ocean on which to form and in the other the ice is pushed out by a continent to the edge of the Polar region onto unconfined waters contiguous to the Pacific, Atlantic, and Indian Oceans.

Antarctic sea ice is thinner than that in the Arctic, and in February and March—late summer in the Antarctic—the pack is limited to a narrow fringe around the edge of the continent. There are a number of places where ships have reached the shore without encountering any pack at all, although at these same places a year later the ice may have been forty or more miles wide. In winter the pack expands greatly and by September and October extends out from shore for several hundred miles, as much as 900 to 1,000 miles along that part of the coast lying south of the Atlantic Ocean. The width of the ice belt here is greater than anywhere else, probably because of cold surface water moving eastward from the Weddell Sea. At this time of the year in the sector south of Australia the pack seldom attains a width of 400 miles. Strong winds blowing off the continent's icy mantle at all seasons drive the ice seaward, creating a wide zone of open water inside the pack along much of the coast.

Because of the ready response of Antarctic floes to wind currents, the northern edge of the pack fluctuates rapidly and is known to have moved over short periods of time as much as twenty to forty miles a day. In the summer of 1936 the *Discovery II* on a due-south course north of the Ross Sea passed through 400 miles of pack ice. Three weeks later on the return trip they found that only 150 miles of ice remained—250 miles of ice had disappeared from the northern edge of the pack.

Antarctic floes, with greater freedom of movement, are not crushed and broken up as much as those in the Arctic, and ships have been navigated through the pack during the winter months. For various reasons, among which are navigability of the pack and the operation of many scientific stations over the Antarctic continent, no drifting stations have been established on Antarctic floes.

The Antarctic pack, however, is not everywhere placid and unruffled. At several places, especially in the western part of the Weddell Sea, the pack is thick and the floes grind against each other, creating pinnacled and blocky icescapes no different from those in the Arctic Ocean. Several vessels have been carried long distances trapped in the pack of the Ross, Bellingshausen, and Weddell Seas. Most dramatic of these enforced cruises was made by the *Endurance*, in which Sir Ernest Shackleton was taking his Imperial Trans-Antarctic Expedition to Antarctica to attempt a crossing of the continent from the Weddell to the Ross Sea. For nearly a month the ship had fought through 800 miles of pack along the eastern edge of the Weddell Sea almost to within sight of land on Luitpold Coast near the present site of Britain's IGY Shackleton Station. But before the expedition even had an opportunity to set foot on land the *Endurance* was frozen fast in the pack and began to drift with the floes— away from their goal, away from the continent they had come to conquer. During the next ten months (January to November 1915) the ship was carried 570 miles in a general northward direction parallel to the Palmer Peninsula before finally being crushed by the grinding floes. During this drift, because of zigzags in the course, the total measured distance, calculated on the basis of observed positions, was 1,186 miles, although Shackleton estimated that they had actually covered more than 1,500 miles. That floes in the eastern Weddell Sea are quite capable of carrying scientific stations is borne out by the fact that, after abandoning ship, Shackleton's expedition drifted for five more months on their floe and covered several hundred additional miles before getting clear of the ice.

11

Ghost Ships of the Arctic

O N THE fourteenth of August 1946 the radarscope of a U.S. Air Force plane winging its way over the icy skin of the Arctic Ocean showed a large object in the sea below, apparently an island. But the location was about 300 miles north of Point Barrow, Alaska, where no island was known to be and where one could hardly have escaped detection. The airmen, not knowing exactly what it was but believing it was land, named it Target X, a name which was later changed to T–1.

Subsequent flights in clear weather showed that T–1 was an island of ice fifteen miles wide and eighteen miles long and that it was moving slowly northward through the pack toward the Pole. Because this ice island was close to the paths of routine reconnaissance flights, airmen were able during the succeeding three years to watch it move, both on radar and visually, for a distance of 1,400 miles. Then it became lost. When again sighted twenty-two months later, it was near the northern coast of Ellesmere Island. Soon afterward it made a sharp turn toward the west and began to move along the shore toward the spot where it was discovered in 1946.

T–1 was readily distinguishable from the shattered sea ice through which it was moving, and under conditions of good visibility could be recognized at a distance of many miles. Even from the air it was possible to determine that its surface was twenty or more feet higher than the pack, indicating a probable thickness of 150 to 200 feet, compared with the seven- to twelve-foot thickness of the pack ice.

The discovery of T–1 caused speculation as to whether there were other ice islands, so airmen of the Air Weather Service, which regularly made flights to the vicinity of the North Pole, kept a close watch on their radarscopes and on the sea, when conditions allowed, for other ice islands. Sure enough, in April 1947 another one, later to be designated T–3, was sighted by a joint USAF/RCAF flight not far north of Cape Isachsen on Ellef Ringnes Island, on the north edge of the Canadian Archipelago. In July 1950 the third ice island, T–2, was discovered in the vicinity of the Pole. Not until after the discovery of T–2, however, was T–3 recognized as an ice island; hence the reversal in the order of numbering. T–3 is considerably smaller than T–1, measuring four and one-half by nine miles, and T–2 is the largest of the three, approximately seventeen by eighteen miles. The Russians reported finding an ice island, presumably T–2, in April 1948.

During the eight years following discovery of T–1, at least fifty other ice islands were found. Some of these were observed to be no more than a quarter of a mile long; others were as large as the first three found. There was in fact a time when ice-island discoveries were made in the office; it wasn't necessary to make a flight. Aerial photographs made by the RCAF, particularly between 1949 and 1951, were taken from the files and re-examined. There were the ice islands, many of them hiding in the sounds and straits among the islands of the Canadian Archipelago. Some of the ice islands found on these pictures have since been observed and rephotographed from the air.

The total number of ice islands now known is probably somewhere between eighty-five and 100. Each one resembles all the others in its tabular form, flat top, and peculiar undulating surface marked by broad, parallel, low ridges with shallow troughs between. The ridges, only a few inches high and in some instances 100 or more yards apart, are barely perceptible as viewed from the surface of the ice island. From the air, especially when the troughs contain melt water, they form a very conspicuous striped or banded pattern, detectable from a distance of miles in periods of good visibility. Because of their hardness and great thickness ice islands seldom break or crack as they push through the pack; their surfaces do not exhibit the irregular fracture pattern so characteristic of the pack. Unlike the pack, they usually carry boulders and clay and occasionally other land-derived materials.

Crews of U.S. Air Force planes were probably not the first to see ice islands. Features so large and so obviously different from the sea ice could hardly have gone unnoticed by veteran Arctic explorers, had they encountered them. Vast areas of the Arctic, of course, even yet have never been traversed either by sledge or motorized parties or by drifting ships frozen in the pack. Explorers' records show, however, that some of these floating ice islands probably had been encountered before. There are many references, as far back as 1861, to features which might have been ice islands.

A. W. Greely reported finding in 1883 a floe with a rolling surface which required two days for his sledge party to pass over. One of the most probable early finds of an ice island was reported by Storker Storkerson of Vilhjalmur Stefansson's Arctic Expedition in 1918. He and several other members of the expedition drifted on it through the Beaufort Sea north of Alaska from April to October. It measured about seven miles wide and more than fifteen miles long. Storkerson's description of it and the manner in which it moved through the pack indicate that it quite probably was an ice island.

A number of explorers, including Peary, have reported finding land at various places in the Arctic Ocean where later investigations have demonstrated conclusively there is none. Since some of these "discoveries" were made by seasoned explorers whose integrity cannot be questioned, there is some probability that the finds were ice islands. One of these was made by an Eskimo, Takpuk, in the Beaufort Sea in 1931. He and members of his party landed on it and took photographs, so it is well documented. Soil, grasses, and mosses were reported on the "island."

Although Dr. Frederick Cook was inclined to regard the truth rather lightly, since he neither reached the Pole nor climbed Mount McKinley, as he maintained, he did write a description of "old ice" which he sledged across and which sounds much like an ice island. Whether or not Peary's "land" in the Arctic Ocean was an ice island we cannot be sure, but that he saw the ice islands' source area on the north coast of Ellesmere Island there can be no doubt. Here he sledged across corrugated shelf ice which stretched for many miles along the coast and extended from the shore thirty or more miles into the sea. He also discovered that great sections of it broke off and floated away. There is no dispute among those who have studied the origin of ice islands that this area indeed is their source. Some aerial photographs show jagged ruptures in the ice-shelf edge into which nearby ice islands would make a perfect fit. All ice islands, including those most distant from the Ellesmere shelf, have the same surface markings as the shelf.

The Russians apparently made their first known contact with ice islands in 1946, the same year that T–1 was discovered. The icebreaker *Mikoyan* put a party of Russian scientists on one in 1947.

OCCUPANCY

Soon after discovery of T–1, Air Force planners realized that ice islands might have value as sites for semipermanent or even permanent bases. This would open up additional unknown sections of the Arctic to scientific investigation and provide weather-observation stations. It was obvious that these ice islands were stable, because of their great thickness, and floated through the pack month after month and apparently year after year with practically no change in size or shape. Because of their flat, smooth surfaces, ice islands could serve as landing places for the largest planes. Occupants of an ice island need have no fear that a fissure would split their camp apart, a danger which constantly faces parties on the much thinner ice floes.

The Air Force planners, realizing that even the largest and most stable floes are not always adequate for drift stations—the Soviets on several occasions have been unable to land large planes satisfactorily on floes which had been selected as sites for drift stations—went ahead with plans to occupy one of the ice islands. Hence, on March 19, 1952, an aircraft landing, the first ever made on an ice island, was carried out on T–3 when it was little more than 100 miles from the Pole. A party of three was put on the island to establish the station and begin scientific work. Thenceforth their "home" was known as "Fletcher's Ice Island" for Lieutenant Colonel J. O. Fletcher, leader of this first party ever to land planes on one of these floating masses of ice. In subsequent months there were some shifts in personnel, but the island was occupied continuously for the next two years, while it passed close to the Pole and then swung southward toward the shore of Ellesmere Island.

In 1957, when Fletcher's Ice Island was headed on a course that would again take it back into the white wastes of the Arctic, it was reoccupied by another scientific party. Within two months after this landing, a mile-long runway had been completed, enabling heavy four-motored planes to make safe wheels-down landings. In June 1960 the island grounded in shallow water about thirty miles north of Point Barrow, Alaska. A little over a year later, after the island had broken loose, made a short drift, then grounded again, its scientific station was abandoned.

The Americans at various times have also occupied T–1 and T–2, and the Soviets are known to have maintained a station, known as Nordpol 6, on an ice island. Normally, drift stations on ice islands are temporarily abandoned while they are passing close to shore. At such times they are not of much value as weather-observation stations because the same information can be obtained by land stations.

Just what can be accomplished by conducting operations on ice islands and ice floes? Several commercial airlines are already making regularly scheduled flights between Europe and North America on a route pioneered by Scandinavian Airlines

System across the Greenland ice sheet and the ice-choked waters of the Canadian Archipelago. And as time goes on there will be an increasing use of the air over the Polar regions, even across the Arctic ice pack and the Pole itself. The most direct air routes between Western Europe and a number of places, including Japan and western parts of Canada and the United States, lie across the Arctic regions. Direct flight lines between the interior of North America and practically any place in the Soviet Union span the Arctic Ocean.

Thus weather observations by the ice-island stations will continue to be of the utmost importance. Many important data on magnetic activity, auroral discharges, and solar radiation have already been gathered. We still do not know much about the circulation of water within the Arctic Basin or how it exchanges with the warmer waters of other oceans. We know very little about the age of the water at various depths. Temperature, current, and salinity determinations at all depths, and studies of marine life must yield clues to some of the problems facing oceanographers. Cores and sediment samples collected from the ocean floor may help to unlock some of the long-range climatic secrets which the Arctic most certainly holds.

Many of the questions scientists have about the Arctic will undoubtedly be answered by photographs taken on the ocean floor. But in the Arctic this method of approach to oceanography is still in an incipient stage. The first photographs—and at this writing, the only ones—ever taken at the bottom of the central Arctic Ocean were made by scientists of Lamont Geological Observatory from Drifting Station Alpha when it was in the vicinity of the Pole of Inaccessibility. One hundred and forty exposures were made at two localities by lowering the camera to the sea floor by means of a steel cable.

Man's first look at the submarinescape in the Arctic abyss revealed the presence of several forms of life and a number of features for which there as yet is no satisfactory explanation. Life is scarce in the areas photographed, but a small bryozoan colony and a sea anemone were recognized. Other doubtful objects may also be forms of life. Several types of "tracks" and other markings in the mud could not be associated with any known life form and remain unexplained. The most striking feature of the ocean floor is an abundance of randomly scattered pebbles and small rock fragments which must have been rafted on floes and ice islands and dropped to the ocean bottom when the ice melted.

Scientists on T–3 measured the depth of the ocean at many places along the drift route by setting off charges of dynamite and timing the returning echo, the same method used in determining the thickness of glaciers. In the vicinity of the Pole the explosions showed that the island was crossing a great submarine mountain range. Subsequently, the erratic course of the island caused it to cross and re-cross this range a number of times. This is the same range discovered by a Russian drifting party in 1948–9 and named by them the Lomonosov Range. From a general oceanic depth of 9,000 to 12,000 feet this range rises in places to within 3,000 feet of the surface, separating the Arctic Ocean into an eastern and western basin. It does to the Arctic Ocean what the Atlantic Mid-Oceanic Ridge, Earth's largest mountain range, does to the Atlantic. Depth of water at the North Pole, despite proximity to the base of the range, is 14,000 feet. General contours have been established on a number of sections on this Arctic ridge. Seismic data collected from drifting stations in the future will make possible the drawing of a detailed map of this large but little-known Earth feature.

The weather and climate of much of the Northern Hemisphere is affected by the Arctic. If man eventually attains his goal of long-range climatic prediction, it is likely that what he learned on the ice islands in the Arctic will have done much to make it possible.

As today's air traveler, comfortable in his heated, pressurized plane, plunges through the rarefied Arctic air at close to the speed of sound, he sips *Château Kirwan* and dines on such culinary achievements as *Châteaubriand à la Portogaise, Tomatoes Duxelles,* and *potatoes gaufrette.** As he may from time to time look down on the serene world of blue and white, let him not be unmindful of the mercilessness with which the elements treated the explorers and the lonely men on the floating drift stations, who made his flight possible.

* From the menu of an SAS flagship flying the Trans-Polar Route.

WHAT ROUTE DO THEY FOLLOW?

Each ice island, though it zigzags and even moves backward at times, follows a roughly circular course, several thousand miles long, on the North American side of the Arctic Ocean. The course starts on the north shore of Ellesmere Island, goes westward along the edge of the Canadian Archipelago, and then veers out into the ocean north of Alaska. Here it swings in a big arc northward to the vicinity of the Pole, thence southward, returning to or near its starting point on the shore of Ellesmere Island. The length of time required to complete this circuit is ten to twelve years, at an average speed of a little over a mile a day.

In 1958 Fletcher's Ice Island began the second circuit of the Arctic since its discovery. Evidence that this probably was only the third circuit it had ever made is borne by the island itself. It carried tufts of live mosses and willow twigs whose growth rings, when matched with live willows on land, showed that the island must have been attached to land as late as 1935.

Sometimes ice islands move independently of the pack, as evidenced by areas of open water frequently appearing on their lee sides. It is likely that the minor zigzags in their paths are caused mainly by shifts in wind direction and from the deflecting action of the pack, but the motion of ice islands seems to be controlled primarily by ocean currents. The general track they follow shows there is a great clockwise-rotating eddy in the Arctic Ocean between the Lomonosov Range and the northern edge of North America. Though some ice islands caught in this circulation may have circled the Arctic Ocean many times, very few remain on this course more than thirty years. With each circuit they move farther toward the outside of the great circulatory path and eventually escape from it by veering toward the left before making the westward swing north of Greenland. Then they move southward toward the edge of the Arctic Ocean and are picked up by the East Greenland Current. A large ice island, after spending thirty years floating around the Arctic, might eventually reach the shipping lanes of the North Atlantic.

This seems to be what is happening to Russia's Station

SP–6, established on an ice island north of Wrangel Island in April 1956. During the time it was manned it drifted for more than three years along a route not differing greatly from that of the *Fram*. In September 1959 the station was abandoned because the ice island, caught in the Greenland Current, was about to leave the Arctic Ocean and follow the route of Papanin's pioneer drift along the east coast of Greenland. Although when abandoned the station was only 1,600 miles from its starting point, it had covered a total distance of 5,800 miles because of zigzags and even reversals in the route followed by the island.

When last sighted, T–1 appeared to be on its way out of the Arctic Ocean, too, as it was then entering the strait between Greenland and Svalbard. Yet most ice islands move southward into the maze of channels among the Canadian Arctic islands, where they become grounded, eventually to disintegrate in the warmer waters.

Despite innumerable plane flights that have been made across the Arctic Ocean, ice islands are still being discovered. In May 1961 a three-plane expedition, en route from the U.S. Navy's Arctic Research Laboratory at Point Barrow, Alaska to establish a drifting station on a previously selected ice floe, spotted a new ice island about two miles by four miles in size. The expedition quickly changed plans, landed on the island, and set up the new station, ARLIS II * (Arctic Research Laboratory Ice Station Number Two), since an ice island would be superior to a floe and could be counted on to carry the station for several years.

That scientific work on ARLIS II will yield exciting results, not only in glaciology and ice-island history, but also in oceanography, meteorology, marine biology, and others, seems assured. Even as the planes were landing, expedition members could see that this island was thinner than the larger ones and that it carried mounds of rock, one as high as fifty feet, with boulders up to ten feet in diameter. Since establishment of the station, polar bear, arctic fox, and other animals have been seen. A number of plants, including grasses, saxifrages, and lichens,

---

* ARLIS I, a floe station, had been abandoned two months earlier because break-up of the floe appeared imminent.

were found. Seven days after they were collected, the grasses and saxifrages blossomed in the Arctic Research Laboratory at Barrow.

So another small group of dedicated scientists have taken up their lonely life of floating across the top of the world (it could be worse; their bunks are hollywood beds with linen and blankets). Before their ship runs aground or sails out of the Arctic these men on ARLIS II, like those who preceded them on other drifting stations, will add much to our knowledge of the forces and processes that make the Earth what it is.*

WHAT MADE THEM?

When Admiral Peary and other early explorers sledged across the peculiar, undulating ice shelf along the north shore of Elles- mere Island, they wondered about its origin. Since then scientists have learned much about the character of the ice in the shelf, but they are still studying it to know the climatic conditions under which it formed and to correlate these with known cli- mates of the past. Drill cores from the shelf and from the ice islands broken away from it show us that some of the ice is more than 1,000 years old. The top layers are largely firn which fell as snow directly on the shelf. At places this material rests upon old glacier ice, recognizable by its interlocking crystals; and below this there is ice which formed on the bottom by freezing of sea water. Except for its relative thinness, the Ellesmere shelf thus resembles the great ice shelves of the Antarctic.

At several places along the Ellesmere coast, especially in the vicinity of the long fiord known as Yelverton Bay, glaciers pour down into tidewater and merge with the ice shelf. They are, at least in part, responsible for this floating ice blanket. Many of the large boulders and accumulations of rocky debris carried around the Arctic by ice islands presumably were con- tributed directly by glaciers. On the other hand, along much of

* Information about ARLIS II was furnished by Louis O. Quam, Director, Earth Sciences Division, Office of Naval Research. Later it was published in *Glaciological Notes*, No. 7, IGY World Data Center A: Glaciology (American Geographical Society; July 1961).

the coast to which the shelf is connected there are no glaciers.

No ice is being added to the top of the Ellesmere shelf now; all of the snow which accumulates each winter and some of the ice upon which it rests melts in the summer. Reports of the early explorers indicate that the shelf was wider in earlier years. Likewise, the great age of the ice bears out the belief that the shelf ice formed many years ago in a period when the climate was colder than it is today—when some of the snow which fell each year on the ice was preserved and when glaciers were larger and perhaps present in some of the areas which are now ice-free. In any event, even though it is getting smaller, the great floating ice apron worn by Ellesmere Island will continue to break up into huge rafts which will float out into the Arctic Ocean and onto their time-consuming journeys through the Polar Sea.

Submarines can surface in summer polynyas and, like whales, can break up through the thin, newly frozen ice of winter polynyas, as *Skate* did at the Pole in March 1959 and *Sargo* in February 1960. But continuous meteorological and other observations cannot be made from submarines; they cannot substitute for large floating bases. So, in their quest for knowledge and also for strategic information about their common frontier, American and Soviet scientists, notwithstanding submarines and icebreakers yet to be invented, will for a long time to come continue to chase each other on ships of ice around the Pole.

12

Life on Ice

ARE GLACIERS inhabited? Are there any types of plants and animals which live on them? Obviously, glaciers are rather poor features on which to look for wildlife, although when animals do go onto glaciers they can be seen to rather spectacular advantage.

Many large animals and some of the smaller ones will cross glaciers to get from one side of a valley to the other or in order to go from one side of a range to the other. I have frequently seen grizzly bears and mountain goats and, on several occasions, mountain sheep and other large animals traveling across glaciers in the northern Rockies. On the firn fields of some glaciers there are regularly traveled goat trails, though in most cases these are merely detours used to circumvent the hazards of travel on the most precipitous parts of cirque walls, which even such sure-footed creatures as goats do not care to face.

A number of animals are known to make frequent jaunts onto the Himalayan glaciers. Among them are the wild yak, Tibetan wild horse, ibex, Tibetan antelope, snow leopard, lynx, wolf, and others. In any event, occupancy of glaciers by these animals is a very brief experience, in most cases probably an expediency.

Another glacier traveler which rivals the Loch Ness Monster in fascination and elusiveness is the *yeti*, or "Abominable Snowman," which has been reported from one end of the high Himalayas to the other. The most credible evidence of his existence is the footprints which have been seen by many persons on the high firn fields and glaciers. So far, a number of these tracks, though examined carefully and photographed, have not been definitely associated with any known animal. The largest average ten to twelve inches in length, four and a half to six inches in width, and presumably are made by a quadruped weighing perhaps as much as 175 pounds. There is no documentary evidence of an actual sighting of this strange creature, although many people, mostly Sherpas, claim to have seen them. Most accounts of actual sightings come from people in whose simple and primitive life superstition plays an important role.

Eric Shipton of Everest fame has seen many *yeti* tracks during the course of a number of expeditions to the Himalayas. On the 1951 reconnaissance of the southern route to Everest he found tracks at a height of 19,000 feet on a glacier in the Menlung Basin. The find caused his Sherpa, Sen Tensing, to describe an actual encounter which he claimed to have had with a Snowman. Shipton's account states:

Sen Tensing, who had no doubt whatever that the creatures (for there had been at least two) that had made the tracks were "Yetis" or wild men, told me that two years before, he and a number of other Sherpas had seen one of them at a distance of about 25 yards at Thyangbochi. He described it as half man and half beast, standing about five feet six inches, with a tall pointed head, its body covered with reddish brown hair, but with a hairless face. When we reached Katmandu at the end of November, I had him cross-examined in Nepali (I conversed with him in Hindustani). He left no doubt as to his sincerity. Whatever it was that he had seen, he was convinced that it was neither a bear nor a monkey, with both of which animals he was, of course, very familiar. Of the various theories that have been advanced to account for these tracks, the only one which is in any way plausible is that they were made by a langur monkey, and

even this is very far from convincing, as I believe those who have suggested it would be the first to admit.*

Most accounts of the alleged sightings depict an animal
similar to Sen Tensing's, a hairy body and a hairless face. A
number of persons who have examined the tracks or their
photographs follow Shipton's view that they are probably made
by a large langur monkey. Others have some conviction that the
culprit is an ape or the Himalayan red bear—some photographs
of the footprints show unmistakable claw marks.

Anyhow, some large animal, perhaps more than one type
not yet identified with the footprints, prowls the glaciers and
firn fields of the high Himalayas. But what are they doing at
such inhospitable high altitudes where there is no apparent
source of food? It seems obvious that they inhabit the lower
elevations but journey onto the glaciers en route to and from the
high passes through which they move when adversity prompts
them to seek new living space on the other side of the divide.
Persons with a less serious view might suspect that, like those
who find his tracks, the *yeti* has a love of high places, which
periodically finds an outlet in excursions into the realm of the
gods. Notwithstanding the failure of several expeditions—
American, British, and Russian—conducted expressly to find a
yeti, the identity of this elusive, high-traveling creature will
surely someday be solved, if Sir Edmund Hillary doesn't already
have the answer—namely, that the *yeti* is any one of a number
of well-known animals that leave their tracks in the snow on the
glaciers.

The summits of hundreds of high Himalayan peaks are still
untrod. But since the greatest peaks of all have fallen before the
onslaught of large expeditions, it is probable that future cam-
paigns will devote increasingly more time to exploration and
science, and possibly to the search for the Snowman. He will
probably turn out to be, as Sir Edmund suspects, one or more of
the well-known Himalayan animals, for we must not overlook
the strong possibility that in the rarefied air of the Himalayas
pink elephants are represented by Abominable Snowmen.

* By permission from Eric Shipton: *The Mount Everest Reconnaissance Expedition 1951.*

The reason some animals have for going onto glaciers is more obvious than in the case of the *yeti*. Several species of birds spend much time on the surfaces of glaciers during the summer months. Among these the most common frequenters of the ice are pipits and rosy finches. The seeds on which these birds feed are very conspicuous after they are blown onto the surface of a glacier. The birds simply recognize an easy method of making a living.

Insects are often blown onto glaciers where the low temperature quickly numbs and eventually kills them. Several glaciers in the Beartooth Range near Yellowstone Park and in the Crazy Mountains of central Montana contain great numbers of grasshoppers which have been imbedded in the ice over a period of many years. The best known of these ice masses is Grasshopper Glacier in the Beartooths about twelve miles north of the little town of Cooke at the northeast entrance to Yellowstone Park. Grasshoppers now yielded by melting of the ice at the terminus of this glacier may have been trapped in the firn as much as 200 years ago. Their abundance on the surface of the ice sometimes attracts bears and birds to the glacier. So numerous have these insects been at times that the odor from their putrefaction has been detected a quarter of a mile away. Grasshoppers in considerable numbers have also been found at an elevation of 16,000 feet in one of the glaciers on lofty Mount Kenya in Africa.

Despite the grief that has come to the grasshoppers, we must go to another group of insects to find one of the few members of the animal kingdom which lives out its entire life span on glaciers. A small, wingless insect belonging to the Order Collembola and known as the glacier flea lives exclusively on snow and ice. These insects are so abundant on some of the glaciers in the Alps, on Mount Rainier, and elsewhere that at times ice surfaces are blackened with them. During the night they freeze fast to the firn and ice. Their food consists of conifer pollen blown onto the ice.

Another animal which apparently spends its entire life cycle in the snow and ice of glaciers is a small worm belonging to the Order Oligochaeta, a group which also includes the omnipresent earthworm. Glacier worms have been found on glaciers and snowbanks all the way from Oregon to Alaska. A half-inch-long variety, with the formidable name, *Mesenchytraeus soli-fugus rainierensis*, lives in great numbers on some of the glaciers of Mount Rainier and the Olympic Mountains. Its eggs, deposited in snow, ice, or pools of water on the ice, must hatch in freezing temperatures.

In the animal world, prey and predator are associated in all types of environments. The glacier flea and worm are no exceptions to the rule; they share their harsh environment with several other minute animals, mostly mites, which prey upon them.

Plants, too, have adapted to living on ice. The color in the "red snow" on glaciers all over the world is really algae, and living among these primitive plants are the glacier worms and the predatory mites and ticks.

Below the firn line on the Greenland ice sheet there are large areas covered with closely spaced, cylindrical holes up to two feet deep, ranging in diameter from an inch or less to more than three feet. During the melting season they are filled with water. In the bottom of every pit is a fine-grained gelatinous material called *cryoconite,* consisting partly of dust blown by the wind from areas beyond the ice margin. But cryoconite contains a considerable amount of organic material in the form of several kinds of blue-green algae and fungi, associated with which are microscopic animals belonging to the rotifers. During the winter, which includes most of the year, the water and the algae freeze solid. In the summer as soon as sunlight can reach down to these tiny plants, they begin growing again. That these algae are not hampered by their life on ice is borne out by evidence that the pits in which they live are formed by heat released by their photosynthesis and metabolism. Scientists actually started a new algae pit by taking a handful of the cryoconite and placing it on the surface of the ice. In ten days this new colony had created a pit nearly a foot deep, and when examined the following summer it was still going strong. At one place where the marginal ice is moving about one mile per 100 years, investigators believe that algae in some of the larger pits may have started out higher on the glacier 100 or 200 years ago.

Though no life dwells permanently on the vast reaches of the Antarctic ice sheet, certain forms of animal life have been found at incredible distances inland, in what is undoubtedly the harshest environment on the face of the Earth. During the IGY, members of a party led by glaciologist Troy Péwé found a large number of well-preserved, mummified seals in the ice-free areas of the McMurdo Sound region. A few were found on the glaciers, and some of the others were in areas surrounded by glacier ice. Some were found up to distances of forty-five miles inland and 2,500 feet above sea level. The cold, arid climate is ideal for retarding organic decay, and Péwé believes that all creatures, seals and birds, that have wandered inland and died during the past 2,000 years remain to attest their last journey.

A half century earlier, members of Scott's expeditions apparently saw some of these same seals, for they reported finding crabeater seals in the McMurdo region forty miles inland and 2,400 feet above sea level. Since the seals found by Scott's men were either dead or dying, it is assumed that their trek from the coast was undertaken to gain seclusion, a habit which a number of animals have when sick or injured. One cannot help feeling, though, that in the case of the crabeater seals they would be near death, or at least in extremely poor physical condition, after floundering forty miles across land and ice, regardless of the state of their health at the start.

But the champion long-distance traveler of the Antarctic appears to be the skua gull. Several parties have seen this bird on the high Polar plateau 500 to 600 miles from the nearest open water, and Scott in January 1912 found it only 160 miles from the Pole. In the summer of 1929 the members of Dr. Laurence Gould's sledge party were amazed to see a skua gull feeding on pieces of dogfood at their camp at the head of the Ross Ice Shelf. To reach this point the bird would have had to have flown at least 500 miles in a straight line from the nearest open water. Since gulls are inveterate opportunists, there is some possibility that they follow the dog teams in order to have a meal ticket.

Although the emperor penguin does not inhabit the Antarctic ice sheet, it is, no matter how you look at it, truly a bird of the ice. It was not until 1952 that the first detailed scientific study of this bird was made—by members of a French Expedition on the Adélie Coast of East Antarctica. Eight of the fourteen known rookeries were discovered only after the IGY had begun.

The emperor has a unique method of living in an environment where almost any kind of living is a terrific ordeal. At the end of the summer when all birds that breed along the rocky Antarctic shores have left and gone north to warmer climes— all, that is, save the emperor penguin—this strange bird comes south from the sea to nest and rear his young on the surface of land-fast sea ice along the coast. In almost all cases the egg and the bird hatched from it never rest on a solid surface other than ice. The single egg is laid in late autumn and incubated during a period when temperatures may fall to 70° or 80° below zero Fahrenheit, and the young is reared in the heart of the winter night. Within three hours after the egg is laid the female turns it over to the male for incubation. During the two-month period of incubation the male does not sit on the egg, but instead stands all the time, the egg held in a fold of skin between the feet and the lower part of the stomach.

As soon as the female turns the egg over to the male for brooding, she takes off—this bird which walks with difficulty and can't fly at all—across the sea ice for open water, perhaps 100 miles away, to break her three-month fast by feeding on fish. It will be two months before she returns to her mate, well fed and carrying extra food in her stomach for the expected youngster.

The arrival of the female back at the rookery is timed to take place just before the chick is hatched. As soon as this event occurs the male, weakened by lack of food during the long period of incubation, takes off in his turn across the ice on the long trek to open water and the feeding grounds, leaving the female to care for and feed the young—with regurgitated food eaten at her last meal. Not for two months will the male come back to his family. After his return there is another two-months period of fasting—before the sea ice breaks up, bringing open water with its feeding grounds close to the rookery. For ten months of each year, except when feeding briefly in the cold water along the edge of the pack, these hardy birds live on ice. During the coldest part of the night and when storms are raging the emperors form themselves into compact, oval-shaped groups. Standing on the ice with their flightless wings held against their sides and pressing tightly against each other, they protect themselves from the bitter cold. Thus they may stand for several days, with the birds on the edge of the group offering only their backs to the elements.

During the IGY, parties traversing the ice from Byrd Station in the interior of West Antarctica reported the discovery of penguin tracks more than 150 miles from the nearest known coast. Even for so amazing a bird as the penguin this is a most incredible exploit. Perhaps a miniature "Abominable Snowman" has invaded Antarctica.

IGY scientists have collected spores and pollen grains from the ice as much as ninety feet below the surface at the South Pole. It is possible that these minute particles, carried in from great distances by the wind, can be preserved for thousands of years in the ice.

The North Polar region, too, is not without its winter bird-life. Little Ross's gull in the fall moves from its nesting grounds in eastern Siberia to the Arctic coast of Alaska and then heads out into the Polar Sea, apparently to spend the winter in icy darkness, eking out a meager living by fishing in the scarce and short-lived leads of open water.

Various forms of animal life wander almost everywhere across the wild wastes of the Arctic pack ice. Polar bears have visited both the Russian and American ice-floe and ice-island stations when they were close to the North Pole and even farther from the nearest land. Arctic foxes, too, because they follow the bears to feed on the leavings of their feasts, have been seen on the ice many miles from the nearest shores. A short time before Drifting Station Alpha cracked apart and had to be abandoned, a polar bear and her cub got tangled in the wires to the runway lights and knocked out all the lights—just as a plane was preparing to land. Evidently the bears resented the intrusion of foreigners into their domain.

The polar bear's incredible strength and endurance may be of little avail in overcoming a new menace which is challenging his survival. The day after a business executive boards a plane in Chicago, a bush pilot can land him on the ice pack off Alaska; he can kill a bear and be back in the office before his associates realize he had left. Hunting polar bears by plane, however, is not without dangers—men have been killed in crashes on the ice, and there is the chance of being attacked by a wounded bear—but it is a sport which, if not rigidly controlled, may bode ill for the bears. Two or more planes, in radio communication with each other, in a few hours can search hundreds of square miles of pack and spot all the bears on it. If a bear is in ice too rough for a landing, he can be followed to a place where the ski-equipped plane can be set down. Alaska game laws are in effect only within the three-mile limit, but fortunately it is illegal to bring into the state any bear not taken in accordance with its game laws. Those who pursue this exciting sport of hunting polar bears from the air will have to use considerable self-restraint. Otherwise the hunters will have to fly farther and farther to find bears, and eventually those who brought about his extermination will wonder what has become of this magnificent former inhabitant of the ice.

The presence of bears on the Polar pack hundreds of miles from shore means that the seals upon which they prey also inhabit these icy waters. Cracking of the relatively thin pack ice in summer creates open leads in which the seals can emerge for air. During the winter when openings are scarce and remain unfrozen only briefly, the seals maintain breathing holes through the young ice covering cracks and leads. In his fight for survival the seal not only must search constantly for fish in the darkness beneath the ice, but he must return to his breathing holes sufficiently often to keep them open—a formidable task when the air temperature is far below zero. Breathing holes which the seal starts in the thin crust of ice over a newly frozen lead may, in the course of a winter, become surrounded by ice nearly ten feet thick. The seal faces the ever-present prospect of losing his life by freezing fast to the ice in the narrow tunnel through which he must force himself up to the air at the top. If the breathing hole should freeze so solidly that the seal cannot break the ice, he is doomed and will drown, unless he can reach another hole or hold his breath long enough to find a newly formed open lead. Few seals, however, get caught in this embarrassing situation, since they seem to have a faculty for finding those places where ice motion is sufficient to create areas of open water. Seals are scarcer the greater the distance from the edge of the pack, but they have been seen within two degrees of the Pole.

Polar bears and arctic foxes pass over the ice islands in their wanderings across the pack. Signs of still earlier inhabitants have been found on some of the islands. Not long after the first landing was made on Fletcher's Ice Island, a set of caribou antlers and the remains of other land animals, including lemmings, were found. But the island undoubtedly acquired these remains while it was part of the ice shelf on the coast of Ellesmere Island.

Life is ubiquitous and capable of adapting to almost any environment, regardless of how inhospitable it might be. No matter where man penetrates with his protective clothing, heated shelters, oxygen tanks, and bathyspheres, there he will find some form of life, not always in its most elemental form, living adjusted to its environment.

✿✿✿✿✿✿

13

✿✿✿✿✿✿

Ice Beneath the Ground

✿✿✿✿✿✿✿ I N 1799 a Tungusian tribesman named
✿✿✿✿✿✿✿ Shumakhov, while hunting near the mouth of the Lena River,
noticed a peculiar object embedded high above his reach in a
cliff of frozen silt. Suspecting that it might be something of
value, he resolved to return the following year in the hope that
it might then have been freed from the cliff by thawing of the
frozen ground. Each year for four more years he returned to the
site only to find that the object, now recognized as the carcass of
a large animal with tusks, was still frozen into the cliff. On the
fifth year, however, Shumakhov's persistence was rewarded; the
animal, released by thawing of the frozen ground, had slid to the
bottom of the cliff. At this time the body of the beast was essentially complete; hide, flesh, and bones were intact. Shumakhov
chopped off the ten-foot-long ivory tusks and bartered them to a
trader for fifty rubles.

During the next two years while the carcass lay partially
covered by silt, its exposed parts were completely destroyed by
bears and wolves, and some of the meat was fed by the local
Yakuts to their dogs. Fortunately, at this time M. F. Adams, a

zoologist and member of the Russian Academy of Sciences, who happened to be traveling across Siberia, heard of the find and visited the site. From a sketch made by a trader who saw the animal soon after it had fallen from the cliff, from Shumakhov's oral description of the carcass, and from Adams's examination it was readily apparent that the animal was a member of the elephant tribe known as the mammoth.

When Adams arrived on the scene there were few remaining soft parts except skin, but there was a lot of this. The largest section of skin came from the side of the carcass which had been in contact with the ground. The skin of the head, except for a missing ear, was complete. The most remarkable part of the find, however, was an eye which still retained its original color. Adams was able to salvage practically all of the bones and a part of the thick hair-covered hide. He also gathered up about thirty-six pounds of hair which wild animals had scattered over the ground.

Although not seen by a scientist until nearly seven years after it had begun to emerge from the crumbling cliff of frozen silt on the Lena delta, this mammoth became the first one to have its remnants exhibited in a museum. The skeleton—with tusks taken from another mammoth—was assembled at the St. Petersburg Zoological Museum. Pieces of skin and hair eventually reached musuems in Moscow, Stuttgart, Berlin, and London.

Adams's mammoth carcass probably was the best one ever found in the frozen ground of the Siberian tundra, but it certainly wasn't the first. There is no way of knowing when the first such discoveries were made, for the record is found only in legend and folklore. But well-documented finds of frozen elephant carcasses were made in the seventeenth century. In a paper published in the Transactions of the American Philosophical Society in 1929, I. P. Tolmachoff listed thirty-four between 1692 and 1924. Most of these were north of the Arctic Circle between the Taimyr and Chuckchi Peninsulas. Many finds were lost to science because they were destroyed before they could be investigated. Many others probably were discovered, but because of remoteness never were reported. In addition to the carcasses, the tusks and bones of thousands upon thousands of mammoths have been found in the Siberian tundra. In places it must have resembled the North American Great Plains when they were strewn with the bones of bison.

Few if any of the carcasses, except the Adams mammoth, were complete. Most of them consisted of tusks, broken bones, and varying amounts of flesh—often in a state of partial putrefaction—pieces of hide, and masses of hair. Many were found because of their odor.

Perhaps the most important of all Siberian fossil elephants is the Beresovka mammoth, discovered in August 1900 by a Lamutian native, S. Tarabukin, while he was chasing a reindeer. Only the head of the animal, minus the trunk and one tusk, protruded from the frozen ground. Tarabukin, like other natives of the region, had a superstitious fear that sickness would overcome anyone who excavated or even touched the flesh of these frozen animals. This, however, did not deter him from cutting off the remaining tusk, which he later sold to a Cossack, Yavlovski. Fortunately Yavlovski realized the scientific importance of the find and visited the site early in the winter after much of the carcass had been exposed by partial thawing and sliding of the frozen ground in which it had been buried. Satisfied that an effort should be made to secure the animal before further deterioration would reduce its value, he reported the discovery to the governor of Yakutsk. About the middle of the following April the report reached the Imperial Academy of Sciences in St. Petersburg (now Leningrad). The Academy must have been delighted with the opportunity to acquire a nearly complete mammoth carcass, for it acted at once. By May 3, an expedition for the recovery of the mammoth, under the leadership of O. F. Herz, had been organized, financed, and was on its way.

But the mammoth lay, only partly protected from the ravages of animals and weather, nearly halfway around the world along the Beresovka River in the taiga of far-eastern Siberia. In June, after having reached Yakutsk on the Lena River north of Manchuria, the expedition still had 1,500 miles to go, through an area in which long trips were limited almost entirely to the winter months, because in summer the trails and roads were—and still are—a sea of mud and practically impassable. But Herz and his assistants, anxious to get to the mammoth as soon as possible, pressed on. Traveling on horseback and transporting their baggage on pack animals, they required more than three harrowing months to cover these 1,500 muddy miles to their goal.

On September 11, a full year after the carcass had been exposed and probably twice that long after the head had appeared above ground, excavation of the mammoth was begun. Even though Yavlovski had cut off several pieces of hide and flesh, and wild animals had destroyed parts of the carcass, it was in surprisingly good condition. By the end of September a house had been constructed over the animal in order to thaw the frozen ground and protect the excavating crew from the cold. Because of the delicacy of the operation and the difficulties involved in excavating in frozen ground, a month was required to exhume the animal. But at the end of that time the hide, the skeleton, large amounts of hair and wool, a considerable quantity of the flesh, and the contents of the stomach were packed and ready for shipment to St. Petersburg. Subsequently the hide and skeleton were mounted and put on display there in the Zoological Museum. In 1922 several pieces of hide and flesh from this mammoth were acquired by the United States National Museum through purchase from one of Herz's assistants, E. W. Pfizenmayer, who had collected them when the animal was being excavated.

While the Beresovka mammoth was being exhumed, Herz and his helpers made a number of important and exciting discoveries. Of course, the mere finding of a large fossil animal "in the flesh" is a thrilling and important event in itself. But as the digging progressed in the little hut on the bank of the Beresovka River, great amounts of well-preserved flesh, covered in places with a thick layer of white, odorless fat, were found beneath the hide. On the animal's side the skin was nine inches thick, and the abdominal skin when cut from the carcass weighed about 470 pounds. There were masses of blood which had formed because of hemorrhage from an injury at the time of death. The tail was short, only fourteen inches in length, and its end was covered with long rusty-brown hair. The color of the hair varied from one part of the body to another. This mammoth differed from all other species of elephant by having only four toes on each foot.

A notable event during the excavating was the discovery of

some partly masticated food between the animal's teeth and the recovery of many pounds of food remains from its stomach. On October 5 Herz entered in his log:

The flesh from under the shoulder, which is fibrous and marbled with fat, is dark red in color and looks as fresh as well-frozen beef or horse meat. It looked so appetizing that we wondered for some time whether we should not taste it, but no one would venture to take it into his mouth, and horseflesh was given the preference. The dogs cleaned up whatever mammoth meat was thrown to them.*

Small wonder, though, that the diggers didn't taste the meat. All the while the work was going on the stench of putrefaction was thick on the air, and Herz wrote that during the first two days it was nearly unbearable. His report states, however, that toward the end of the work the stench did not seem "near so intolerable" as at the start, though he admitted this might be a state of mind resulting from the fact that they had grown accustomed to it.

Just how palatable is mammoth meat? The scientists who dig out the remains don't find it appetizing enough to eat because of the odor associated with it. The natives of northern Siberia who have made practically all the finds, though they may find the odor less objectionable than their "civilized" brothers, have not eaten it because of superstitious fear. Dogs, on the other hand, relish it. But dogs can't talk. In 1951 it appeared that we were going to get the answer to our questions from the members of the Explorers Club, who reportedly were to be given the rare privilege of tasting hors d'oeuvres of mammoth meat brought from Alaska for the club's annual dinner. Unfortunately, though those who partook of these tidbits thought they were eating the real thing, the meat didn't belong to a mammoth at all. I have the feeling, however, that had the flag of the Explorers Club been flying over the little hut along the Beresovka, we would now have a vivid description of the flavor of mammoth steaks and possibly the soup made from the bones.

Several times during the nineteenth century the Russian Academy of Sciences, in order to avoid delay between the time

* From O. F. Herz: "Frozen Mammoth in Siberia," in *Annual Report of the Smithsonian Institution for the Year Ending June 30, 1903* (Washington; 1904) p. 621.

a mammoth carcass was discovered and the time an expedition could reach it, endeavored to establish a resident scientist in the Siberian Arctic. His mission would be to rush to the scene as soon as a find was reported. This plan of the Academy never met with success; exile in Siberia apparently was no more attractive then than it is now. So expeditions for the recovery of frozen mammoths continue to be late.

A discovery made on the Taimyr Peninsula in the summer of 1948 and reported in the autumn was finally excavated a year later, but by then it consisted only of the skeleton with some flesh and ligaments adhering. In 1956 the Zoological Institute of the Academy sent out a special appeal, requesting anyone finding a mammoth to telegraph immediately to the Committee for Mammoth Study.

About the same time the Taimyr mammoth was discovered in 1948, placer miners uncovered a baby mammoth, later determined to be about one year old, from the frozen muck near Fairbanks, Alaska. There is no telling how much of the animal lay buried in the muck, but when the high-pressure hydraulic jets had washed it out, nothing was left except the trunk and the skin covering the face and one forelimb. The remains were embalmed and shipped by air express to the American Museum of Natural History.

More important than the flavor of mammoth meat are answers to these questions: What is the material in which these heavy animals are embedded, and how have they been preserved for such a long time? In spite of the apparent freshness of some of the flesh of these animals when they are found, not a single live mammoth has trod the Earth for thousands of years.

The mammoths and the rhinoceroses and other large mammals with which they were associated, wherever they lie buried today, are frozen simply because the ground in which they rest has been in a continuously frozen state for a long time. Technically, perennially frozen ground, known most commonly as *permafrost,* includes bedrock, soil, ice, sand, gravel, and any other types of materials in which the temperature has been below freezing for more than two years. On the other hand, nearly all permafrost, and certainly that in which the mammoths have been preserved, is thousands of years old.

Although some permafrost is dry, most of it contains varying amounts of ice in the form of grains, small irregularly
shaped masses, and even large masses and layers several feet
thick. It is this *ground ice,* especially small interstitial particles,
which makes frozen ground hard.

Since the limits of permafrost, both in area and thickness,
are not definitely known, and because it is a phenomenon which
lies hidden beneath the ground, it is impossible to know the
quantity of ice within it. But, armed with a few rough statistics
about the known extent of permafrost, we need very little
imagination to arrive at the conclusion that the amount of ice
locked up in it is enormous. The area underlain by permafrost
is at least as large as that occupied by glaciers, which at the
moment is ten per cent of the Earth's land surface.

Since permafrost depends for its existence mostly upon
temperature there is little relation between its distribution and
that of glaciers, which depend equally or more upon other
factors. Permafrost in the Northern Hemisphere is circumpolar
in its distribution, occurring around the rim of the Arctic Ocean
in a wide band which extends far to the south in eastern Canada
and across central Siberia deep into Mongolia and Manchuria.
Narrower arms reach southward in the Rocky and Ural Mountains. The zone is narrowest in northernmost Europe, where the
effect of the Gulf Stream drives its edge northward, just as it
does the pack ice in the Arctic Ocean.

Nearly half of Canada is underlain by permafrost. In the
U.S.S.R. an area fully twice the size of the United States is
within the zone of perennially frozen ground. Perennially frozen
ground also caps the tops of high mountain ranges—the Alps,
Himalayas, Rockies, Andes, and many others—and may occur in
isolated patches on much lower mountains far outside the main
permafrost zone.

Permafrost is everywhere present on the exposed rim of
Antarctica and may also exist under part or all of the ice sheet.
The islands between South America and Antarctica are also in
the zone of perennially frozen ground. The permafrost line in a
way resembles the snowline, for it surrounds the top and bottom
of the world and a number of isolated "islands" in the mountains
of all continents except Australia.

Along its southern border the permafrost zone in the Northern Hemisphere is only a few inches thick and is not continuous. In general the thickness increases northward, and beyond a certain line every part of the land is underlain by an unbroken layer of frozen ground.

On top of the permafrost is the ground known as the *active layer*, which freezes in winter and thaws in summer. It may be several feet thick, but in northern Alaska and Siberia there are places where its thickness is only a few inches.

At Point Barrow, the northernmost point of Alaska, permafrost extends to a depth of 1,030 feet. At a number of places in northern Canada it is just as thick, and on the Taimyr Peninsula, between the Lena and Yenesei Rivers, there is a large area where it reaches twice that depth. Some of the coal mines in Svalbard extend through more than 1,000 feet of permafrost into the unfrozen rock beneath it.

The thickness of permafrost, of course, can be measured in wells and mines which penetrate entirely through it, as in Svalbard. Where wells have failed to penetrate to the base of the permafrost, its thickness can be extrapolated from the temperature gradient in the holes. Seismic methods, such as those employed to determine the thickness of glaciers, have not proved satisfactory for finding the base of the frozen zone because there is very little difference between the velocities of the waves in frozen and unfrozen bedrock.

Under certain conditions permafrost thickness can be ascertained by using electrical methods similar to those employed in the crevasse detector. In the case of permafrost, however, the electrodes, instead of being carried by a vehicle, are placed on the ground at some distance from each other. Knowing the depth to which a current passed from one electrode to the other will penetrate, and because unfrozen ground offers greater resistance to the flow of the current than does frozen ground, the distance to both the top and bottom of permafrost can be calculated. But over the vast far northern lands deep wells and mines are scarce and practically no resistivity prospecting has been done. So the thickness of permafrost throughout much of this domain can only be inferred.

Now that we have some conception of the extent of permafrost, let's try to think of the amount of ice in it. It is common knowledge that bedrock almost everywhere outside the permafrost zone is permeable to water, either because of pore space between the grains or because of fractures and larger openings such as caves. The amount of pore space within rocks varies widely, but a common rock such as sandstone is considered to have only a medium porosity if from five to fifteen per cent of its volume consists of voids. Many sandstones have more than twenty per cent pore space. Unconsolidated materials—soil, silt, sand, and gravel—may have porosities as high as fifty per cent. On the other hand, some granites and other igneous rocks have practically no pore space and are impervious to water. But in all of these rocks there are fractures which may hold sizable volumes of water. Further, in all humid regions there is some moisture in these openings, and below a depth which varies usually from a few inches to several tens of feet, all interconnected openings—pores, fractures, caves—are completely filled with water. Even under a number of arid regions there is a zone in which water saturates all the openings.

The extent and volume of this great subterranean reservoir are incredibly large. This certainly is a conclusion you would reach if you visited Silver Spring or any of the other large springs in Florida, the source of which is an interconnected maze of water-filled caverns which honeycomb the limestone lying beneath practically the entire state. The yield of Silver Spring, one of the largest in the United States, is several hundred millions of gallons a day—enough to supply Chicago or Philadelphia. And there are other Florida springs nearly as large. Springs yielding 500,000 gallons a day are abundant.

Of course, we would expect to find a lot of ground water in Florida because of heavy rainfall and the cavernous limestone, but there are places in the world where rainfall is light and the bedrock is not limestone which also yield enormous quantities of ground water. The vast Columbia Plateau, especially the Channeled Scablands in eastern Washington and the Snake River Plain in southern Idaho, is an arid region. Yet stored in the rock under this land is a tremendous subterranean reservoir of fresh water. Many of the wells drilled down through the lava flows, which, one upon the other, constitute the bedrock of the plateau, yield incredible quantities of water. For long stretches along the sides of the deep gorge which the Snake River has cut down through the lava, water pours out continuously in some of the most spectacular springs known in the world, and the names of two of these places—Thousand Springs and Niagara Springs— are unexaggerated descriptions of these amazing outflowings. At Thousand Springs, opposite the mouth of the Salmon River, the water issues from the side of the canyon at a rate of ten or more millions of gallons an hour and drops to the river in a 200-foot series of foaming cascades. Along the forty-mile stretch of canyon centered on Thousand Springs the quantity of water issuing from beneath the ground is between two and three billion gallons a day, more than twice as much as the Catskill and Delaware Aqueducts together deliver to New York City. And this water pours forth into the Snake day after day, year after year, in a never-lessening volume, even during periods when rain, the ultimate source of all ground water, has not fallen for weeks or even months.

The cavernous limestones of Florida and the highly permeable basalt of the Columbia Plateau afford extremely favorable conditions for the storage of ground water, but rocks similar to these underlie vast areas of the Earth's surface. Furthermore, there are other types of porous rocks through which water can readily pass. Anywhere you go you will find people taking water from the ground. In the country every farmer has a well. In many cases it may be capable of delivering no more than ten or fifteen gallons a minute, but in a single county in Iowa or Illinois or Pennsylvania you could multiply this figure by thousands. Almost every village and small town and many cities, some of them large, get their water from wells. Although not all wells yield huge quantities of water, it is almost impossible to drill a well from which some water cannot be obtained—that is the reason "water witches" are so successful.

How is all this related to ground ice? Simply in this way: The kinds of rocks in the permafrost zones of the world are no different from those elsewhere; they have similar degrees of porosity and permeability. But in permafrost there is no circulating ground water—it is all in the form of ice. In the sands and silts and other materials which overlie the bedrock the volume of ice may be even greater than the original volume of pore space, because water in freezing to ice increases approximately one tenth in volume. In the process it exerts a pressure of more than 2,000 pounds per square inch on the enclosing materials, forcing them aside to make space for itself. In many regions where permafrost is hundreds of feet thick ground water simply isn't available, except in those rare places where wells have been drilled through it to unfrozen water-bearing rock beneath. In the winter, when even the active layer is frozen solid, water can be obtained throughout much of northern Canada, Alaska, and Siberia only by artificially melting ice and snow, and at no time are large supplies available.

Within bedrock the subterranean ice occupies the pore spaces, either partly or completely filling them, and it also occurs in the form of thin veins which are nothing more than ice-filled cracks. Ground ice thus seldom constitutes more than one fifth, usually much less, of the total rock volume. But in the mantle of soil, silt, and other superficial materials covering the bedrock, ground ice may be present in far greater volume. It occupies the spaces between fragments, cementing them firmly together, but in a number of localities it also occurs in the form of massive vertical wedges and extensive layers which may be fifteen or more feet thick.

There are large sections of Alaska where, mainly because of the presence of ice layers, lenses, and wedges, the silts and similar fine-grained superficial materials on top of the bedrock may be fifty or sixty per cent or even as much as eighty per cent ice. And in northernmost Siberia, east of the Taimyr Peninsula, there is an area far larger than the state of Texas in which the permafrost contains similar unbelievably high percentages of ice.

The ice wedges, widest at the top, extend from the base of the active layer downward. A wedge, two or three feet wide at the top, may extend to a depth of ten feet. The largest ones observed in Alaska are more than ten feet wide and thirty feet high. In many areas these wedges are not single masses of ice. They intersect other similar masses, creating a ramifying network of subterranean ice walls, partitioning off the ground into cell-like columns. In several districts in Alaska, including Fairbanks and Nome, where placer miners have washed away the overlying and enclosing soil and silt, extensive ice structures looking like giant if somewhat irregular honeycombs have been uncovered. There undoubtedly are many thousands of square miles in Alaska and northern Canada underlain by ice structures of this type. Even where these ice networks have not been exposed, their presence and even their design can be detected by the effect they have upon the surface. As the ice wedges and veins grow they heave up the overlying ground into an intersecting maze of low ridges. If the ice should melt, the ridges would be replaced by a system of shallow trenches having a similar pattern. Such surface markings are common over immense areas of the Arctic tundra, and viewed from the air they are a most striking feature of the landscape. As soon as they come into view one is apt to receive the impression that here the Earth is held in a gigantic net, or if we should drop down a little lower for a better view, we might conclude that the surface had been broken by a maze of intersecting cracks.

And this may be what has happened. At least that is what many students of permafrost believe. Contraction of the ground in the intense and prolonged cold of winter causes it to crack. As soon as thawing occurs in the active layer, water enters these cracks and enlarges them by freezing. Further expansion of the cracks is caused by freezing of more water from thawing ground, melting snow, and moist air, and possibly from continued shrinkage of the ground in the following winters. The result is innumerable wedgelike veins of ice surrounding irregular polygonal columns of frozen soil, varying in width from several to more than thirty feet. The distinctly marked surface above existing or former ice wedges goes by many names, but *polygonal ground* and *patterned ground* are two of the most frequently used.

As in the case of ice wedges, a satisfactory explanation for the presence of thick layers of clear ice beneath the surface is something on which scientists are not fully agreed. Some of these beds undoubtedly formed on the surface and were then buried. Where Arctic rivers freeze to the bottom in the shallow reaches, the water from farther upstream flows over this ice, freezes, and makes the deposit thicker. Continued breaking out of water and the formation of new ice on top of the old results in thick accumulations which spread beyond the river channels and cover entire floodplains. These accumulations may be many feet thick, a mile or two wide, and much greater in length. With the coming of the spring flood this layer of ice stranded on the floodplain may be covered with silt and thus preserved. This has been observed in recent times, and must have happened often in the past.

There is also evidence which indicates that some of the ice layers were never at the surface; rather, they originated and developed below ground. After a thin layer of permafrost forms just below the surface, its growth would have to take place at its base, because water could not penetrate the impermeable frozen ground from above. In seeping upward toward the surface, water already in the ground would freeze when it encountered the base of the permafrost. Likewise, water could enter unfrozen ground beneath the permafrost from streams and other places where the permafrost was absent. During their growth, the crystals of ice from this continuous supply of water would exclude the silt and soil particles and grow into clear ice. The tremendous force exerted by myriads of growing crystals would raise the overlying ground as the layer of ice grew ever thicker.

We do not know, even within crude limits, the total amount of subterranean ice. But if it could be brought to the surface and spread on top of the ground beneath which it now lies, one fifth of the world's land area surely would be covered by ice.

Why does permafrost exist and why is it where it is? We know that it is a temperature phenomenon and that it is present only where the ground is continuously below freezing and that its presence is related to the mean annual air temperature. The outer edge of the permafrost zone roughly parallels and is not far from the line marking a mean annual air temperature of 25°F. This is especially true in Canada. In places it lies farther south and locally may extend almost to the 30° isotherm. Yet Siberia's permafrost line extends far to the south of the mean annual 25°F. isotherm. So several factors other than temperature guide the distribution of permafrost. Permafrost exists because freezing temperatures in winter penetrate the ground more deeply than the thaws of summer. Therefore where the surface of the ground is insulated by thick moss, peat, various other types of vegetable matter, or by deep snows, freezing temperatures do not readily penetrate. In such places permafrost may be thin or even absent. Conversely, these protective covers, if placed on ground already frozen, tend to preserve it from seasonal thawing, much as do soil and moraine on top of stagnant masses of glacier ice. In very cold climates where snowfall is light or where the bulk of the snow comes late in the season after the ground has frozen deeply, permafrost is thick. Where snow is deep throughout the winter the permafrost zone normally is relatively thin and may be absent. On the west side of Hudson Bay and James Bay, for example, where the snowfall in October to December is about forty inches, the permafrost line extends 200 miles farther south than on the east side where snowfall during the same period averages about sixty inches.

Water also acts as an insulating blanket, and even in the Far North the ground immediately beneath large rivers, lakes, and the sea is not frozen. Beneath glaciers, because they insulate the underlying ground from the winter cold, permafrost is also thin or absent.

Though permafrost is thickest and most widespread in the Arctic tundra, in certain areas it extends southward far into the forested zone. Trees and other plants with long taproots cannot grow over permafrost, and many of the trees which do grow over it, especially if the active layer is thin, are stunted because the ground is always refrigerated. But dense stands of tall trees —cottonwood, spruce, larch, birch—are present in places where the top of permafrost is no more than four or five feet below the surface. Areas in which the active layer is as thin as eighteen inches can support luxuriant growths of shrubs and stunted trees. Ice within the permafrost prevents the water from draining downward, thus holding it in the soil. In very dry summers when the rainfall is below normal the top of the permafrost may thaw and thus supply even more water. This abundance of water in the ground is favorable for plant growth; it even makes plant growth possible in a region which otherwise would be too dry to support vegetation. But poor drainage and the resulting saturated condition of the ground everywhere help create one of the most favorable environments for mosquitoes—and their number in the Far North is astronomical.

In temperate regions when the ground thaws in the spring,

it of course remains wet and muddy for a brief period until the water seeps downward, eventually emerging into streams through springs and other places of seepage, thus leaving the soil dry. Not so in the permafrost areas. When the active layer thaws it becomes a layer of mud and remains in this soggy condition until it freezes again in the fall. Very fine soil and other supersaturated materials resting on permafrost become plastic and are capable of flowing like viscous liquids. This soupy material is known by the euphonious name *slud* to distinguish it from mud formed in other ways. Since the top of the frozen ground on which it rests is a natural sliding board, the slud, even on very gentle slopes, constantly moves downhill. Where the vegetative cover has been removed or where it is thin, the slud may break out into more rapidly moving slides and flows. Such phenomena are common throughout the Arctic and those parts of the Subarctic underlain by permafrost.

It is this characteristic of the active layer which has constituted one of the chief obstacles to the advance of settlements into the Arctic. Construction of roads and railroads is greatly hampered by it. A house placed on a slope may be carried away by flow of the active layer, or the weight of a structure may squeeze out the slud on which it rests, damaging or tilting the building.

A great deal of cross-country travel could be done in the treeless tundra if it weren't for the active layer. Unless the active layer is thin enough for vehicles to ride on the top of frozen ground beneath it, they become hopelessly mired in the mud. But there are few places where the active layer is so thin. Thus except in winter when the active layer is frozen, heavy vehicles are useless in great expanses of the Far North where there are few obstacles, other than the mud, to their use in overland operations.

Where the active layer is thin the problems it causes can be overcome. It is the artificial disturbance of the temperature of permafrost that often starts a chain reaction of troubles. Permafrost is as suitable as any bedrock for foundations of buildings, dams, towers, and other structures—if it remains frozen. But permafrost can be thawed by the warmth passing through the floor of a heated building. If the thawed ground does not have adequate bearing strength, the building will tilt or slump and may be severely damaged. In some localities in Alaska, especially noticeable in the Seward Peninsula, many of the "bush" houses are tilted. Before entering one of these houses you can easily determine the location of the kitchen by the direction in which the building is tilted; the deepest sinking is always under the warmest part of the house.

The tilting of a shack may not be very serious, but permafrost is no respecter of size. Larger and more substantial buildings can be damaged when ice in permafrost thaws beneath them. Buildings in which the furnace is located near the center will tilt from both ends.

Most trouble arises because of failure to take proper precautions. Disaster can be averted by raising the floor of a building above the ground on piles; this keeps the permafrost in an undisturbed condition by insulating it from the heat of the building. One system of installing piles is to drive them into ground previously thawed by the injection of steam. When the thawed ground refreezes around the piles they are held immovably, summer and winter, especially if the part embedded in the permafrost is notched.

Where the permafrost layer is thin the ground in the foundation area can be artifically thawed before the building is constructed, but it must be kept in a thawed condition in order to prevent future damage. Since the greatest damage results when the permafrost thaws, the ground beneath some buildings is artifically maintained in a frozen condition by a refrigerating system. This operation can be rather costly, but it may be far less expensive than the bill for repairs. In any event, erection of buildings in the permafrost zone is a lot more complicated than in places where there is no ground ice.

Although roads and railroads can be built successfully in permafrost areas there is a variety of headaches that the engineer constantly has to deal with when constructing transportation lines. Removal of the insulating cover of vegetation, moss, and so on will cause melting of permafrost and consequent slumping and caving, if the permafrost under the road contains masses of ground ice. Constant regrading, rebuilding, realigning, and even abandonment of sections are necessary. Where thick fills are required, however, permafrost may actually have a salutary effect, because the permafrost table will rise up into the fill, thus helping to stabilize it. If the permafrost can be prevented from melting, heavy-duty highways and airplane runways can be constructed and successfully maintained on top of it.

The city of Fairbanks, Alaska and several adjacent large airfields lie over permafrost in places 200 to 300 feet thick. The huge Air Force base at Thule, Greenland is deep within the zone of continuous permafrost, and a number of sizable Russian cities, Norilsk, Tiksi, Verkhoyansk, and Sredne Kolymsk, are located in regions where the permafrost is 1,000 or more feet thick.

Maintenance of railroads in permafrost areas poses even more problems than the highways. Slumps and cave-ins on a highway can be bulldozed and graded, but railroad track must be leveled and realigned with great care. On some stretches of the Alaska Railroad where it lies over permafrost containing much ground ice, such maintenance during the summer months is never-ending.

Gold miners look with mixed emotions upon permafrost. Where it is present the sands and gravels from which they extract placer gold are as solid as a rock and the gold cannot be successfully washed out by the jets of water used in hydraulic mining or extracted by dredges unless the ground has been thawed. This is a time-consuming and expensive operation which placer miners in other regions are not burdened with. In Alaska several means of thawing the gold-bearing gravels are employed. One is simply the removal of the insulating moss or sod blanket, allowing the frozen ground to thaw naturally. This is slow, and where surface drainage is poor, thawing may penetrate no deeper than two to four feet during a summer season. A more successful method is the injection of steam or water into the frozen ground. In a large operation, to keep the ground thawed ahead of the dredge, an area of several acres may be completely covered with a network of steam or water pipes, both above and below the ground.

On the other hand, where underground mining operations are conducted in perennially frozen ground containing much ice, timbering is not necessary. Ice in all the cracks and voids so firmly cements the rock fragments together that there is no danger of their falling from the walls and ceilings of the mines.

Even agriculture does not escape the destructive effects of permafrost. Thawing of ice under newly cleared fields causes sinkholes, mounds, and other sharp irregularities to develop on the surface. Fields cleared initially for cultivation may have to be converted to pasture or even abandoned. Just as in the case of roads, the cave-ins can be filled and the land leveled off by continual grading and bulldozing, but this is an expense few farmers, especially homesteaders in northern lands, can afford, and the topsoil is frequently destroyed in the process.

Government geologists have wisely recommended that before land is opened up for agriculture in Alaska, surveys be made to determine which parts are unfavorable because of permafrost. Actually, it should not stop at this; the government should zone the land, on the basis of permafrost investigations, into areas suitable for cultivation, those suitable for pasture, and those unsuited for agricultural development, and restrict its use accordingly. It is because of failure to do this in the past on other types of land that many millions of acres of our country are unproductive, that people are still trying to eke out a living by cultivating the too-steep, almost soil-less slopes of the Southern Appalachians, the too-dry fields on the far western Great Plains which never should have felt the plow, and the marshlands which should never have been drained. Will the North have the same hit-or-miss development so characteristic elsewhere of the past and present use of the land?

Roads, railroads, airfields, buildings, bridges, and other structures can, however, be successfully maintained in permafrost areas, and agriculture can be carried on, but there is one problem faced by communities in the Far North for which in some localities there seems to be no satisfactory solution in sight. Cities, towns, large camps, and other centers of civilization in the Far North have a difficult time getting a water supply, but they fare even worse when it comes to sewage disposal. And much of the problem is related either directly or indirectly to the presence of permafrost. In most places where permafrost is continuous and thick, large supplies of water cannot be obtained from the ground, but must come from deep lakes or large rivers, the only surface bodies of fresh water which do not freeze solid in the winter.

The city of Yakutsk in eastern Siberia, where the mean January temperature is 46°F. below zero and where the snow cover seldom exceeds four inches, is one of the few places where water wells have been drilled through thick permafrost. But they have to be pumped constantly, summer as well as winter, to prevent the water from freezing on the way up. At some places in the Soviet Union heaters are used to prevent freezing of well water rising through the permafrost.

A number of attempts to drill through thick permafrost have been unsuccessful. At Resolute Bay on Cornwallis Island in the Canadian Archipelago an effort was made in the summers of 1950 to 1953 to drill to a depth of 1,000 feet to determine the temperature gradient in the permafrost. But the drillers were unable to extend the holes much below 600 feet because the drilling water froze—even when near-boiling water was circulated in the holes. Although the use of heavier equipment would have resulted in success, this example illustrates that the drilling of a single well in the high Arctic can be a major operation.

Since aeration and oxidation of sewage is very slow in cold climates and because the flow of rivers is much reduced in winter, lakes and streams cannot be used as repositories for sewage. And permafrost prevents the disposal of sewage in underground passageways. People will have to become reconciled to the fact that their sewage-disposal operation will be costly—by evaporation of the liquids and burning of the solids or by chemical treatment. Perhaps the lakes and streams of the Far North, unlike those in developed lands, will remain unpolluted, even during a period of extensive settlement, though I fear it will be for reasons other than aesthetic.

Despite the grief that it has caused, the effect of permafrost is not wholly bad. Because of its constant subfreezing temperature it makes an ideal place for cold storage, especially at large camps and other places where storage space is required for large volumes of perishable materials. At a number of places in northern Canada large underground chambers, excavated in frozen ground twenty or more feet below the surface, are used for cold storage. Individual families also have cold cellars, and even the

Eskimos, whom we usually do not think of as needing refrigeration facilities, have used them since prehistoric times. They excavated them by placing heated stones on the permafrost or by building fires on it, then removing the water and thawed ground. By repeating this operation a number of times they could excavate a cellar to the desired size and shape.

When a large earth-fill dam is under construction in the Far North, the permafrost slowly moves up into it from below, thus converting the dam into a solid impermeable rock. Even if cracks develop in the structure they can be healed quickly by freezing of water seeping from the surface or forced into the dam by artificial means. The process of freezing can be hastened by building the dam during the long winter when cold can be accumulated within it. To insure that a dam remain solidly frozen, holes penetrating it are kept open in winter so that cold air can circulate through it.

The stability and impermeability of frozen ground are properties that have been made use of far beyond the boundaries of the permafrost zone. While the excavation for the east abutment of Grand Coulee Dam was being dug, a large slide of water-soaked silt and sand began to move into it at a rate faster than the material could be removed by power shovels. Since none of the ordinary methods for stopping the slide was economically feasible, the engineers decided to block it by freezing its lower portion. This they did by circulating a refrigerating brine through pipes driven into the slide. They maintained the slide in a rocklike frozen condition until excavating was completed and the concrete abutments were in place.

This method of stopping slides may have wide future application where highways and railroads are menaced by earth movements. Where the investment in construction has been large it may even be desirable to maintain ground in a frozen condition permanently by making artificial permafrost. This method of land stabilization may soon be necessary on long strips of coastal California, where housing developers make a fetish of disregarding Nature's laws by placing huge housing projects not only in the paths of but even on moving masses of earth.

How old is the permafrost? How long has the ice been in the ground and how did it get there? Since permafrost occurs in those lands which have a low mean annual air temperature its presence certainly bears some relationship to the present climate. Much of the permafrost is in equilibrium with the existing climate. This is borne out clearly in those places in the North where the permafrost table has risen into road fills, mine dumps and tailings, and other unfrozen materials which have been piled on the surface. That some permafrost is youthful and actively forming today is also attested by its growth in new islands and sand and gravel bars in Arctic rivers and in recent landslides and mud flows. The volcanic ash and pumice thrown out by Katmai in 1912 is now part of the permafrost zone, and since this material covers the remnants of glaciers beheaded by the explosion, these streams of ice, now largely stagnant because their source of nourishment has been destroyed, will be preserved indefinitely as masses of ground ice in the permafrost.

That some, if not most, permafrost is very old is proved, of course, by the frozen carcasses of mammoths and other animals extinct for thousands of years. Though it was created long ago, the permafrost in which these animals are preserved could have formed under climatic conditions very similar to if not the same as those existing in the same areas today. Calculations based upon temperature gradients in mines and wells, upon the diffusivity of various types of ground, and upon other factors have indicated that several thousand years might be required to create permafrost 1,000 feet thick in the present climate of northern Siberia—but it could be done.

There is irrefutable evidence, however, that in the southernmost regions of permafrost the perennially subfreezing temperature and the ground ice are relics of a colder climate than exists today. In these places there is a perennially unfrozen zone between the bottom of the active layer and the top of the permafrost. Obviously if this permafrost were of recent origin it would have to be in contact with the active layer so that winter cold, the maker of permafrost, could be conducted downward into it. This relict permafrost may, if the climate does not become colder, slowly recede and eventually disappear under the influence of heat conducted outward from the Earth's interior.

Now that we have had a look at perennially frozen ground it is time to consider how the mammoths got into it. The food found in the stomachs and mouths of the Beresovka and other mammoths consisted of remains of plants characteristic of northern Siberia at the present time. So the climate during the age of the mammoths probably was little different from that of today, and permafrost was present when the animals lived. But if this were the case, how did these animals get buried in the frozen ground? This is a question scientists wish they knew more about, but by carefully studying the materials in which the carcasses lie, they think they have found the right answers.

Practically all mammoth remains have been found in silts and clays deposited by streams or mud flows. Most of the carcasses are on former river floodplains. It is possible that old, sick, or injured animals sought seclusion or protection from wolves in the sloughs and swamps on the river floodplains where many of them died or were drowned. During subsequent floods some of these carcasses were buried in silt deposited by the overflowing river; others were carried downstream, coming to rest on the delta where they were either partly or entirely buried in sediment deposited by the receding floodwaters. Other mammoths undoubtedly were mired in sticky slud which had flowed down from nearby slopes.

It would not have been necessary for these carcasses to have been completely buried immediately or even soon after death. Parts of the Beresovka mammoth lay exposed for two years before the team of scientists finally reached it. Adams's mammoth lay almost fully exposed for at least four years, and some parts of it had been uncovered even longer. Putrefaction proceeds much more slowly in arctic than in temperate climates. Bacterial action is hindered not only because the summers are short and dry but because the temperature frequently falls below freezing during the nights in early and late parts of the summer. Today when whales meet death by becoming grounded along Arctic shores, putrefaction is slow to start, and the carcasses may lie for weeks without showing pronounced signs of decay. Burial under a thin covering of wave-washed or wind-blown material may help to preserve them until they freeze in the ensuing winter.

The condition of the plant remains recovered from mammoth digestive tracts indicates that most animals, at least among those examined by scientists, met death late in the summer.

Even those animals which were not immediately buried probably underwent very little putrefaction before the winter freeze set in. The following spring they might have been partly or entirely covered by additional sediment when the river went into flood. There was always a chance, too, that the carcasses might be covered by silt drifted by the wind across the rapidly drying floodplain. Rising of the permafrost table up into the newly deposited sediment would assure preservation for the carcass, at least for that part of it lying within the permafrost. And, too, a mammoth's thick, tough hide undoubtedly was a factor in slowing the processes of decay.

Actually, the known finds indicate that very few complete mammoth carcasses were preserved. Most were partly destroyed either by decay or predatory animals before burial and freezing. This is one reason for the foul odor which all mammoths have, no matter how well preserved they appear to be. As indicated by the condition of the food remains in some mammoths, notably the Beresovka carcass, a number of these ancient animals met death suddenly by drowning, burial in a landslide, or perhaps even at the hands of another animal.

Additional finds of carcasses may yield all the answers, but it is clear that the animals whose remains have been preserved in the perennially frozen ground lived in an environment not much different from the present. It is just as clear that these large animals did not have to be frozen immediately after death in order to be preserved in the condition in which they are found today. And it is not necessary to concoct such absurd notions—and some have done it—as a quick freeze made by changing the climate even faster than the weather.

It is probable that the first primitive men to enter the Arctic regions saw masses of exposed ground ice on the banks of rivers and along the sea coast. And the finders of the first frozen mammoths must have noticed it. But it wasn't until early in the nineteenth century that scientists began to observe it carefully and write intelligent descriptions of it—M. F. Adams in 1806 was the first. The first recorded discovery of ground ice in North America seems to have been made by Lieutenant Otto von Kotzebue in 1816 along the shore of what is now Kotzebue Sound at a locality that has since become well known for its ground ice and bones of mammoths and other extinct animals. The first scientific expedition to Siberia for the study of permafrost was led by A. T. von Middendorf in 1844 to 1846. Very few people, however, paid any attention to this phenomenon until they were forced to do so by the problems it created. This era began in Siberia with the construction of the Trans-Siberian Railroad and the influx of settlers it brought after 1873. The Russians lost little time in tackling the investigation of permafrost, and ever since then have been carrying on scientific studies, now directed largely by the Institute of Permafrostology.

The United States and Canada, the only other countries having extensive areas of permafrost, were slower getting started. The gold rush into Alaska and the Yukon at the turn of the century brought prospectors and others into contact with a new problem—ice in the ground—which they could not successfully cope with. They couldn't dig into it and they couldn't wash it away with their high-pressure hydraulic giants. In their desperation some of the miners dug their mines as the Eskimos had dug cold cellars—by piling heated stones on the ground to thaw the ice in it. Between then and 1941 several geologists of the U.S. Geological Survey made intensive investigations of permafrost, but little was done to organize systematic studies of permafrost until World War II finally convinced the proper authorities of the strategic importance of Alaska and the Canadian North. Construction of the Alaska Highway probably did for the study of permafrost in North America what the Trans-Siberian Railroad did for Russia more than fifty years earlier. Now, however, rapid strides are being made in the study of permafrost by a number of organizations, especially the U.S. Army's CRREL, the United States Geological Survey, and the Division of Building Research of the National Research Council of Canada. This much-needed work has come none too soon. The North American Arctic still is a land of vast vacant spaces, but it will not remain so for long. Already huge military bases are in operation, and the DEW line has been strung across the full breadth of the continent. Each year farmers are breaking new land and have not yet reached the northern limit of agricultural expansion.

Soon there will be more military bases, more mines, more airfields for trans-Polar flights, and more oil wells. Virtually the

whole Arctic Archipelago—from Baffin and Ellesmere Islands on
the east to Banks on the west—is underlain by thick series of potentially oil-bearing sedimentary rocks, and today millions of
acres of this land, some of it only 700 miles from the Pole, are
under lease to major oil-exploration companies. Even now they
are beginning the search which may yield the last major oil
strikes on the North American continent. Every well drilled will
have to penetrate the permafrost, and every pipeline will have to
be buried in it.

A taste of what may be in store for the pipeliners was experienced by the crew which in 1954 laid the pipeline from the
port of Haines in southeastern Alaska 620 miles to Fairbanks. On
the 100-mile stretch of the route which lay over permafrost a
specially designed ditching machine had to be used, and the
usual sequence of ditching, stringing, welding, and then covering
the pipe could not be followed. By the time the pipe was welded
and strung the ditch had been completely destroyed and converted into a quagmire by thawing. This difficulty was overcome
by excavating the ditch after the pipe was welded and strung.
But after the pipe was covered, permafrost, moving up into the
fill from below, heaved the pipe out of the ground. The next step
was to weight the pipe at forty-foot intervals with 300-pound
blocks of concrete and rebury it. Farther north where permafrost
is closer to the surface the difficulties will probably be even
greater.

All these developments mean an influx of people. New settlements will spring up; they will require water and sewage systems and more roads. Sources of power will be exploited. Two of
North America's largest rivers, the McKenzie and the Yukon, are
in the Arctic. For the production of power these streams will
someday be dammed. These tasks may require more engineering
ingenuity than any others affected by permafrost. Although none
of the problems posed by ice beneath the ground is apt to be insurmountable, there is much yet to be learned. That is why settlement of the Arctic, long delayed by ice beneath the ground,
will proceed at a future rate dependent, not upon man's ability
to combat it, but upon his ingenuity in determining how to live
with it.

❀❀❀❀❀❀

14

❀❀❀❀❀❀

Ice and Our
Changing Climate

❀❀❀❀❀❀
❀❀❀❀❀❀ $\mathcal{S}$OMETHING is happening to the World of
Ice—to the snowline, to the glaciers, the sea ice, and the permafrost. They are not what they used to be. During our lifetime evidence of the change has been coming in from all directions of
the compass and from almost all parts of the globe where snow
and ice hold sway—from the Alps, the Himalayas, and the Rockies; from Greenland, Iceland, and Alaska; from the North Atlantic and from the Polar Sea.

The most obvious victims of the change—a change in the
world's climate—are the glaciers. For about 100 years in all parts
of the world, with the possible exception of Antarctica, they have
been growing smaller. To be sure, this decline has not been constant. At various times glaciers have even reversed the trend by
expanding, but in nearly all cases after a brief period of extension these glaciers again have fallen into the general pattern of
recession.

Though the climatic change which initiated this current period of glacier shrinkage began around the middle of the last century—in some places a little earlier, in others a little later—the
most pronounced dwindling of glaciers occurred in the 1920's
and 1930's. It was during this period that the late François Matthes referred to the recession of glaciers as "catastrophic." It was
then that people dependent upon glaciers for their water supply
began to become concerned about their future. It was then that
the Mount Rainier and several other long-term mapping projects
were undertaken to find out just what was happening to the glaciers.

This change in the glaciers means, of course, that the snowline has been rising on a world-wide scale. By direct observation
it is known to have gone up in Scandinavia 300 feet between
1905 and 1955. In the Alps the rise has been just as great.
Even the migration of the seasonal snowline and the changing
duration of the winter snow cover in lands far from the glaciers
are reflecting what is happening in the lands of permanent ice
and snow.

There may be something to Grandfather's nostalgic and
challenging statement that it doesn't snow the way it did when he
was a boy. Almost everywhere in the eastern United States and
Canada—Washington, Philadelphia, Boston, Montreal—where
accurate measurements have been made for many years, the
records show clearly that the seasonal snowfall and the duration
of the snow cover are decreasing.

When considering changes in the elevation of the snowline
one can hardly avoid giving heed to the influence of temperature, since the recent and perhaps continuing rise of the snowline has been caused by a noticeable warming of the atmosphere
in temperate and Arctic regions. Although almost all parts of the
world outside of the Equatorial Zone have felt this warming, it
seems to have been most pronounced in the lands bordering the
North Atlantic and in the waters connecting it with the Arctic
Ocean.

During the last 100 years at New Haven and Philadelphia
the average annual temperature has risen more than 2°F. and
the average winter temperature more than 3°. Other places on
the eastern seaboard have experienced comparable warming. In

Western Europe the rise of the mean winter temperature between 1850 and 1900 was 5°F.

Some of this increased warmth can be credited to heat from factories and homes which have crowded in on the weather-observation stations, but this is a factor that can hardly be regarded as important in Greenland, Iceland, and Svalbard, three areas in which warming of the climate probably has been more pronounced than anywhere else. Not only that, but there has been a rise in the temperature of the surface water in the North Atlantic Ocean commensurate with the increase in air temperature.

According to Thorarinsson, the climate of Iceland during the 1950's was warmer than at any time during the preceding 750 years. And the average temperature of Svalbard is 10°F. higher now than it was early in the present century; winter temperatures have risen even more.

Although continuous long-range weather observations have been made nowhere in Antarctica, temperatures recorded in the vicinity of Little America, where the traffic has been relatively heavy ever since the days of Scott, Amundsen, and Shackleton, indicate a temperature rise of about 5°F. in the past fifty years. Whether this rise is limited to the Ross Shelf area or is characteristic of larger areas is not known, but it has had no effect upon the Antarctic glaciers. Slight fluctuations in the elevation of the snowline, since practically the entire ice sheet lies above it, cause no change in the area in which the ice accumulates; so here the ice remains in equilibrium with the climate despite the rise in temperature.

Surely, if seasonal snow accumulation increases because of greater snowfall or lower temperatures, the snowline will fall and glaciers will expand. If the climate warms, as it has been doing for nearly two combined human lifetimes, the snowline will rise.

To see the most spectacular manifestation of the recent climatic change the place to go is to the glaciers. And no matter where we go, provided it isn't Antarctica, there will be plenty of evidence that things have been changing.

Most glaciers in the Alps have been shrinking noticeably since the middle of the nineteenth century. The Rhone Glacier, one of the longest, is nearly three miles shorter than it was 100 years ago. Since 1920 several hundred small Alpine glaciers have disappeared, and more will follow if the present climatic trend continues.

Strangely enough, the fluctuations of Alpine glaciers were recorded in written form for several hundred years prior to the middle of the nineteenth century, yet there was no reference to glaciers in the local laws. Even in the Alps where the land had been under population pressure for centuries, no one seemed particularly concerned about ownership of steep, sterile, and rocky land when it was exposed by shrinkage of glaciers. But after 1750 when several long glacier tongues, especially the Mer de Glace and the Upper Grindelwald, uncovered relatively flat and potentially valuable land, the law had to take a stand. Apparently there was considerable difference of opinion among the jurists themselves about the ownership of this new land. Some favored the State as the legal owner, some the local community or parish, and others felt that it was private property. Large glaciers, like navigable rivers and large lakes, were regarded by some as property of the State, whereas the smaller ones, like small streams and ponds, were the property of the individuals owning adjacent lands. In any event, there was a time when landowners charged a fee for the privilege of passing over an adjacent glacier.

In America when the current period of glacier shrinkage began, the glacier regions were uninhabited. Later most of them were included in public land—national parks and forests—and so there were no arguments as to ownership of the land exposed as the glaciers shrank from it. In fact, until the present century was well on its way very little was known about what was happening even to some of our best-known glaciers. Not until 1918 were yearly accurate measurements made of the terminus of Nisqually Glacier on Mount Rainier. When the road was constructed from Longmire to Paradise Park in 1907 it crossed the Nisqually River about 280 yards below the end of the glacier. Twenty-four years earlier the glacier had extended as far as the bridge site, and in 1750 the ice was 100 or more feet thick where today park visitors drive their cars across the river bridge nearly a mile downstream from the glacier terminus.

Nowhere is the world of mountain glaciation, both past and present, more

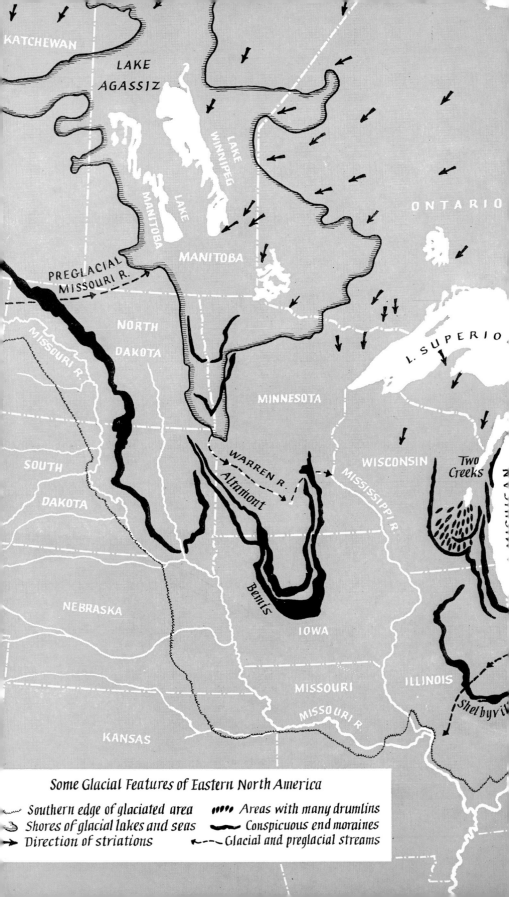

Some Glacial Features of Eastern North America

〜 Southern edge of glaciated area   ♦♦♦♦ Areas with many drumlins
🝆 Shores of glacial lakes and seas   〜 Conspicuous end moraines
➤ Direction of striations   ←·· Glacial and preglacial streams

JAMES
BAY

QUEBEC

ST. LAWRENCE SEA

L. HURON

L. ONTARIO

NEW
YORK

MASS.

CONN.

VT.

N.H.

MAINE

MICHIGAN

L. ERIE

Valparaiso

Defiance

INDIANA

TEAYS R.

OHIO

W.VA.

OHIO R.

PENNSYLVANIA

N.J.

ATLANTIC

OCEAN

VIRGINIA

KENTUCKY

NORTH
CAROLINA

TENNESSEE

Miles

0   50   100   15

Ten thousand years ago this view would have resembled the Matterhorn today, with hanging glaciers clinging to peak on right. Though no glaciers have worked on these horns for several thousand years, they still retain form given them by ice. Glacier National Park, Montana.

Planes of the Wallis Section, Swiss Aero Club, on firn of Grand Combin Glacier, Valais, Switzerland. Snow is very deep, but pilots guard against hidden crevasses beneath.

An eight-place "Pilatus Porter" taking off from firn. Plateau du Trient, Valais, Switzerland. Bergschrund crevasses, partly snow-filled, slice across glacier in distance.

The Great Gorge of Ruth Glacier, Mount McKinley. South side of North America's highest mountain—a superb example of an ice-made landscape, with an intricate maze of long valley glaciers. Unfortunately it is not part of Mount McKin-

Ruth Glacier at entrance to the Great Gorge, eighteen miles from Mount Mc-Kinley's summit. The ice, probably more than 1,000 feet thick, slices great slabs of rock from valley's side. Deep snow smooths badly crevassed glacier surface.

A pack train crosses a glacier in Dongus Oren Pass, Central Caucasus. For 100 miles there are no glacier-free passes across range.

Fourteen-mile long Lake George, largest glacier-dammed lake in Alaska, in Chugach Mountains near Anchorage, is formed by melt water from Knik Glacier
(foreground) and two other large ice streams. Late each summer lake overflows

This ice-dammed lake at right of Tana Glacier, Alaska, was
created when a tributary glacier, through shrinking, became
separated from main glacier.

Marjelen Lake and Great Aletsch Glacier, which holds it in. High-water mark, made before lake waters were diverted through a tunnel, is visible on right of lake. Swiss Alps.

Berg stranded by bursting of ice-dammed Tulsequah Lake. Coast Mountains, British Columbia. Minutes after photo was taken 100-foot ice pinnacle on left collapsed. Streaks in ice are shears or dirt layers between ice strata.

A berg has just calved from Miles Glacier. Melting has enlarged a network

Electrical crevasse detector at work on Greenland ice sheet. A crevasse has been located and marked.

The panlike electrodes of electrical crevasse detector. Army-Navy trail party en route between IGY, Little America, and Byrd Stations.

Sno-Cat and cargo sled stuck in narrow crevasse after breaking through a snow bridge. Another vehicle remains at safe distance. Edith Ronne Land, Antarctica.

XLII

A thermal drilling rig in one of Camp Century's roofed "streets," Greenland.

Removing ice core from barrel of the drill. This apparatus has successfully more than 1,000 feet, bringing up ice over ten centuries old.

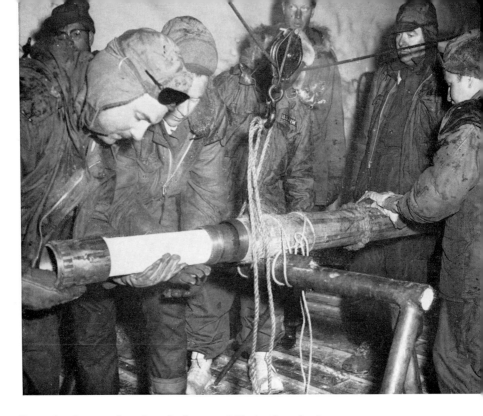

Removing ice core from barrel of rotary drill rig. Greenland.

Firn strata in crevasse. Juneau Ice Field Research Project, Alaska. Rubber tubes and buckets collect melt water.

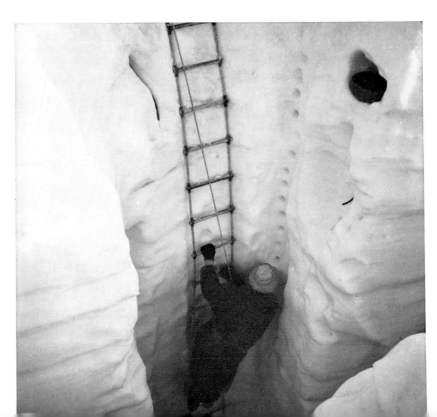

V

Corrugations on Ellesmere Island's ice shelf—here more than ten miles wide—are made by ridges only a few feet high but several hundred yards wide. They may have been caused by movement of glaciers when shelf was more extensive, or by pressure from sea ice and tides, or by other means. Melt water (dark) lies in the troughs between them.

Tabular Antarctic bergs may rise more than 100 feet above pack ice. Here several of them are trapped in land-fast sea ice, separated from drifting floes by wide lead. Victoria Land coast near Hallett IGY Station, Antarctica.

Navy icebreaker, *U.S.S. Glacier,* cutting path through ice on
newly frozen lead between old snow-covered floes—large one
in foreground, smaller ones in distance. On this trip in 1960
the *Glacier* and another Navy icebreaker, the *U.S.S. Burton
Island,* became the first ships to penetrate to the Antarctic
coast through the Bellingshausen Sea.

Alaska has been not only the scene of some of the most spectacular recent glacier advances, but it is also there that we must go to see the most phenomenal ice shrinkage. When Captain George Vancouver, the first European to probe a number of the fiords along the southeast Alaska coast, in 1794 sailed into the fiord now known as Icy Strait, he found a tributary bay on the north side of the Strait blocked at its head by a wall of ice nearly five miles wide. This was the tidewater terminus of a great sloping sheet of ice extending northward for a hundred miles into the St. Elias Mountains, completely burying most of the intervening lesser mountains and ranges.

For another 100 years no one except the natives—and who could care less about glaciers?—saw Vancouver's ice-bound bay. Then in 1879 John Muir, with his Indian guides, boated into the bay. But the great ice cliff that blocked the bay a century earlier was not there, and the bay extended beyond this point farther than the eye could see, with no glacier in sight. Another twenty miles up the bay Muir's guides had to row before they found the first tidewater glacier—in a tributary fiord now known as Muir Inlet. But the head of the bay, barred by the main wall of glacier ice, lay yet another twenty-five miles beyond Muir's inlet.

In 1890 to 1892 Harry Fielding Reid, then professor of geology at Johns Hopkins University, mapped the newly exposed bay —named Glacier Bay after Muir had "rediscovered" it—and the surrounding glaciers, giving present-day surveyors a number of reference points from which to accurately figure the amount of change in the glaciers since that time. Reid found that tremendous shrinkage had taken place since Muir had visited the Bay. So rapid had been the deglaciation that some large masses of ice, each several square miles in extent, had been separated from the main glacier and lay stagnating in low valleys far below the snowline. One of these Reid named Dying Glacier. It has since disappeared, but a part of its ice could still be found in 1946.

So now we know that the vast sea of ice that Vancouver encountered little more than 150 years ago has largely melted away. In so doing it has created a whole new world by uncovering a huge branching system of fiords with a combined length of 160 miles and in places a water depth of more than 1,500 feet.

While withdrawing from the fiords, the ice also disappeared from several hundred square miles of adjacent land. Mountains now 2,000 to 4,000 feet high were completely covered by glaciers in Vancouver's time. As late as 1892, when Reid made his map, the ice was more than 2,000 feet thick in places where today there is none.

Not all glacier regions of Alaska have experienced as striking an ice shrinkage as Glacier Bay. What has been happening to glaciers here, however, is typical of what has been happening on a somewhat less grand scale elsewhere in Alaska and in the mountains of Yukon and British Columbia. Few, indeed, are the large glacier tongues which have not been shortened from one to two miles during the past 100 years. Even Taku Glacier, which, unlike other Alaskan ice streams, has extended itself more than three miles since 1900, seems to be suffering over-all shrinkage rather than expansion. The advance of its terminus, like that of Black Rapids in the 1930's, apparently is caused by a more rapid drainage of ice from the collection area, which is resulting in thinning there rather than thickening.

While other glaciers have been shrinking, those in Washington's northern Cascade Mountains have been enlarging. The expansion began about 1948 because of increased seasonal snowfall and slightly lower temperatures. So pronounced was this heightening of glacier activity that some observers regarded it as heralding a reversal in the long-continued period of widespread glacier shrinkage. But this local expansion, though still going on in the glacier region along the International Boundary, seems to have reached its peak around 1956 and has now about run its course.

The effect of the current period of glacier shrinkage is being felt far beyond the borders of Alaska and other ice-adorned regions. In recent years the sea level has been rising—not much, but it is measurable—as the glaciers pour more water into the seas than is removed by evaporation and converted into precipitation. This rise in the level of the sea wasn't noticed until 1880, and at some places not until after 1900, because of the lag in the rise along those shores far distant from the center of greatest glacier shrinkage. Some of the rise undoubtedly results from thermal expansion of the water because of climatic warming, but it has been calculated that this means alone could not account for all of the rise that has been measured. In recent decades the sea has been going up at a rate, according to Ahlmann, of nearly four inches per century. Others have calculated the rise at even more—as much as two feet per century in the most extreme case. Whatever the rate—two inches or two feet—it is bound to have significant though possibly subtle effects. Who knows but that it may even now be causing slight shifts of local currents along certain shores, with consequent added eating away of the land here and increased transport of sediment and shoaling of navigable waters there? There will be—and certainly is now—an effect on man-made structures along all tidal bodies of water.

In another fifty to 100 years will ships be able to navigate the central Arctic Basin unimpeded by an ice pack? Some people believe so. And they base their opinion on what has been happening to the sea ice in the recent past. The climatic amelioration that has been the chief cause of the recent widespread deglaciation has had, and apparently still is having, a similar effect on the Polar pack. The pack certainly isn't what it used to be.

During the long drift of Nansen's *Fram* across the ice-packed Polar Sea the thickness of the ice was recorded regularly as the seasons came and went. Its average thickness was twelve feet. But during the drift of the *Sedov* along roughly the same path in 1937–40 the average thickness of the pack was only a little over seven feet. There had been a forty per cent loss of thickness in the forty-five years between drifts.

As the pack has thinned, its edge has retreated inward. The Russians have estimated that between 1924 and 1944 the area of the pack in their sector of the Arctic alone lost 1,000,000 square kilometers in area.

Since 1900 there has been less drifting sea ice along the coast of Iceland than at any other time during the past 400 years, and the period since 1925 has been the longest nearly ice-free time since the first settlers reached the island 1,000 years ago. The length of the shipping season in Vest Spitsbergen increased from three months in 1900 to seven by 1950. In recent years the last boats of the season have been leaving Longyearbyen, the island's coal-shipping port, in late November and early December.

These dramatic changes in the volume of sea ice have led some to make predictions that in another 100 years there would be no ice at all in the Arctic Ocean. Such predictions, of course, are predicated upon the assumption that the warming trend of recent decades will continue. But at the moment we have no assurance that such will be the case—neither can we say that it won't.

Because the permafrost lies hidden beneath the surface, it has been very difficult to find out whether or not the recent climatic change has any appreciable effect on it. But the Russians, who have kept it under the closest surveillance, report that the permafrost limit in Siberia migrated northward thirty miles during the first half of the century. It is possible that some of this retreat has been caused by man himself. The constant development of new, more frost-resistant varieties of wheat and other plants is enabling agriculture to be pushed constantly farther north in the permafrost zone. The removal of the natural cover of vegetation to make way for domestic crops destroys the insulation of the permafrost and causes it to disappear.

It is not just the snow and ice that bear testimony to the recent climatic amelioration. There is much extra evidence, some of it spectacular, of the warming trend. The length of the growing season has extended throughout the higher latitudes of both the Eastern and Western Hemispheres. It is not only the Russians who are pushing agriculture into the Arctic. As the snowline goes up, the cropline cannot be far behind, because the ever-increasing pressure of human population drives man onto every potential agricultural acre as it becomes available. And he relinquishes with extreme reluctance his hold on any land he has thus gained. With a two- to three-week lengthening of the frost-free season the cropline in Scandinavia moved upward 300 feet during the first half of this century. In the Canadian Northwest in the same period ten or more additional frost-free days each year have carried the cropline fifty to 100 miles closer to the Arctic.

Trees have reacted to the changing climate by growing faster and by extending their ranges into lands formerly treeless.

In Scandinavia since 1900 annual rings, especially in pine, spruce, and birch, have increased in width. As a result of more favorable growing conditions the treeline has been moving upward, as much as several hundred feet in the past 100 years. The same thing has occurred in the timberline zone of northern Quebec. In the Northern Rockies many cirques and hanging valleys, bleak and rocky fifty years ago, are now verdant. In these mountains in the short space of time between 1935 and 1950 I have seen grass-covered alpine meadows yield to an invasion by spruce and fir, an invasion which had started several decades earlier at lower elevations.

Animals, too, like the ice and the plants, have responded to the changing climatic conditions. The warming of the sea has had the most pronounced effect. Entire populations of fish in the North Atlantic have shifted their ranges far to the north. In recent years many kinds of fish, including herring, haddock, and cod, in enormous numbers have appeared for the first time along the coast of Greenland. Before 1920 cod were essentially unknown in Greenland. Now the cod fishery there is one of the richest in the world.

Another possible result of the warming of northern waters is the appearance since 1945 of sharks off Cape Cod and Martha's Vineyard earlier in the summer than ever recorded before. On both the Atlantic and Pacific coasts of North America swordfish, tuna, and lobsters have extended their ranges to the north.

Many species of birds, too, have displayed a remarkable sensitivity to slight climatic changes by moving northward, especially since about 1920, into lands where they have never been seen before. Many new species have arrived in Greenland and Iceland from both North America and Europe and many have taken up residence in their new homes. Fully a fourth of all the North European species have to some degree expanded their ranges to the north.

American bird watchers have had no less exciting a time. We have seen the cardinal extend its range across New York and into Ontario, and now it has even invaded northern Maine. Other species which have made similar movements are the Carolina wren, the mockingbird, and the tufted titmouse. Many of the records turned in by winter bird watchers during the last

few years have been astounding in the number of species reported far north of their normal ranges. Olive-backed thrushes,
Baltimore orioles, yellowthroats, and yellow-breasted chats have
been reported from many places in New England and the Middle
Atlantic States on the Christmas bird census. These are only a
few of the newcomers. Rose-breasted grosbeaks have been seen
in the dead of winter in New York and Wisconsin, glossy ibis at
Chincoteague, Virginia, and palm warblers in Nova Scotia. And
each new year adds additional invaders to the list.

It may be that the northern influx is due in part to the tremendous amount of winter bird feeding and that, because of
great numbers of observers, birds are now being seen for the first
time, or at least in greater numbers, in areas where they previously were present but escaped notice. Many bird watchers go at
the Christmas census with a passion seldom seen in other avoca-
tions. The rivalry among groups is keen, and some observers
probably find a few birds which are not there. But among these
people there are many competent and careful observers, including experienced ornithologists who have been, and still are, finding birds where they simply did not occur some years ago.

Artificial feeding may hold some southern birds in the north,
but it can hardly be held responsible for what has happened to
the cod. The evidence weighs heavily in favor of the view that
the same warming of the climate which has been forcing the
snowline and the treeline upward and northward has been having an equally profound effect upon the birds.

Despite rising temperatures and their effect on glaciers and
snowlines and on the migration of fish and birds, residents of the
northern states should not prepare to plant palm trees in their
back yards yet. Even had they anticipated such a possibility, the
sting of several recent winters probably has effectively dispelled
any such ideas. Even at the height of the warming phase of a
climatic cycle some years can be extraordinarily cold.

Then, too, there is some indication that temperature rise
and glacier shrinkage have lessened somewhat since the late
1940's. This may herald, as some people believe, the beginning of
a climatic reversal which will see the glaciers again expand and
regain some or all of the ground they have lost in their recent
period of widespread retreat.

If this happens, the cod will leave the coastal waters of Greenland and Svalbard and will depart from the Barents Sea as quickly and as mysteriously as they invaded them during the past generation. And Greenland's most vital industry will become a thing of the past.

At this point we can't predict with any certainty the immediate climatic future, but recorded history, as well as the geological record, leave no doubt that this recent warming is merely one of innumerable minor climatic fluctuations, which are part of a far larger cycle, in turn one of many through which the Earth has passed and will continue to do interminably. Hopefully, however, as the Swedish geologist, Hans Ahlmann says: ". . . this recent climatic fluctuation is the first in the endless series of climatic variations in the history of the earth which we can study, measure, and possibly also explain."

Man has left a written record of some of these earlier climatic fluctuations, and perhaps by looking back beyond the last 100 years we can find something in the record which will give us a clue as to what we might expect in the future. Man has lived and worked close to the glaciers in the Alps for several thousand years, but throughout most of this time he was too preoccupied with making a living to show much interest in these streams of ice. So the glaciers, especially those in the higher mountains, remained virtually unknown until comparatively recent times. During the several hundred years of the Middle Ages, and perhaps for a long time preceding them, Alpine peoples lived more or less at peace with their environment. The glaciers were there, but most of them were hidden in cirques and high hanging valleys. Even the larger ones, like the Mer de Glace, where they extended into the main valleys, lay nearly motionless, buried in their own debris.

Then, late in the sixteenth and early in the seventeenth centuries the climate became cooler, because the glaciers came suddenly to life and began to advance. New glaciers were born in formerly empty cirques. The larger ice streams began to throw off their cloak of debris and to push forward over the top of it.

For the preceding several hundred years, the inactivity of these glaciers had lured the natives closer and closer to the ice with their farms and villages. Now they had the experience of watching helplessly as the ice came forward, destroying their homes and burying their lands.

The glaciers in the Mont Blanc range were particularly active. Documents found in the archives of Chamonix show that several villages were practically destroyed during this period. After this catastrophe the ice retreated slightly, but a few years later, in 1609 to 1611, it made another spectacular advance, completing the destruction of the villages. Still another ruinous advance occurred in 1640 to 1644. As the walls of ice at the front of the glaciers crept slowly down the valleys to the villages and then began to pile up against the houses, finally to crush in their walls, some of the desperate villagers, in a last futile attempt to save their properties, chopped pieces of ice from the glaciers and hauled them away.

At the same time that the glaciers were bringing hardship to the Alpine peoples the increased snowfall heightened the frequency of the rumbling white death of avalanches. In a matter of seconds, these masses of sliding snow, breaking loose with little or no warning, can snuff out the lives of people unfortunate enough to be in their paths. This menace, although it has taken many lives in the Alps, has not always brought complete destruction to property. Sometimes buildings can be repaired after the snow has melted or been dug away from them. And pasture land across which the snow moves may suffer no ill effects whatsoever.

On the other hand, advancing glaciers claim no lives, but buildings cannot withstand their crushing force. Destruction of such objects when a glacier passes over them is complete. Frequently, the land over which they pass is stripped bare of its soil or plastered with a sterile blanket of rock debris, unfit for agriculture until it has weathered for many, many years.

Theodule Pass is a notch high above Zermatt in the mountain wall separating Switzerland from Italy. In the Middle Ages, especially around the seventh century, heavy traffic flowed across it and other high passes on the main route from Italy to Germany. Then the Theodule Glacier, moving down from the east flank of the Matterhorn, crept across the pass and severed this important mountain road. Now only skiers, hauled up the mountain by lifts from both its sides, tread this ice-choked former artery of heavy trans-Alpine traffic.

There are well-documented accounts of advances of other Swiss glaciers. Near the end of the sixteenth century the Upper and Lower Grindelwald glaciers in the Bernese Alps began to spill out of their high hanging valleys. For about twenty-five years their fronts advanced, not coming to a halt until they extended down into the lowlands almost to the village of Grindelwald. Then followed nearly 100 years of slow recession, after which they again moved forward, this time so fast that the frightened villagers reputedly sought the aid of the authorities to somehow force the glaciers back. And as the glaciers did then retreat, those in political power, as sometimes happens even to this day, probably received credit for an act of community improvement for which they were not responsible. From that time on, the records show that the Grindelwald and other Alpine glaciers had a history of alternate advances separated by minor retreats. A major advance took place in 1743, and one of nine years' duration began in 1770. Between 1814 and 1820 and between 1850 and 1855 they advanced almost as far as they did at the end of the sixteenth century, which to this day stands as the greatest glacial advance of historical times.

During these periods of glacier expansion lakes were formed in some of the tributary valleys when glaciers blocked their outlets. Each time this happened some of the inhabitants of these valleys lost their land under the rising waters of the new ice-dammed lakes.

Since about 1850 recession has been dominant, but some of the Alpine glaciers are still larger than they were before their great expansion at the end of the sixteenth century. Under the ice of the Brenva Glacier are the ruins of the village of St. Jean de Perthuis in the Veni Valley near the Italian portal of the Mont Blanc Tunnel. In the Valley of Chamonix on the opposite side of Mont Blanc is the village of Argentière, but the silver mine for which it was named, and which was worked during the Middle Ages, still lies buried beneath a glacier. And, of course, only skiers are able to cross Theodule Pass.

In the Alps, according to F. E. Matthes, there was a total of fourteen recorded advances, separated by minor retreats, between 1595 and 1939. Almost certainly a number of other less significant advances went unlisted, since the natives paid little or no attention to the glaciers unless their advances seemed to be leading to catastrophe.

For centuries the people of Iceland and Scandinavia, like those in the Alps, have put in writing a record from which we can reconstruct a fairly accurate picture of glacier comings and goings. And the record shows that the major periods of advance and retreat were essentially synchronous in all these areas. Whatever it was that affected the glaciers, it was the same over the whole of Europe.

Iceland, from the time of its settlement by the Norsemen in the ninth century until the fourteenth century, experienced a relatively mild climate, and its glaciers were less extensive than in the several following centuries. But this period of bland climate, under the influence of which the island was colonized, began to show signs of becoming less favorable as early as the latter part of the thirteenth century. Late in the seventeenth century climatic conditions had deteriorated to the point where a number of farms, which had been under cultivation for 700 or 800 years, were buried by the expanding outlet glaciers of the icecap Vatnajökull. Not until the pronounced glacier retreat of the 1930's were the sites of these farms exposed from beneath the ice which had concealed them for several centuries.

That conditions in the northern seas closely parallel the waxing and waning of glaciers is evident from the accounts of Iceland's early history. For the first three centuries after its settlement, a period when its glaciers were at reduced size, drifting ice in the sea along its northern shores was of no consequence as far as sailing was concerned. Erik the Red, and other intrepid seamen who followed him, sailed directly west from Iceland to Greenland in boats unsuited for navigation through sea ice. For several hundred years while the Norse colonies were flourishing on the west coast of Greenland, trading vessels maintained frequent contact with Europe, apparently with little trouble from ice.

But in the thirteenth century when Europe's glaciers began to expand, something also began to happen to the ice in the sea.

The route from Iceland to Greenland had to be moved farther south because of increasing drift ice. As the East Greenland Current continued to bring down more and more ice, the route was shifted still farther south. Fewer and fewer vessels made the trip to Greenland, and finally early in the fifteenth century trade with Europe was terminated altogether. Political and economic conditions in the homeland, certainly none too good during this period, had much to do with this lessening of traffic and with its eventual end, but that sailing conditions had become more and more hazardous because of drifting ice there can be little doubt.

During the ensuing 100 or so years when there was no communication between Greenland and Europe the colonies disappeared. When the next vessels from Europe reached Greenland in the sixteenth century they found no trace of the long-neglected Norsemen.

What were the circumstances under which these people vanished? The severance of ties with Europe probably contributed more to the final disappearance of these Europeans than any other factor. They needed imported iron for weapons and implements and wood with which to build their ships. Without corn and flour they would have to subsist largely on a diet of meat and fat, which in the harsh Arctic environment over a prolonged period of time is known to cause physical and mental deterioration among Europeans exposed to it. So it is almost certain that those few Norse who were able to survive the rigors of isolation eventually merged with the Eskimos who during this period came out of the north, following the seal and walrus which heavier ice in Baffin Bay and Davis Strait was driving southward.

The fate of the earliest European settlers of North America may not have been sealed entirely by changing climate and response of the ice to it, but nonetheless these factors exercised a strong power in guiding human events of those times. These unfortunate Greenlanders unintentionally left a record which tells unmistakably that their little world was invaded by ice.

In a little cemetery in the former Norse settlement at Herjolfsnes on the southwest coast of Greenland not far from Cape Farewell, for 500 years the remains of some of the last Norse colonists lay buried, disturbed only by minor excavations and by the relentless sea which washed some of the graves away. Then in 1921 a Danish archaeological expedition under the leadership of Dr. Poul Nörland excavated the remaining graves, and in so doing discovered much evidence that after the burial of these people the climate became much harsher. Many skeletons still remained, and both wooden objects and costumes in which the dead were buried were preserved, despite the great length of time in the soil.

When they were excavated, the bodies were in permafrost, and the excellent preservation of the clothing is a sure sign that the ground in which it lay must have been frozen throughout most of the 500-year period of burial. Since the graves would not have been dug in the hard frozen ground—even today this is not done in permafrost regions—it must be assumed that the ground was not permanently frozen, at least not close to the surface, at the time the bodies were interred. The oldest burials were the deepest; later graves were dug to lesser and lesser depth as the permafrost zone moved upward, enveloping the bodies of those buried earlier. Further—and this leaves no room for doubt about the condition of the ground—the coffins, clothes, and even the bodies were enmeshed in plant roots which, of course, could not have penetrated into permanently frozen ground.

So after the earliest Norsemen at Herjolfsnes were laid to rest, the summer thaw, under the influence of a cooling climate, penetrated to less and less depth, and finally, about the time Columbus began his epic voyages to the West Indies, the remains of the last surviving Norsemen in Greenland were claimed by the permanently frozen ground, in whose grip they remained until removed by the Danes in 1921. The extent of the frozen ground remains unchanged to the present time.

We know that during these early centuries the climatic changes which now favored, now restrained, the ice left substantial imprints on lands and peoples far beyond the borders of the lands of ice and snow. Each time that the glaciers expanded and the Arctic drift ice came farther south, elsewhere in the North Temperate Zone the climate became cooler and more moist; each time the ice receded, the climate in these same places warmed and became drier.

Geological and archaeological findings tell us that many of

the lakes, both large and small, in the western United States were reduced to very low levels or dried out completely around the fifth century. And in the seventh century, when heavy traffic was pressing across now ice-locked Alpine passes, trees growing in the American Southwest, with growth stunted by the pervasive drought, left a record which we can read like a book today. Again, the American tree rings tell us that they were not particularly favored by the climate when the Norse were passing back and forth between Greenland, Iceland, and Norway in nearly ice-free waters. And the Nile, that ever faithful renewer of the Egyptian soil, also rose and fell in synchronism with the changes of climate. During the times of greatest ice recession in Alpine and other regions, the Nile's floods were low; at the other extreme of a glacial cycle they appear to have been high.

What is the cause of these minor fluctuations of climate which we know have occurred repeatedly throughout historical times? That is a good question with which to start an argument, but it perhaps will generate less heat than one about the major, much longer changes measurable only over long periods of geologic time.

Though these historical changes—measured in tens of years or at most a few hundreds—are inconsequential moments in the Earth's long history, they have, as we know, exercised a lot of control over man's activities. And they cannot help but become ever more important as man comes to populate larger and larger portions of the globe.

Among the several most probable causes of these recent climatic variations and glacier fluctuations are changes in the amount of solar radiation. Unfortunately, in order to know accurately the variation in the sun's energy output, it would be necessary to obtain measurements over a long period of time from instruments carried by satellites in orbit near the outer limit of the Earth's atmosphere. Enough observations have been made, however, to show that there is quite a variation in the amount of ultraviolet radiation received by the Earth, and that it is correlated with changes in the number of sunspots that can be seen on the solar surface. During the periods when sunspots are at a maximum, and these occur from seven to seventeen years apart, glaciers apparently are mainly in a state of recession, and in the intervening periods of minimum sunspot activity they advance. And we have enough information about sunspot activity for the past 200 years to know that minor climatic variations correlate well with it.

Variations in receipt of solar radiation also cause changes in the general pattern of atmospheric circulation. When the jet streams, those high-altitude, whirling streams of air encircling the globe in middle latitudes, wander from the normal routes for any length of time, the Polar Front goes with them, storm tracks take new courses, and the permanent high- and low-pressure areas shift positions, with the result that large sections of the Earth experience pronounced climatic changes. Perhaps this is why the glaciers of the northern Cascade Mountains have been expanding while those in the rest of the Northern Hemisphere, where warm tropical air has invaded high latitudes, are shrinking.

Whether or not the Earth is receiving more or less solar energy than it returns to space is, of course, controlled in part by the Earth itself. Some scientists believe that some of the recent warming is caused by the increasing quantity of carbon dioxide poured into the atmosphere from the combustion of fuels— mainly through the exhaust pipes of automobiles and the smoke-stacks of industrial plants. Carbon dioxide absorbs outgoing long-wave radiation which the Earth is sending back into space and thus warms the atmosphere by what some people refer to as the "greenhouse effect." That far greater quantities of carbon dioxide have been added to the atmosphere in recent years than at any time during the historical period is unarguable. But beyond that the situation becomes quickly clouded. The sea absorbs carbon dioxide, but the rate is not known. Some scientists have interpreted the measurements to mean that the content of atmospheric carbon dioxide has increased by several per cent since the turn of the century. Others interpret the apparent equilibrium of carbon dioxide in the air over Antarctica, though the observations were carried on for a relatively brief period, to mean that the sea is absorbing the excess carbon dioxide almost as soon as it forms, and that only in heavily industrialized regions has the concentration noticeably increased. But the problem will require the attention of scientists for some time to come.

It has been estimated that at the present rate of burning of our mineral fuels (coal, oil, and gas) the amount of carbon dioxide in the atmosphere will double by the end of the century—if it is not absorbed by the oceans. Regardless of the effect of the added carbon dioxide in the air today, we cannot call upon it for an answer to the minor warm periods which came and went prior to the time of the Industrial Revolution, when the gift of carbon dioxide to the air by the burning of fossil fuels was nil.

Each time a volcano erupts, a quantity of dust and ash is thrown into the atmosphere. During some of the larger eruptions thick clouds of volcanic ash are ejected to tremendous heights, and eventually some of the material is carried through the stratosphere by high-altitude winds over all parts of the world. Two weeks after the great explosive eruption of Krakatoa in 1883, which destroyed not only the volcano but also the East Indies island on which it was located, its wind-borne ash had encircled the world in the Equatorial Zone and three months later had spread northward across Western Europe. In France solar radiation for the next three years averaged about ten per cent below normal. And there was a significant drop in world-wide temperature for at least a year after the eruption. In the few days immediately following the eruption the decks of ships steaming across the Indian Ocean 2,000 miles from Krakatoa were covered with thin films of fine white dust from the volcano. Elsewhere in the world the falls of ash were not detectable, but nonetheless the dust was there, and its presence created a series of remarkable occurrences that none could fail to observe. For a full year following August 27, 1883, unusual greenish-yellow to brilliantly red sunsets and halos around both sun and moon, seen on practically all clear days in the United States, Europe, Africa, and throughout the world, were caused by the dust thrown into the atmosphere by this small but extraordinarily violent volcano on an island in the Sunda Strait off the west end of Java.

Krakatoa has not been alone in its effect on the climate of the world. Historical records since the beginning of the sixteenth century show that a number of other volcanoes have made their contributions. On several occasions Hecla in Iceland has dropped ash on Norway and the British Isles, and for varying periods following its greatest eruptions peculiar sunsets and other atmospheric marvels were observed over Europe. For several months following the eruptions of another Iceland volcano, Skaptar Jökull, in 1783, colored sunsets and peculiar haze were visible over Europe and Asia, and the succeeding winter was one of the severest recorded up to that time in both Europe and North America.

Significant drops in world temperature followed eruptions of Tomboro, on the island of Sumbawa, east of Java, in 1815, of Mont Pelée in the West Indies in 1902, and of Katmai in 1912. The air-borne ash clouds thrown out by Tomboro were so thick that total darkness prevailed for three days over an area extending 300 miles from the volcano. On June 19, two weeks after Katmai's eruption, a haze created by its dust appeared in North Africa and within ten days had become so thick that measurements of solar radiation being made by an expedition from the Smithsonian Institution had to be discontinued for the summer.

No one has yet been able to calculate how much air-borne volcanic ash is needed to depress world temperatures by any given amount. It is quite obvious that the concentration of the minute ash particles is extremely tenuous. The amount of solid material ejected by the Katmai eruption, certainly one of the largest in historical times, was estimated to have been between six and seven cubic miles, most of which dropped to earth close to the volcano itself. At Kodiak, the nearest town, 100 miles from the crater, the ash fall was about one foot deep. And 1,500 miles away on the Greenland icecap the fall of ash, though preserved within the glacier, perhaps would not have been noticeable, though unusual colored sunsets and related atmospheric effects caused by its presence might have been spectacular.

When most of the large eruptions took place the means of communication were slow and the science of meteorology was in its infancy. Further, and this holds true even today, observations from all over the world have to be collected, correlated, and studied before we can tell if a volcanic eruption has had any effect upon climate. In some cases years have passed before the answer was forthcoming. There are still large sections of the world in which systematic observations have never been made. Even so, the effect of volcanoes on climate was suspected many years ago, and as far back as 1784 Benjamin Franklin, in one of his numerous but lesser-known contributions to science, made public his view that volcanic dust in the air might be a cause of climatic change.

The fact that volcanic ash may remain in the upper atmosphere for years has led some scientists to believe that the period of cool climate which began to wane just prior to the beginning of the current century was caused by volcanic ash in the air, from the large-scale eruptions of the preceding 100 or more years. The slow settling of this ash, particularly since about 1920, has enabled more solar radiation to penetrate to the Earth and is thus the cause for the current marked warming of climate.

Whatever the cause or causes of variations in climate since the beginning of historical time, we can be certain that a number of factors, including an inadequate system of observations, join to make the problem complex. At the moment we do not really know whether the Earth as a whole is warming up or cooling off.

15

Nature Keeps the Record

W E HAVE the archives of Chamonix and other Alpine places and the written records of the Icelanders and Scandinavians to give us direct evidence of what was happening to the glaciers in those places during earlier centuries. On papyrus and on plates of clay retrieved from tombs and dug from buried cities we have been able to reconstruct climatic changes far back beyond the Christian Era. By accounts such as these we have obtained a documented record, much of it indirect, of natural events back to the misty beginnings of historical time.

But the historical period began much later in some places than in others; there are places where it is only just beginning today. Before the historical period Nature was the only scribe who kept the record. For tens of thousands of years she has been faithfully recording the comings and goings of glaciers wherever they have been. And since she still continues to inscribe as she has done in the past, glacial geologists of future millenniums will have plenty of opportunity to determine whose recordings—man's or Nature's—are more enduring.

There undoubtedly were occasions when Indian villages in

southeastern Alaska were swept away by the outpourings of ice-dammed lakes. We can also visualize many an occasion when an Indian village was wiped out by an advancing glacier or when a hunter returned to a valley campsite he occupied several years before only to find the valley clogged with ice. If there were any survivors of these harrowing experiences they have bequeathed us no written word, because there are essentially no written records of Alaska before the nineteenth century. The vague Indian legends handed down from one generation to the next do not give us the slightest inkling as to when these events were witnessed, yet not only do we know they occurred, but with the aid of Nature's diary we have been able to find out when and where.

Almost 200 years ago—around 1768—the front of Mendenhall Glacier lay two miles closer to the present site of the Juneau airport than it does today. We know also that at no time during the past 600 or 700 years did Mendenhall Glacier extend beyond this point. In 1755 Taku Glacier, another large stream of ice draining the Juneau Ice Field, was three and one half miles longer than it is today, and at that time it blocked the Taku River, creating a lake that extended many miles upstream. The past habits of many other Alaskan glaciers are as well known as those of Mendenhall and Taku, even though man has left no record of them.

How does Nature document these events? What kinds of marks does she leave behind for us to read? We have already found out that the ice itself holds the key to some of the history. If the annual ice layers are separated by dust films we can count them to determine the age of the ice. The spores, pollen, and volcanic ash in these dust films yield clues to events happening at the time they were deposited. Where there are no visible dust films, as in Antarctica and Greenland, oxygen isotope ratios reveal not only the age of the ice, but also the temperature when the snow accumulated.

But what about the reconstruction of history where glaciers have disappeared or where, as at Mendenhall and Taku, they have retreated from the ground they formerly occupied? It is here that Nature has done some of her most lucid writing.

When the end of a glacier remains in one place long enough, the terminal moraine of rock debris carried down the glacier gradually builds up into a ridge. Even though the ice front oscillates because of changing weather conditions from year to year, the moraine ridge may eventually reach a height of several hundred feet. During this period of glacier stability the adjacent forest, especially in southeastern Alaska where the glaciers descend far below the treeline, will crowd in against the outer edge of the moraine. Of course no trees grow on terminal moraines while the glaciers are dumping their loads of debris onto them, and no plant or animal can survive the scraping and grinding constantly going on beneath a glacier. So when a change in climate causes a glacier to shrink and its end to retreat to a new position farther up the valley, the area it formerly occupied is a denuded barren strip hemmed in by undisturbed forest. Vegetation, at least in the mild, moist climate of southeastern Alaska, almost immediately begins to reclothe this barren ground. But long after the glacier has retreated, the edge of the undisturbed forest will remain as a forest trimline marking the former edge of the glacier, because the new-generation forest on the newly exposed land will be much younger and possibly of different composition than the undisturbed forest outside of the moraine. These trimlines are formed in a much less spectacular manner than those made by the crashing waves in Lituya Bay, but there is essentially no difference in appearance and they both tell a similar story.

Pioneer plants, however, cannot take root on the new land until their seeds are carried in by the wind or by birds and other animals. Since the terminal moraine is the part of the barren zone closest to the undisturbed area and its source of seeds, the first new plants spring up on its rock-rubble surface. Only the seeds of plants tolerant of sunlight and able to germinate and grow in the sterile ground appear during the first few years.

In the vicinity of Juneau, willows and alders are among the first trees to become established, and within several years a dense forest of these small trees is usually growing inside the trimline. But close on the heels of these smaller trees, usually within five to ten years from the time of ice withdrawal, scattered Sitka spruce and other long-lived species begin to grow. For a long time, hidden within the dense stand of alder, they grow very slowly. But in time they punch up into the sunlight through the canopy of alders. Soon the lesser trees are squeezed out and this new generation of conifers will dominate the forest for the next several hundred years.

The time lapse between glacier disappearance and the establishment of a forest is, of course, not everywhere the same as adjacent to the Juneau Ice Field. Where the climate is dryer or colder the forest is slower in getting started. In the Northern Rockies tree seedlings may not become established until fifteen or twenty years after the glaciers have retreated. And at Glacier Bay glacier recession has been so incredibly rapid that it has far outdistanced the encroaching edge of the forest. Vast newly exposed land surfaces are so far from the edge of the old forest that very few wind-blown seeds can reach them, and they may not be covered with a new forest for fifty or even 100 years after they are exposed.

So all that is necessary to find out when a glacier began retreating from a certain point is to determine the age of the oldest living tree on the abandoned moraine. Since each tree adds a growth ring every year, the most direct method for computing age would be to cut down the largest, oldest tree on the moraine and count its rings. Then, if we knew how long a time was required for that particular species of tree to establish itself on moraines after the withdrawal of a glacier, we would know, at least within a few years, the year in which glacier recession began.

But the problem is not quite as simple as that. First of all, the oldest trees are not always the largest, so a large number of trees might have to be examined before the oldest is found. Obviously it would be a near-impossible task to go through the forest felling large trees in an effort to find the elusive oldest one, and this method would cause needless destruction of trees. So whenever possible the tree-ring expert uses a coring tool known as the Swedish increment borer to extract a core about the diameter of a lead pencil from the tree. After the core has been polished the annual rings, like annual strata in a core from the Greenland or Antarctic ice sheets, can be counted, and the age of the tree accurately figured—if the borer intersected the earliest growth ring.

Even ring-counting is not as easy as it sounds. The rings in some deciduous trees are very indistinct, and near timberline, where growth is extraordinarily slow, trees may be so small that a core cannot be obtained. Trees only three to four feet tall may be several hundred years old. Some trees have more than 200 annual rings to the inch. The only way to find the age of these dwarfs is to cut them down, polish the complete cross sections, and count the rings with the aid of a magnifier. The age of even very small conifer trees can usually be determined with great accuracy because the conifer annual growth ring consists of two sharply contrasting layers, an inner light-colored one added in the spring and an outer dark one in summer.

In narrow valleys where no part of the uncovered land is more than a few hundred yards from the edge of the undisturbed forest, plants spread over the area inside the end moraine almost as soon as they spring up on the moraine itself. And before long a new generation of forest has established itself on practically the entire area between abandoned moraine and glacier. In a like manner, a still younger forest will spread over the area inside the next recessional moraine. Thus progressively younger forests, each separated from the others by trimlines and moraines, follow the edge of a retreating glacier. And the slower the retreat, the narrower will be the unforested zone in front of the ice.

But climate being what it is, a glacier will make advances as well as retreats, and when the ice comes forward, the new forest which has been struggling to take over the land vacated by the glacier will go down before the wall of advancing ice and be ground into dust beneath it. If the advance carries the ice down the valley and beyond the innermost moraine, the newest-generation forest will be obliterated. Should the advance continue far enough, all trimlines may be destroyed as the glacier pushes across the oldest one and into undisturbed forest beyond, obliterating its own record of former advances and retreats.

But when this major push finally loses its momentum, whether the ice makes a stand at the new position or immediately begins to retreat, a new trimline will remain to mark the location of this farthest extent of the ice. If such an advance occurred now it would of course be observed, documented by photographs and a map; and an accurate written description would add the event to the recorded history of glacier fluctuations for the benefit of scientists, say, some several thousand years hence. Similarly, we would be able to record and document the future retreat when it came.

But let us assume that several centuries ago a glacier in southeastern Alaska made such an advance and that its front remained stationary for several decades before beginning to retreat. The age of the oldest trees on the moraine, just inside the trimline, would date the time that the glacier began to withdraw. But how could we calculate the time when the advancing glacier front had come to a stop? Using one of the most fundamental concepts of geological study, "the present is the key to the past," set forth over 175 years ago by James Hutton, we must find our clue along the fronts of glaciers which have actually been observed in the act of invading forests.

As the front of a glacier, in reaching the limit of its advance, moves forward the last foot or two before coming to a stop, it will, like a bulldozer, merely push some of the trees over into a leaning position and scrape off some of their bark without uprooting them. Some of these leaning trees will continue to grow, and though straining to straighten up, they will remain bent and gnarled. But unfailingly over the years they will continue to add annual rings recording both time and the vagaries of weather and climate. Long after the glacier has retreated, the lumberman with his ax and chain saw will pass these scarred old veterans by, but the tree-ring expert, with his increment borer, will see that here are special trees, indeed. To him they may be the most valuable in the entire forest. The core taken from one of these injured trees will plainly show the scar made by the last dying push of the glacier, and covering this wound will be an annual ring for each year since the disaster. The count of these newer rings will pin down the exact year the ice advance halted.

Though most glaciers in southeastern Alaska have experienced one or more periods of advance during the past 300 years, retreat has been dominant. So the fronts of most glaciers there are paralleled by several well-preserved trimlines marking the places where retreat of the glacier front was punctuated by either a minor advance or a pause in the general retreat. Even Taku Glacier, which, unlike practically every other glacier in the world, has been advancing steadily for more than sixty years, has not yet reached the trimline marking the maximum extent of the last major advance, from which, the tree rings tell us, the glacier began to withdraw about the year 1750.

Several of the glaciers draining the Juneau Ice Field have especially well-developed recessional moraines and trimlines. The road from Juneau to Mendenhall Glacier crosses some very conspicuous ones. They are most striking when viewed from the air because the color of the younger forests is a lighter green than the more mature forests. At Herbert Glacier a few miles north of Juneau, twenty distinct trimlines and moraines have been identified.

Trimlines are by no means an exclusive feature of southeastern Alaska. They just happen to be very well developed there because many of the glaciers extend into the forested zone. The same relationships are present around many of the British Columbia glaciers and those in the Cascades in Washington and Oregon. Tree-ring experts have found the same timetable of glacier events in the trimlines around these glaciers as they have in Alaska. The age of trees just inside the oldest trimline at Nisqually Glacier on Mount Rainier, where it is crossed by the Paradise Highway not far from the Nisqually River bridge, shows that the glacier began to retreat from this point about 1750, over 100 years before the glacier was discovered by Lieutenant A. V. Kautz. The age of mature trees outside this trimline shows that the glacier had not advanced beyond its 1750 position during the preceding several hundred years.

The same story is repeated on Oregon's Mount Hood. At the oldest trimline of Eliot Glacier on the northeast side of the peak not far from Cloudcap Inn, Professor Donald B. Lawrence counted the rings of a tree scarred and pushed over by the ice and found that this forward shove of the glacier occurred in the year 1740. Outside of the trimline the forest had not been disturbed since some time before the year 1300.

So the picture of recent glacier history in North America emerges: Around the middle of the eighteenth century the glaciers made a major advance, greater than at any time since before 1300 and possibly greater than any in the last several thousand years. Between this great advance and the present time, retreat, punctuated by pauses and minor advances, has been the rule. In all this Pacific coastal region few glaciers have shortened more than two miles during the past two centuries except at Glacier Bay, where the principal glacier has receded more than sixty miles.

All this the tree rings have told us, and it corresponds almost exactly with what European observers wrote into the record for the glaciers of Iceland, Norway, and the Alps. Man wrote about Nature; then years later other men went into the field to check Nature's record—the moraines and trimlines—to see if man's observations and recordings were correct. So we do not need Captain George Vancouver's account to tell where the terminus of the big Glacier Bay ice sheet lay when he confronted it in 1794. Tree rings tell us something Vancouver never knew— that when he saw it, this immense blanket of ice had been shrinking for fifty years and that its spectacular terminal wall had already retreated five miles up the bay.

Although dendrochronology has revealed what the glaciers have been doing only for the past 600 or 700 years, it has extended the record of climatic changes far beyond that time. This record comes mainly from trees growing under harsh conditions—rocky wind-swept slopes and places where the soil is thin and sterile—because such trees are very sensitive to changes in soil moisture. Annual rings of dry years are much narrower than those laid down in years of greater moisture.

High up in California's White Mountains, their roots anchored in crevices among the limestone slabs, stands a group of bristlecone pines which have been parched and buffeted by searing winds from the surrounding deserts and subjected to both great heat and intense cold through a span of life longer than that of any other living thing. These patriarchs were ancient when the oldest sequoia was a sapling.

In the summer of 1957, after several years' search for the oldest bristlecone pines, the late Dr. Edmund Schulman, dendrochronologist from the University of Arizona, knew that he was getting close to his goal. A quick field count of rings on the cores collected during the summer from one of the largest bristlecones indicated a tremendous longevity. But now the exciting work of making an accurate count had begun. Ring after ring passed across the microscope field, taking Dr. Schulman back across the centuries. His count was hardly more than well under way before he passed the year when Columbus landed on San Salvador. At the birth of Christ the tree was already ancient. While the Greeks fought the Trojan War and the Phoenicians were building their great maritime empire, this pine faithfully recorded each passing year, carefully distinguishing in its heart-wood those years which were lean and those which were fat. And yet another thousand years and still another—practically all of it before the birth of the oldest-known living giant sequoias —passed across the stage. And still the count continued, to a time more than 4,600 years ago when this ancient sprouted from a seed that had found a resting place in a crevice high on a California mountain slope.

But because of the bristlecone pine's preference for high barren slopes, few if any of these trees have been pushed over by the farthest shove of an advancing glacier. At least if there were any, they have not yet been found.

How then can we date these more ancient climatic changes and glacier advances? We know they took place. At Mount Hood, at Mount Rainier, in southeastern Alaska, and wherever glaciers are or have been there are, far beyond the earliest eighteenth-century moraines, still more ancient ones. On them stand mature forests growing in a thick layer of humus, itself resulting from the growth and subsequent decay of several, perhaps many, earlier generations of forests. And beneath this soil the moraine itself has been intensely weathered to depths of several feet. Rock fragments have been softened and decomposed or completely dissolved away during their long exposure to the elements. From observations of the rate of weathering over short but accurately determined lengths of time, we know that such changes required far more time than that spanned by the lives of even the oldest bristlecone pines.

If there is a considerable age difference between two moraines, their relative ages can be found by the depth to which they have been weathered. The weathered zone will be thicker on the older moraine because of its longer exposure to the elements. As time passes, the continuous percolation of surface water carrying organic acids derived from the plant cover and carbon dioxide gathered by rain as it fell through the air decomposes and dissolves the rocks within the moraine to greater and greater depth. The rate of penetration, however, varies from place to place because of differences in climate. It proceeds much faster in the warm, humid climate of the Amazon Basin than in the cool climate of northern New England or in the nearly moisture-less Sahara. So the mantle of soil and decayed rock waste in Brazil may be 300 to 400 feet thick and in New England, on the same kind of rock, only twenty feet. So as far as age is concerned, the depth of weathering in moraines can tell us little more than that one moraine is older or younger than another.

A method of actually attaching an age in years to ancient glacial events had its inception in 1879 when Swedish geologist Baron Gerard De Geer began his lifelong study of thin rhythmic sediment layers in the exposed beds of former glacial lakes. A peculiarity of these layers, which De Geer called *varves*, is their dual character; each varve consists of two layers, a lower thicker layer of silt and fine sand and an upper thinner layer of clay. Most varves are only a few millimeters thick, few as much as an inch. De Geer assumed, because of their regularity and uniformity over wide areas, that each varve represented a year's deposit of sediment.

Each summer, into lakes along or near glaciers, melt-water streams dump a load of sediment. In the quiet lake water the coarse material quickly settles to form the bottom layer of the varve. The fine clay is held in suspension much longer in the cold dense glacier water, not settling until the following fall and winter when the lake is no longer agitated by inflowing melt water.

This type of sedimentation can be observed in glacial lakes today. Varves are being deposited on the bottom of Lake Louise in the Alberta Rockies. During the spring and summer the melting of Victoria Glacier supplies a large quantity of sediment to the lake. The coarse material settles first to make the bottom layer of an annual varve. Much of the fine clay which gives the lake its milky tint remains in suspension all summer but settles slowly during the winter to complete the varve and make the lake water perfectly clear by early spring. The varve of a cold year is thin, that of a warm year thick, so varves, like annual rings in a tree, can be correlated from place to place.

Glacial lakes are born as soon as the ice uncovers the land on which they lie, and the melt-water streams immediately begin to fill them. Thus the lowest varve in any deposit must have been laid down in the year that the glacier retreated beyond that point. As new lakes come into being, new varve series begin to form. All varves—in many lakes—deposited in the same year, especially if it is either a cold or a warm year, will be quite similar, and the student of varves can easily recognize and correlate them one with the other.

Because of this unique property of varves, De Geer was able to time the retreat of the last ice sheet all the way across Sweden and to make a count of the years since it disappeared—a total close to 12,000 years. De Geer's announcement of this feat before the Eleventh International Geological Congress in Stockholm in 1910 was epochal. Now for the first time it was possible for men to measure in years the length of a division of geologic time.

This method of chronology, however, is not without its weak points. Thick undisturbed varve exposures are not common, and in North America particularly they are so scattered in some areas that correlation from one to the other has not been possible. Thus there are a number of gaps in the varve chronology for this part of the world. It has also been found that in some of the old lakes, storm-created waves and currents stirred up varve sediment and then redeposited several layers in place of the original two.

Since 1947 geologists have been able to realize their long-cherished dream of obtaining precise dates for many of the glacial events beyond the time of the tree-ring chronology and even well beyond the time of the varves. It was in that year that nuclear chemist Willard F. Libby, after he had discovered radioactive carbon in the atmosphere, found a method of determining the age of materials containing this radiocarbon, an achievement for which in 1960 he was awarded the Nobel Prize in chemistry.

Dr. Libby's time clock is based upon the fortunate circumstance that the radioactive isotope of carbon, which has an atomic weight of 14, in contrast to 12 in the normal carbon atom, changes, as do all other radioactive elements, at a constant rate into another element. Atoms of carbon–14, as radiocarbon is known, are created in the Earth's upper atmosphere by the bombardment of nitrogen atoms by neutrons. When one of these fast-moving neutrons collides with an atom of nitrogen it knocks a proton out of the nucleus, thus transmuting nitrogen–14 into radioactive carbon–14. Once created, the carbon–14 atom begins a slow disintegration and eventually reverts to nitrogen. If the production of neutrons in the upper atmosphere should cease today, there would be no additional carbon–14 created, and in about 70,000 years practically all the radioactive carbon would have disappeared. The half-life of carbon–14 is about 5,700 years, meaning that in that span of time half the original radiocarbon disappears and that half of what is left disappears in the next 5,700 years, until after 70,000 years essentially none remains.

But because the formation of carbon–14 in the atmosphere has been going on for a much longer time than 70,000 years and because it is disappearing as fast as it forms, its concentration in the atmosphere remains constant. Radiocarbon enters the tissues of all plants as they absorb carbon dioxide during the process of photosynthesis. Animals eat plants and thus also absorb radiocarbon. And so in living plants and animals the amount of radiocarbon, as in the atmosphere, remains in a steady state—the supply is renewed at the rate it is dissipated.

Dr. Libby and his colleagues found that the proportion of radiocarbon to carbon in living materials all over the Earth was essentially the same and could be determined by sensitive Geiger counters which record each disintegration of a carbon–14 atom as it converts to nitrogen. No matter whether the material was Norway spruce from Scandinavia, pine wood and needles from timberline in New Mexico, oak from Palestine, or seal oil from Antarctica, the counters recorded essentially the same number of exploding atoms per gram of carbon.

But the moment a plant or animal dies the absorption of carbon dioxide, and thus radiocarbon, ceases. And from that time on, with each disintegrating atom the radiocarbon in the organism steadily dissipates, one half of it in 5,700 years, three fourths of it in 11,400 years, until eventually the remaining amount is so small as to be undetectable. So all one has to do is to measure with Geiger counters the amount of radioactivity in the remains of a long-dead plant or animal to determine the year in which it died if, while it lived, it had the same concentration of carbon–14 as in similar plants or animals today. Obviously, here was a calendar which could be of tremendous value to geologists as well as archaeologists and others interested in prehistoric events.

So Dr. Libby's next step was to test his method on some ancient objects of known age. The oldest more or less accurately dated archaeological finds were the 5,000-year-old tombs of the First Egyptian Dynasty. Radiocarbon dates, determined from wooden objects—from the floors, beams, and coffins—in these tombs have matched very closely the dates documented by the calendars these ancient people obligingly kept.

In the years since radiocarbon dating began, many other similar checks of its accuracy have been made in every one of the nearly forty radiocarbon dating laboratories scattered throughout the world. Scientists at the Lamont Geological Observatory determined an age of $1,830 \pm 50$ years for a charred loaf of bread found in a storehouse in the ruins of Pompeii, which apparently had been covered by volcanic ash when the city was destroyed by a violent eruption of Vesuvius in A.D. 79. Since grain probably was not stored more than two years in ancient Pompeii before being used, the wheat used in this loaf of bread was harvested about 1,800 years before its age was determined at Lamont. It may be going too far to pass judgment on the baking methods used by the baker who made this loaf, but the fact remains that had the Neapolitans left us no documentary record of the date on which one of their proud cities was destroyed, we would now be able to record it because of a single little charred loaf of bread dug from the ash of the ruins.

So here indeed is an age-determining method to warm the heart of the glacial geologist. And geologists, in an effort to reconstruct a chronology of glacial events, have submitted thousands of samples of wood, bone, shell, and peat to the radiocarbon daters. And this collection of materials, taken from such places as the swamp, the cave, and the beach as well as the moraine, have extended the yearly calendar of glacial and climatic events backward for nearly 70,000 years. Samples coming from a time earlier than this just do not have sufficient remaining radiocarbon to enable an age determination to be made.

Soon after Dr. Libby's discovery of the method, radiocarbon

made its first big hit in glacier dating by yielding an absolute date for the last major invasion of the northern states by the great ice sheet. In the shore cliffs along Lake Michigan a few miles north of Manitowoc, Wisconsin, geologists have long been examining and re-examining layers of moraine and other materials which tell with great clarity a most interesting sequence of events which transpired when the region was in the throes of the last stages of its glacial history. Exposed in these cliffs, near a place known as Two Creeks, there is a buried layer of peat in which there are stumps, some with roots extending into the clay below, and shattered trunks of spruce, pine, and birch. This ancient forest floor is covered with a layer of glacial till in the base of which many of the shattered tree trunks, broken from the stumps, lie pointing toward the southwest. Beneath the peat are thin layers of lake clay under which there is another layer of glacial moraine.

The story told by this series of deposits is quite clear. The lowest moraine was deposited beneath the ice sheet when it covered Two Creeks and extended many miles to the south. Next, because of a change in climate the ice sheet began to shrink, and as its terminus withdrew northward across Two Creeks, the area was covered by water ponded in the Lake Michigan Basin against the retreating ice front. This lake, called Glacial Lake Chicago, its north shore one of ice, overflowed at its southern end, where the city of Chicago is now located, through the Illinois River and into the Mississippi. Several feet of thin-layered clay were deposited in the lake. Lake Chicago grew larger and larger as the edge of the glacier retreated to the north. Finally the edge of the ice withdrew into Canada, uncovering a lower outlet through the Straits of Mackinac and the St. Lawrence Valley. The surface of Lake Chicago immediately fell to the level of the new outlet, exposing dry land at Two Creeks. Soon trees and other plants invaded the land vacated by the glacier, as they are doing around glaciers today, and in time a dense forest of spruce had taken over the land. While the edge of the shrunken ice sheet rested somewhere in Ontario the first trees in the forest grew to maturity and a peaty soil developed from moss and rotting leaves and wood on the forest floor. The climate at the time, as reflected by the kinds of trees and other plants in the Two Creeks forest, probably was very similar to the present climate in northern Minnesota and the region north of Lake Superior.

After a time the climate cooled—the outer growth rings on the buried stumps at Two Creeks are thinner than the earlier ones—and the edge of the awakening ice sheet moved out from Canada, down across the St. Lawrence Valley, and over the Straits of Mackinac, again blocking off the northern outlet of the Lake Michigan Basin and re-creating Lake Chicago. The rising waters slowly engulfed the Two Creeks forest, killing all the trees. For a number of years these drowned ghosts stood under sixty feet of water while thin layers of mud and clay settled around them. But the front of the ice sheet, crawling relentlessly down the Lake Michigan Basin, pushing the lake ahead of it, finally plowed into the forest, breaking off the trees, and burying them in a new layer of moraine which it had scraped from the land and the lake basin to the north.

The ice age had returned to southern Wisconsin. The ice sheet had overrun and destroyed the forest. It had driven out the forest animals and caused the Great Lakes people, who had moved into the new forests after the last ice retreat, to pack up and move south.

After overrunning the Two Creeks forest, this advance of the ice, which goes by the name Valders, didn't extend much farther south. In the Lake Michigan Basin its farthest projection reached about as far as the location of Milwaukee. But it covered practically all of northern Michigan, extended as far as Niagara Falls and Rochester, and probably blanketed much of northern New England.

Since this was the last major advance of the former North American ice sheet, the time of its occurrence is of great interest to geologists and archaeologists. Prior to the advent of radiocarbon dating, the best estimates, based on the varve chronology, gave an age close to 25,000 years.

But what does radiocarbon tell us about this last act of the great glacier? Actually it does not give us an exact answer, but it does tell us that the ice overwhelmed the Two Creeks forest less than 11,400 years ago. That is how long ago, determined since

1950 by scientists in several radiocarbon laboratories, the rising waters of Glacial Lake Chicago drowned the trees in the forest at Two Creeks. This date, 11,400 B.P. (before the present), marks the time when the ice sheet crossed over the Straits of Mackinac and began crawling down across Wisconsin and the lower peninsula of Michigan. A number of recent age determinations show us that it passed over Two Creeks close to 11,000 years ago and inched the last 100 miles to Milwaukee in another 150 years. Other radiocarbon dates indicate that the European ice sheet was also advancing at this same time.

Other well-established dates reveal that the edge of the ice sheet did not retreat northward beyond the Great Lakes for the last time until about 8,000 years ago and that when the Pharaohs were building the great Pyramids of Gizeh the edge of the great ice sheet lay not far north of the site where the capital of Canada now stands.

Thousands of samples of wood, bone, shell, and other organic materials have been dated in the world's radiocarbon laboratories, but the method is still in its infancy. Many new exciting finds will be dated, and soon we shall have an almost year-to-year calendar of every important event of late Pleistocene time.

Even the time when the mammoths trod the Earth will be known. In fact a start has already been made in getting the answer to this riddle. In casting around for interesting material to date, the eyes of the radiocarbon daters soon fell upon the mammoths which for years had been ensconced in museums around the world. So some skin and flesh of the baby mammoth made the trip from the freezer at the American Museum of Natural History to Columbia University's Lamont radiocarbon laboratory. The answer—roughly 21,300 years.

From a piece of the skin of the famous Siberian mammoth found by Adams in 1799, the Geiger counters in Yale University's laboratory ticked off an amount of radiocarbon equivalent to an age in excess of 30,000 years. The Beresovka mammoth, since it lived in a climate slightly warmer than the present, apparently also lived more than 30,000 years ago in an interglacial period prior to the last major glaciation. According to the Russians, however, the mammoths represented by most of the remains lived during a later interglacial time, when the forest at Two Creeks was establishing itself prior to the Valders advance about 11,000 years ago.

More age determinations will, of course, have to be made on mammoth remains, but from what has already been done it appears that these bulky animals lived in a climate not very different from that in their former stamping grounds today—sometimes it was a little colder, sometimes a little warmer. And they persisted for thousands of years, at least from an interglacial period prior to 30,000 years ago until about the time the last big ice sheet started to wane.

There is yet another depository for the records of ancient climatic fluctuations from which we can find out what was happening to life on the lands and from which we can draw inferences about the sea ice, the permafrost, and how the glaciers were faring during the 10,000-year interval since the ice sheets made their last major push. Everywhere the ice sheets went the debris they plastered over the landscape blocked streams and created depressions which became lakes and ponds as soon as the ice retreated. This rubble-strewn, water-dotted landscape didn't remain barren for long. For, just as the mosses and the sedges and the alders and willows are encroaching now on the barren moraines in southeastern Alaska, so they followed in the wake of the ice sheets' slow retreat across the northern states and Canada and over the Baltic and North Sea plains in Europe. Soon these pioneer plants were joined by spruces and other trees in colonizing the land so long denied to countless generations of their forebears. The green carpet of vegetation crept irresistibly onward, now keeping pace with the retreating glacier edge, now losing ground as a period of warmer years pulled the ice edge back faster, now closing the gap as the glacier edge faltered in its northward flight.

Into this new land of lakes came the ducks and geese and other water birds. In ever-multiplying hordes they came—there was no holding them back from this rapidly expanding favorable environment—until they had taken over for their summer home half the North American continent.

Other animal groups found the new lands to their liking, but some were favored more than others in this new and largest real-estate boom in 100,000 years. The moose, living in a geo-graphically restricted area near the margins of the ice sheets, could now return to eat his fill of aquatic plants in a vast land from which he had been driven by the last expansion of the glaciers.

The plant cover did not confine itself to the land. Aquatic vegetation spread over the floors of shallow lakes and ponds, the newer generations growing year after year on the ever-thickening blanket of the rotting remains of earlier generations. Each lake and pond also received its annual quota of leaves, twigs, and other remains of plants growing along the shores. Water-logged, many of these materials sank, to be added to the organic pot-pourri on the bottom. This detritus, subjected to only partial de-cay under its protective cover of water, was slowly converted into peat.

In the new forest uncountable billions of pollen grains from the flowers of spruce, pine, alder, and all the other trees and flowering plants were cast into the air each spring and summer. Only an infinitesimally small number of these minute grains, though they perpetuated the species, hit the targets for which Nature intended them. The rest, crowding the spring and sum-mer air in atomlike profusion, were wafted far and wide by the winds. Some of this pollen fell in the forests, some on the ice sheet, and some came down to float as thin films on the lakes and ponds, eventually to sink to the bottom and mix with the peat.

It so happens that pollen is the most nearly indestructible of all plant materials. The shell of the pollen grain is an extraor-dinarily hard substance, and though softened when it comes into contact with the seductive fluids exuded by the ovary in a flower of its own species, it can remain unchanged for an in-credibly long time when buried in peat and other sediments. The ducks and the geese of those faraway times have gone and practically all the bones of the moose and the giant beaver have weathered away, but in the peat that has filled the myriads of glacier-made lakes and ponds, layer upon layer of pollen grains remain to attest to the life and climate of the times.

All the pollen grains of a single plant species are identical, and they differ unmistakably from those of any other species.

Thus it is a simple matter for a palynologist to determine to which species of plant a pollen grain belongs.

During the several thousands of years since the ice sheets have disappeared, immense numbers of shallow glacial lakes and ponds have been converted to bogs and marshes by filling with peat. Within this peat there is a record of the surrounding plant life from the present back to the time when the ice sheet withdrew.

To get a complete sample of peat from one of these bogs, the sampler uses a tubelike device with which he can collect a continuous core of peat from top to bottom through the bog. The pollen in the bottoms of these cores, produced by the first plants to invade the barren moraine, is mainly from tundra plants, willows, alders, and birches, followed a little higher in the core by dominant spruce and pine. At any one level in these cores there is a mixture of pollen grains from many species of plants, but one or more species is always dominant. These assemblages accurately indicate the major changes in the composition of the forests, which in turn reflect climatic fluctuations. And the times when these various forests clothed the land can be determined by the carbon–14 content of the peat in which the pollen is enclosed.

Though there have been many minor climatic fluctuations since the last ice withdrawal began, pollen studies clearly show that there were three major climatic periods in these last 10,000 to 11,000 years. Pollen sequences in the bogs south of the Great Lakes show that from the time the ice withdrew until about 9,500 years ago, although the temperature was rising the climate was cool and moist, as indicated by the dominance of spruce and fir in the surrounding forests. Then followed a long warmer and drier period until about 2,500 years ago (500 B.C.), during which spruce and fir yielded their dominant position first to pine and then to oak. But a slightly cooler period set in—pine and spruce began to increase again—and with minor fluctuations continued to the present time. Pollen profiles from bogs in the British Isles, the Low Countries, northern Germany, and the Scandinavian countries paint the same changing climatic picture for Europe since the Fennoscandian ice sheet—the correlative of the Valders—withdrew.

Of course, the forest succession did not everywhere involve

the same species of trees. The sequence in northern Ontario obviously was different from that at Columbus, Ohio, but in all cases the same climatic sequence—cool, warm, and cool again—can be read in the pollen grains.

Although these climatic changes are recorded by the pollen grains buried in the peat, a lifetime may be too short to witness the changes in the act of taking place. But had it been possible to take time-lapse aerial motion pictures, say, at intervals of fifty years or more, for several thousands of years prior to the coming of the great ice sheet to eastern North America, we would now be able to see these dynamic forces in full and obvious operation.

At the start of the show we would see the edge of a vast ice sheet in northern Ontario and Quebec, bordered by a treeless tundra zone, and south of that a wide dark-green band of spruce and fir stretching across southern Canada. South of these conifers is another wide band of pine and northern hardwoods—beech, maple, and birch. As the glacier slowly creeps forward, along with it go the bands of tundra, spruce, and others, never mixing, always retaining their identity.

Now the camera moves slowly down for a close-up view to show how the migration of the forest takes place. In the northern edge of the spruce belt growth is slower and slower as the climate cools, and as spruce trees die they are replaced by dwarfs of their own species and by willows and alders, and finally as the dwarfs die there are no more spruces to take their places—only willows and tundra plants. So the treeline has moved south. And at the southern edge of the spruce belt the climate most favorable to spruce moves south. As the pines and northern hardwoods die out, their places are taken by the more-favored spruce, and the spruceline moves on toward the south, pushing the less hardy species before it. Farther south still, the pines and northern hardwoods are pushing into and displacing the oaks.

Everything, in wave after wave, is moving southward—the glacier front, the snowline, the spruceline, the pineline, and all the animals and other plants. Here and there, because of locally greater snowfall or favorable slope of the land surface, the edge of the glacier temporarily spurts forward across the tundra, and before the spruce forest can retreat, the ice is upon it, burying the ripped-out trees in rock debris under the ice.

Finally, when the ice has crept as far as it can go, the great spruce belt, now much narrower than it had been before the ice invasion, stretches from Maryland, Virginia, and North Carolina westward across Tennessee and Arkansas to the Rocky Mountains. By subtraction at the north and addition at the south the northern oak forest has been pushed all the way to Florida. And if there had been any human residents of the land now occupied by Jacksonville and Tallahassee they would have experienced the same cool temperate climate—without the smoke and other pollutants—in which New Yorkers and Philadelphians now live. This brings to an end the first part of our film.

After a brief intermission the second part of our time-consuming cinema begins. There has been a long gap in time. We now see that the great glacier has begun to retreat, and huge streams of melt water are flowing from it. Back to the north, keeping pace with the ice, go the snowline, the spruceline, the pineline, the oakline, and the permafrost. Back toward the home of their ancestors, moving along in the environment they prefer, go the animal refugees from northern climes—the musk ox and the caribou, the mammoths, the lemmings, the juncos, and many others.

But just like the snowline, the forests and their animals not only move north but they advance, as the snowline rises, up into the mountains. Ever higher and higher they go, dwindling in numbers as the living space diminishes, until finally there is no space at all, and the last surviving animals are replaced by others ascending the mountain below them.

On the higher mountains, though, our film shows remnants of some of the northern species that had been driven the greatest distance to the south, still clinging to summit areas. The big crown of red spruce and balsam fir atop the Great Smoky Mountains is an outlying remnant of the vast spruce belt which has again reached southern Canada in its northward journey. On the flanks of the Great Smokies, trying to move upward into the spruce, are the pines and the northern hardwoods. Here, high on the spruce-clad summits, for several thousand years the wild, sweet song of the blue-headed vireo has floated on the summer air and the junco has flitted through the underbrush, while their nearest relatives have had summer homes in the forests of northern New England and the region around the Great Lakes.

On the top of New Hampshire's Mount Washington the tundra zone still lingers on as one of the most interesting of the remnant biotic islands in eastern North America. For several thousand years it has held out against the spruce pressing hard against it from below.

So on our film we see these ever-shrinking mountaintop islands, as the main band of tundra moves across Ontario and Quebec with the forest zones in hot pursuit. Most of the displaced animals find their way back to former haunts, but some are unable to survive the long trek. The mammoth never got all the way home. Somewhere between the time the ice began its withdrawal and the time it reached Hudson Bay the mammoth perished from the Earth.

Here is where our film ends. What will happen to treelines —the spruce, the pine, the oak—in the future? We know that during the past 100 years or so they made a very slight northward and upward push. But in order to find out we almost certainly will have to see Part Three of our film—10,000 years hence—to tell.

Now let us return again to the period embracing the last 10,000 years. What to name this period seems to have posed a real problem for geologists, and the more we learn about it the more confusing the situation becomes. Names currently in use are *Post-Pleistocene, Post-Wisconsin, Postglacial, Post-Valders,* and the United States Geological Survey tenaciously clings to *Recent.* Each of these has been rather sharply criticized by various individuals from time to time. It can hardly be said, for example, that Postglacial time has come to Antarctica and Greenland or even to much of southeastern Alaska. The current period —so far only ten millenniums in length—is far shorter and not as warm as the last major interglacial period in the Pleistocene. So how can we be certain that the Pleistocene Epoch has passed? And as Professor W. S. Cooper, of tree-ring-glacier-chronology fame, puts it: "With respect to the validity of the term Post-Wisconsin, in order to be quite sure, a waiting period of some thousands of years is prescribed." Professor Cooper has recommended the term *Neothermal,* proposed earlier by Antevs, for this important but as yet unsatisfactorily named part of what he considers Pleistocene time.

The namers are having even more difficulty reaching agreement on titles for the three subdivisions of Neothermal time, especially the long middle part of it. Such products of verbal acrobatics as *Xerothermic, Altithermal, Megathermal,* and *Hypsithermal* are in use, and the less sophisticated name-coiners have contributed *Postglacial Thermal Maximum* and *Climatic Optimum* for this part of geologic time, at the height of which average temperatures apparently were 4° to 5°F. higher than they are today.

For some reason, the first subunit of Neothermal time, the "warming-up" period when temperatures were rising and the ice sheets were rapidly receding, has been neglected by the namers. Though the European pollen stratigraphers recognize distinct pollen zones in this interval, the only name that seems to have been proposed for the time as a whole is *Anathermal.*

The most recent of the three Neothermal time divisions has drawn nearly as much attention from the name-makers as the preceding warmer, much longer period. *Katathermal, Medithermal,* and even *Little Ice Age* have been proposed, but only the latter has appeared much in literature, even though expansion of glaciers during this interval has been minor, actually insignificant when compared with previous ice ages of the Pleistocene. In desperation, some scientists simply refer to this time as "the last third of Postglacial time" or by some similar appellation. And to be constructive as well as critical, Professor Cooper has proposed the term *Hypothermal* for this interval. At the other extreme, Professors R. F. Flint and E. S. Deevey of Yale University, who have contributed much to our knowledge of the Pleistocene, apparently do not feel that this relatively short span of geologic time needs a name.

But this latest time division has distinctive features which do set it apart from the preceding period. Though glaciers have been shrinking more or less steadily for about 100 years in response to rising world temperatures, these ice bodies are still larger than they were at any time since the last remnants of the continental ice sheets vanished from Europe and North America. Pollen profiles in both Europe and North America show clearly by an increase in spruce, and farther south by beech, that the climate of the past 2,000 to 3,000 years has been distinctly cooler than in the preceding longer time interval. In order to see just how different the present (Hypothermal, Little Ice Age, or other term of your choice) is from the Hypsithermal, we should examine the features and events which characterized that warmer period.

It is obvious from the study of pollen profiles that during the maximum warmth of the Hypsithermal interval deciduous forests spread north in Europe and North America into regions which are far too cold to permit their growth today. In temperate and subarctic zones temperatures were several degrees higher than now, and the mean annual temperature of Svalbard rose above the freezing point.

In the Alps peat deposits and the remains of forests at least 1,000 feet above the present treeline indicate the relative mildness of the climate there during the Hypsithermal as compared with today. If the treeline were so much higher, the snowline, too, must have been far higher then than now. Many of the glaciers fed by firn fields which today lie only a few feet above the snowline could not have been there during those warmer times, and today's largest ice streams most certainly were much smaller then.

The same kind of evidence comes from Iceland. Parts of the land now under the icecap Vatnajökull were clothed with dense forests a few thousand years ago, because the outlet glaciers every now and then bring out peat and the trunks of birch trees far larger than any growing in Iceland today. The firnline on Vatnajökull must have been nearly 1,000 feet higher in those warmer times.

Proof of a correspondingly high snowline is also present in many places in North America. Ever since the glaciers at Glacier Bay, Alaska started their big retreat more than 150 years ago, they have been uncovering the remains of forests destroyed and partially buried in rocky debris when the glaciers made their last widespread advance. In places some of the trees, now only shattered stumps, have 300 to 400 annual rings, and at the time they were destroyed they were growing on decayed logs from a much older forest. There were no glaciers in the Rockies south of the Forty-ninth Parallel and none in the Sierra Nevada for several thousand years during Hypsithermal time.

Geologists for a long time have known that many of the saline lakes in the Great Basin and other parts of the arid American Southwest were much larger and that many basins which today are dry contained lakes, some of them fresh-water, during the times when ice sheets lay on the continents. Increased rainfall and the melt water from heavier snow and from the glaciers it formed in the surrounding mountains furnished the water to make these expanded lakes. During these pluvial times Nevada contained more water than Minnesota does today. Much of the northwestern part of the state was covered with a single body of water known now as Lake Lahontan. The shallow and very salty Carson Sink and Pyramid Lake, not far from Reno, are two remnants of this former huge lake.

Death Valley in California, now perhaps the driest and hottest place in North America, contained a lake over 100 miles long. In this lake and in the streams draining into it lived several species of fish.

By far the largest of the pluvial lakes was Bonneville. Occupying the basin in which its principal remnant, Great Salt Lake, now lies, this vast body of water extended into both Nevada and Idaho, and one of its arms reached almost to Arizona. For a while Lake Bonneville was nearly 1,000 feet deep where now the depth of Great Salt Lake is only thirty feet. At that time it overflowed through Red Rock Pass into the Snake River and out through the Columbia to the Pacific Ocean. The lake waters remained at this level long enough for the waves to create beaches, shore cliffs, and other marks of the conspicuous Bonneville shoreline, which today is a pronounced feature high on the mountains surrounding the Great Salt Lake Basin. The Provo, a prominent shoreline about 300 feet below the Bonneville, and a number of others show where the water level made temporary stands as the lake shrank to lower and lower levels.

Eventually, almost all of these lakes dried up, and for several thousand years there were few if any permanent bodies of water in these arid basins. A change to a warmer climate had reduced snowfall in the surrounding mountains and caused the glaciers to disappear. The extraordinary Bonneville Flats, so firm and so flat that they are one of the world's best testing grounds for high-speed automobiles, are composed of salt pre-

TIME (MILLIONS OF YEARS)

ERA	PERIOD	EPOCH	PLEISTOCENE TIME	
			NORTH AMERICA	EUROPE
CENOZOIC (50)	CENOZOIC	PLEISTOCENE(ICE AGE)	Wisconsin	Main Würm
			Minor Interglacial	
			Early Wisconsin	Early Würm
			Sangamon	Riss/Würm Interglacial
			Illinoian	Riss
MESOZOIC (100)	CRETACEOUS		Yarmouth	Mindel/Riss Interglacial
(150)	JURASSIC		Kansan	Mindel
			Aftonian	Günz/Mindel Interglacial
(200)	TRIASSIC		Nebraskan	Günz
PALEOZOIC (250)	PERMIAN	(ICE AGE)		
(300)	PENNSYLVANIAN			
	MISSISSIPPIAN			
(350)	DEVONIAN			
(400)	SILURIAN			
(450)	ORDOVICIAN			
(500)				
(550)	CAMBRIAN			
(600)	PRECAMBRIAN	(ICE AGE)		

300,000 TO 600,000 YEARS B.P.?

1,000,000 TO 2,000,000 YEARS B.P.?

Scale of geologic time, with the Pleistocene Epoch expanded on the right

cipitated from the waters of ancient Lake Bonneville as it dried
up. Radiocarbon dating of lime deposits that formed in these
shrinking bodies of water shows that the time of greatest dryness
came during the Hypsithermal Interval.

With the return of cooler conditions mountain snowfall increased, the present glaciers were born, and the lakes re-formed.
As measured by their salt content and the rate at which salts are
being carried into them today, these new lakes could not have
formed more than 3,000 to 4,000 years ago. Thus their birth
coincides very closely with the onset of the cool period—documented by innumerable pollen profiles elsewhere—which with
minor fluctuations has continued to the present time.

At many places along the shores of all seas and oceans there
are the marks of a former shoreline five to six feet above present
sea level. Its features are unmistakable—wave-cut cliffs, ter-
races, and beaches. Here and there along tropical shores coral
reefs, now abandoned and lifeless, extend to five and six feet
above the sea. So widespread are these features and so uniform
the height at which they occur that the only conclusion one
can draw is that they were made in the not-very-distant geologic
past when sea level the world over stood several feet higher than
it is today. The reason—the climate was warm enough to melt
sufficient ice from the glaciers and icecaps to raise sea level that
much.

Buried in the sands of some of the raised beaches are shells
of types of mollusks which show that the water was warmer
when they lived than it is now. This is especially true in northern
latitudes where a change of a few degrees in water temperature
has a much greater effect on animal life than it does in Low-
Temperate and Equatorial Zones. Some of the species associated
with this ancient strand in the Canadian Arctic islands and along
the North Atlantic coast have perished because now the water is
too cold. For the same reason other species have dwindled in
both size and number. But when the air and the northern sea
waters were as warm as the fossil shells and pollen grains tell
us they once were, it is almost certain that pack ice was absent
from the Arctic Ocean.

And so the present—and to encompass it we are going back
for nearly 3,000 years—has seen the temperature fall to the

point where increased snowfall has caused the rebirth of thousands of mountain glaciers in places where they had been absent for several millenniums. It has seen the formation of lakes in parched valleys in the American West, Mexico, Asia, and in other regions. It has seen plant and animal life make mass migrations under the influence of climatic change. And it has seen the fall of the sea and the return of an ice cover to the Arctic Ocean.

None of these changes has been great in terms of those which took place earlier in the Pleistocene Epoch, but this most recent of all geologic periods has left its mark on the landscape and its own distinctive record has been and is being recorded in the Book of Peat. Even if we are fast approaching the end of this time—and the last 100 years have given us reason to believe so—the record of the period will remain, and as time goes by the diggings of both the archaeologist and the geologist will tell us more about how the life of the world, including man, was affected by its coming.

BEFORE THE NEOTHERMAL

There can be no doubt that long before the first scientific discourses were written about glaciers, Swiss peasants knew that Alpine glaciers at an earlier time had been far more extensive and had covered areas long since occupied by farms and villages. Perhaps it was some of these people who first implanted the idea of an ice age in the minds of scientists.

Hadn't these mountain people on more than one occasion seen ice streams advance across their farms and into their settlements? Hadn't they seen these advances of the ice scrape up rock rubble and pile up masses of scratched and polished boulders in the form of moraines? And after the glaciers had begun to retreat, hadn't they seen the grooved and scraped bedrock surfaces over which the ice had passed? Certainly they must have realized that similar features—moraines, scattered rock rubble, and grooved bedrock—miles down the valleys beyond the glaciers were formed in the same manner when the glaciers were larger.

We don't know when the theory of greatly expanded Alpine

glaciers first came into the mind of man, but the first detailed presentation of it was made in a paper read to the Helvetic Society in 1821 by a Swiss engineer, J. Venetz. Three years later the Norwegian geologist, Jens Esmark, published a paper in which he not only set forth the idea that Norwegian mountains had practically been engulfed by glaciers, but that these streams of ice had also carved out the fiords. Neither Venetz nor Esmark gained many converts to their ideas. In 1834, after Venetz had come to the view that glaciers had covered all of northern Europe as well as the Alps, another Swiss, Jean de Charpentier, went before the Helvetic Society to uphold Venetz's views and to corroborate them with additional proof.

Charpentier's paper drew notable attention, especially from a skeptic and fellow member of the Society by the name of Jean Louis Rodolphe Agassiz. In the summer of 1836 Agassiz, with the avowed purpose of convincing his colleague that his glacier theory was wrong, accompanied Charpentier on a trip to examine glaciers and moraines in the Upper Rhone Valley. The result of the trip was the complete conversion of Agassiz to Charpentier's side. From then on there was no holding Agassiz back. He soon visualized a vast ice sheet extending from the Polar regions as far as the Alps and central Asia.

In 1837 he presented his ideas about an ice age to the Helvetic Society and in 1840 published them in a book, *Études sur les glaciers*, a year before his friend Charpentier, who had been the one to kindle his interest in the idea of an ice age in the first place, was able to publish his own book on the subject. Neither Agassiz nor Charpentier, however, was the first to write about former vast ice sheets over northern Europe. The theory had been set forth by A. Bernhardi, a German forestry professor, in a paper published in 1832. But as sometimes happens, this paper drew very little attention and until a number of years later was not given the credit that was its due. The work of these men—Venetz, Agassiz, Charpentier, and Bernhardi—seems all the more remarkable when we realize that their theories were proposed before any of the world's ice sheets had yet been explored.

Regardless of who was first to propose the glacier theory, it was Agassiz's enthusiasm that really put it across. He took his ideas to Great Britain and finally to America, where his travels over New England and the Great Lakes states soon revealed the scattered boulders and rock rubble which told him an ice age had vanished from America just as it had from Europe.

Though a number of prominent scientists, among them Charles Darwin, were convinced from the start that Agassiz was right, his theory was not generally accepted in England or in America until after the Civil War. And some scientific opposition clung on until the beginning of the present century.

Even while the argument raged, geologists found that there had been not one but several great ice invasions and that each one had plastered its own distinctive layer of debris over the landscape. The times when these great glacier advances of the Pleistocene were made—and at least four of them are recognized—are known as glacial stages. In America the names of these stages, from oldest to youngest, are *Nebraskan, Kansan, Illinoian,* and *Wisconsin.* Another stage, called *Iowan,* is regarded by some geologists as equivalent in status to the other four, and by some as an early substage of the Wisconsin. It is obvious from the names of the various drift sheets that during the early days when geologists were studying and describing them, the Midwest was the scene of the greatest activity.

Nowhere did the Nebraskan ice sheet advance as far as the Kansan, so the only remnants of its drift sheet lie buried beneath later deposits. Wherever they have been found (and there are many places where later ice sheets failed to remove them) they are much more intensely weathered than any of the later drifts.

Though each successively younger drift sheet is less weathered than its immediate predecessor, the intense weathering of all drifts laid down prior to Wisconsin time is a sure sign that each of these ice advances was followed by a long interval—certainly tens of thousands of years in duration—during which the climate warmed up and the ice sheets vanished. In these long, warmer interglacial intervals, vegetation clothed the formerly denuded land and weathering produced a deep soil on the most recent sheet of drift and deepened the soils on the older drifts.

In North America all four of these ice sheets covered essentially the same area even though the intervals between glacier advances were many thousands of years long. In most places, though, the margin of the Wisconsin sheet advanced slightly far-

ther than any of the others, and thus its drift obscures much of
the older ones. But between Indiana and South Dakota it failed,
by as much as 200 miles, to reach the limits of the preceding
sheets. Its till is the least weathered of the four, and because
there are no later tills to cover it, we know far more about the
Wisconsin stage than we do about any of the others.

In America the interglacial stages, like the glacials, have received Midwest names. The warm period following the Nebraskan glaciation is the *Aftonian* interglacial stage. The *Yarmouth*
followed the Kansan glaciation, and the *Sangamon* followed the
Illinoian.

The European continental glacier grew and waned in time
with the North American. In various parts of Europe different
names are used for the corresponding glacial stages. In the Alps
they are—in order of decreasing age—*Günz, Mindel, Riss,* and
Würm. During Würm time the ice sheets made two major advances. It is the earliest one of these which in America is known
as Iowan.

Radiocarbon dating is able to span the entire Wisconsin-
Würm stage which, with its several advances and retreats of the
ice sheets, began nearly 70,000 years ago. Its last major advance
culminated when the North American ice sheet reached as far
as southern Ohio 18,000 to 20,000 years ago.

And we even have a fairly accurate picture of the rate of
advance of this last great glacier across the countryside, because
radiocarbon daters have determined when trees lived which were
overrun by the advancing glacier and buried in the till as the ice
pressed on to the south. Just as at Two Creeks several thousand
years later, the forests in Ohio over which the ice advanced were
largely spruce, and the growth rings of the trees grew progressively thinner during the last fifty to 100 years of their lives, indicating more rigorous conditions as the ice sheet approached.

The advance of the ice was no hasty movement. It reached
the vicinity of Cleveland about 25,000 years ago and then con-
sumed 5,000 years in spreading south across Ohio. In northern
Ohio the ice had edged forward several hundred feet a year, but
by the time it was approaching its limit near the site of Cincinnati
it had slowed to about forty feet annually—less than half a mile
in a lifetime.

On top of the till put down by this ice sheet are the lake deposits and peat bogs which, if we interpret Nature's record correctly, tell us the rate at which the ice edge withdrew to the north whence it had come. The big recession, which began about 18,-000 years ago, was more rapid than the advance. Six thousand years after the retreat had begun the ice front stood, ready to make its last-gasp Valders advance, beyond the Straits of Mackinac 500 miles to the north. This retreat, however, was punctuated with a number of minor advances, each now documented by a terminal moraine.

So the events of the Wisconsin and even some in the later part of the preceding interglacial stage have been timed, thanks to radiocarbon and varves. But what do we do about the earlier glacial stages—the Illinoian, the Kansan, and the Nebraskan—which lie beyond the reach of radiocarbon? For a long time geologists have stamped an estimated age of about 1,000,000 years on the Pleistocene Epoch, based on the amount of weathering of the various till sheets and upon other even more tenuous evidence. But now that radiocarbon has shortened the Wisconsin and brought it closer to the present, some geologists are beginning to feel that the entire Pleistocene may have extended over little more than half that span of time.

Longer-range radioactive time indicators (isotopes of uranium, thorium, potassium, rubidium, and others), though they take us back for billions of years—almost to the beginning of time for the Earth—can bring us no closer to the present than about 1,000,000 years. They decay so slowly that until at least this much time elapses their decay products are too small to be measurable. Uranium–238, an isotope commonly used for age determination, has a half-life of 4,500 million years. The half-life of thorium–232 is much longer—14,000 million years. Furthermore, not only are the minerals which contain these radioactive isotopes rather rare, but they must be collected from an igneous rock if the age determination is to be valid. As soon as such a mineral crystallizes from a molten rock its uranium begins to decay, eventually into lead (uranium–238 yields lead–206; thorium–232 yields lead–208). The amount of this residual lead, provided it was trapped in the mineral so that none escaped over the years, tells the age of the mineral. Since the mineral had its origin at the same time the rock solidified from the molten state, this is also the age of the rock.

The age of a number of uranium-bearing zircon crystals taken from a boulder in an ancient glacial moraine would tell us nothing about the time at which the former glacier existed. Such crystals might tell us the age of the enclosing rock, but that might be millions or even billions of years older than the period of glaciation. In order to determine the age of the glaciation we would have to find a lava flow or other igneous rock associated with the moraine in such a way that we could see the two were about the same age. But unless we could find a sufficient quantity of suitable radioactive minerals in the fine-grained lava we would still be unable to determine when the moraine was deposited. Such fortuitous occurrences are rare—so rare that we are not yet quite certain when the Pleistocene began, nor how long were its glacial and interglacial stages before the Wisconsin. But the gap is fast being closed as scientists find new isotopes with which they can make refinements in the clock of Pleistocene time.

Perhaps Dr. L. S. B. Leakey and his colleagues, who have been digging bones of ancient men (or ape-men) from the rocks of Olduvai Gorge in northern Tanganyika, are close to giving us the answer to the full age of the Pleistocene. The hominid remains at Olduvai are associated with bones of other animals and with tools that almost certainly were used by these primitive "men." This association has led Dr. Leakey to believe this rare hominid, *Zinjanthropus boisei,* lived in early Pleistocene time. Fortunately some of the strata bearing these bones are deposits of volcanic ash. Age determinations on radioactive potassium–40 in feldspars from the ash have yielded an age of 1,750,000 years. But an underlying lava flow, geologically older than the bones, was dated in another laboratory at 1,300,000 years. So at the moment there is a discrepancy, but apparently we have the materials —human remains associated with igneous rocks—with which to date the Pleistocene. After these deposits are better correlated with known early Pleistocene strata elsewhere and after additional analyses are made, a reliable answer probably will be forthcoming. Whether the Pleistocene is nearly 2,000,000 years old, as Leakey believes, or 1,000,000, a more generally accepted figure, it may be that a man was here to witness its dawn.

THOSE OXYGEN ISOTOPES AGAIN

Even in the sunless depths of the sea there are answers to some of the questions about the length of the various subdivisions of Pleistocene time. At the same time Libby was devising his radiocarbon method for determining age, another University of Chicago chemist, Dr. Harold C. Urey, already a Nobel laureate, discovered how to find out the temperature of the water in which a shelled animal—a clam or an oyster, for example—lived at any time for millions of years back into the geologic past.

As in the case of dating with radioactive elements, it was an isotope that did it—this time oxygen–18. Urey found that the ratio of oxygen–18 to oxygen–16 in the calcium carbonate of a shell indicated the temperature of the water at the time the shell was growing—the greater the proportion of oxygen–18, the higher the temperature of the water. It is this same property that has marked the separation of winter and summer layers in the snow, firn, and ice of glaciers.

Among the countless numbers of organisms that comprise the plankton floating in the sunlit surface waters of the sea is a group of one-celled animals known as *Foraminifera*—"Forams" for short—the various members of which secrete some of the most delicately beautiful shells known in Nature. For millions of years these animals have lived in the sea, and for millions of years their dead have rained down into the darkness in what Rachel Carson has termed the "great snowfall" to collect, layer upon layer, in the most changeless environment on the face of the Earth, the bottom of the sea. Their ultimate resting place they share only with shells of other sea-dwelling animals and small quantities of mud, much of it from wind-blown dust and volcanic ash.

Not long after Urey discovered his method of determining paleotemperatures, geochemists were working with oxygen isotopes in tiny Foram shells retrieved from the bottom of the sea. As might be expected, shells from animals that live in the constantly near-freezing temperatures at the bottom of the Caribbean and the Equatorial sections of the Pacific and Atlantic have a different oxygen-isotope ratio than those which float in the warmer surface waters.

But in the dark quietness over large areas at the bottom of
the oceans, sediment, including shells, has been accumulating
uninterruptedly for a tremendously long time. And Foram shells
in cores bored from these bottom sediments have oxygen-isotope ratios showing that surface-water temperatures during the
Pleistocene fluctuated through a range of more than 12°F.

Oxygen-isotope analyses of the shells in these deep sea
cores tell us the temperature and from their radiocarbon content
we can determine the time when they lived. By these means
scientists at the Lamont Observatory have found that around
11,000 years ago, about the time the edge of the Valders ice sheet
began to retreat from its farthest advance in Wisconsin and
Michigan, ocean temperatures rose rather abruptly (in considerably less than 1,000 years) by several degrees. Thus on land
and in the sea there is corroborating evidence for a pronounced
climatic change.

Oxygen isotopes also show an earlier warming of the climate
soon after 18,000 radiocarbon years B.P., which we infer coincides with the beginning of the end for the Wisconsin ice sheet,
soon after it had made its greatest advance—into southern Ohio
and Indiana. Isotopic analyses of shells from several of the longest sediment cores show three main periods of low temperature
preceding the Wisconsin-Würm stage, which probably corre-
spond with the three earlier glacial stages—Illinoian (Riss),
Kansan (Mindel), and Nebraskan (Günz)—though they are beyond the range of radiocarbon and cannot be dated by that
means.

Among the various radioactive elements present in minute
amounts in the mud and ooze on the floor of the ocean abyss are
protactinium and ionium. These two elements are the latest to be
used in what apparently have been successful attempts to figure
the age of ocean sediments. Both elements form from uranium
in sea water, and since they decay at different rates, their ratio is
a direct function of time. Using this method, scientists have extended the Pleistocene time clock to about 150,000 years—at
least for sediment on the ocean floor.

Fortunately, oxygen isotopes tell us the temperature of these
sediments when deposited, and this in turn reflects what was
happening to the World of Ice on land. Radiocarbon and pro-

LATE WISCONSIN CALENDAR

YEARS B.P.	NAMES	DOMINANT POLLEN NORTHERN NEW ENGLAND		IMPORTANT EVENTS	YEARS A.D./B.C.
0	HYPOTHERMAL	Beech declines			
		Beech maximum			
2,000		Hemlock, Spruce return			0
	HYPSITHERMAL / NEOTHERMAL	Oak maximum		*For the first time outflow of → Great Lakes is confined to Niagara and St. Lawrence Rivers*	
4,000		Hemlock, Beech at minimum	LAKE AGASSIZ II		2,000
6,000		Hemlock, Oak, Beech	ST. LAWRENCE SEA	*Ireland severed from Britain*	4,000
8,000		Pine		*Britain separated from → mainland* *Great Lakes outlet through → Mohawk River*	6,000
10,000	WISCONSIN / ANATHERMAL	Spruce, Fir			8,000
	VALDERS	Tundra (ice)			
12,000	TWO CREEKS	Spruce, Birch Tundra		*Lake Bonneville at high stages*	10,000
14,000		Ice sheet covers the land		MAKING OF MIDWEST MORAINES: ALTAMONT, BEMIS, DEFIANCE, VALPARAISO, ETC.	12,000
16,000					14,000
18,000					16,000

Calendar of Late Wisconsin time. *(From various sources)*

tactinium-ionium dating have let us know the rate of sediment accumulation on the sea floor. By applying this yardstick to the lower, older sediments beyond the range of these two methods and by use of temperature determinations, it is possible to make an appoximate time scale for the entire Pleistocene—a scale that shows not only the duration in years of each glacial and interglacial interval, but the temperature of the ocean water as well.

Using this system, Professor Cesare Emiliani of the University of Miami puts the beginning of the first major glacial stage of the Pleistocene (Nebraskan-Günz) at 300,000 years ago, though he believes the Pleistocene itself extends back to 600,000 or more years B.P. There are a number of other workers who also believe that the ice ages began quite some time after the inception of the Pleistocene, but most of these people place both events farther in the past than Emiliani does. The evidence Professor Emiliani has found in the cores leads him to believe that in this early half of the Pleistocene there were no continental ice sheets, but periods of mountain glaciation occurred many times.

Whether Professor Emiliani's time scale is accurate or not—and he has stated that his conclusions are only preliminary—what he and others have done presages a time in the not far future when mud and shells from the bottom of the sea shall give us a precise time-temperature scale for the whole of the Pleistocene, and perhaps for much more of geologic time. Already, because each year's contribution of sediment and shells to the ocean bottom in places is microscopically thin, some of the cores brought to the surface span tens of millions of years. Two cores collected from the bottom of the central Caribbean by research vessels of Woods Hole Oceanographic Institute and Lamont Observatory revealed that nearly 2,000 years were required to deposit one inch of sediment.

There are other vast areas on the ocean floors where the rate of deposition is infinitely slower. In longer cores, to be obtained with equipment like that used for the Mohole or by deep-diving submarines that will enable drilling to be done directly on the ocean floor, scientists face the exciting prospect of being able to date the primeval sea that filled the first ocean basin on Earth.

❀❀❀❀❀❀❀

16

❀❀❀❀❀❀❀

The Ice Sheet Makes
a New World

❀❀❀❀❀❀❀

❀❀❀❀❀❀❀ THE BOTTOM of the sea will someday lay
bare its most guarded secrets about the World of Ice, but the
account which Nature has embedded there is now open only to
the eyes of the scientist, and so far even he must rely on dredges,
coring devices, and cameras to secure it, so that it may be studied
in the laboratory. And only after days, weeks, or months of careful analysis will the story these things have to tell be known.

But it is the marks on the face of the land that tell us
most about what has happened to the World of Ice. These are the
tumbling waterfalls, the lakes and the swamps, the boulder-
strewn moraines, the scoured and grooved hilltops over more
than a fourth of the Earth's surface, and the ancient shorelines
and abandoned coral reefs thousands of miles beyond the borders of former icy lands. These signs of early dramatic events are
not reserved for the scientist. They are the ones that all of us can
see and, in seeing, understand. And their number is legion.

We have already looked at some of these signs of conflict between Earth and ice: mountain ranges scored by great ice-carved cirques, horns, and deep U-shaped valleys; the magnificent fiords and countless lakes and bogs. These are but a few of the numberless traces of the ice of yore. Most likely there isn't a country in all the world that doesn't bear somewhere within its borders signs of the World of Ice.

During one of the earlier Pleistocene glacial stages glaciers spread over nearly a third of the Earth's land, including areas now covered by many of the world's largest cities—New York, Chicago, Montreal, Glasgow, London, Hamburg, Berlin, Leningrad, and Moscow are only a few. Today the landscape over this vast expanse—larger than the entire North American continent—bears conspicuous features directly attributable to the ice which earlier moved across it.

By virtue of their newness, the marks left by the latest major glacial advances (in Wisconsin-Würm time) are by far the sharpest, and it is from them that we have learned most about Pleistocene glacial activity. One of the greatest performances of the former ice sheets was the dumping of billions of tons of rock debris scraped from the vast stretches over which they passed. All this material, whether it now lies where the ice dumped it or where streams of melt water flowing out from the glacier spread it, is known as *drift*, a name given to it long before Agassiz's time by Englishmen when they realized that the boulders and other rock rubble covering much of their land could not have been deposited by streams. So they called upon an unusual origin—a great but brief inundation by the sea during which the material was dropped from drifting icebergs. The name *drift* was so firmly entrenched by the time Agassiz convinced the scientific world of the true origin of the stuff that the word persisted, and today it is firmly established in the glacial vocabulary.

Much of the glacial drift is now in the form of great parallel hummocky moraines stretching across the northern United States and southern Canada and across north-central Europe. Each of these moraines, a narrow strip of hilly, hummocky land noticeably higher and more irregular than its surroundings, marks the line where the ice sheet temporarily paused or to which it made a minor advance during its retreat to the north.

The ice, perhaps rarely moving more than a few hundred feet a year, pushed and carried rock forward to these recessional terminal moraines, and so they grew slowly. At times when the edge of the ice moved along, plowing into and uprooting the moraine previously deposited, blocks of ice broken from the much-crevassed terminus were buried in the growing moraine. Melting of these blocks after withdrawal of the glacier created water-filled depressions which we call *kettle-holes*, or just plain *kettles*. Such oscillations of the ice-front gave individual moraines a width of several miles and their very irregular but distinctive surface topography—knobs and kettles.

In eastern North America the ice in its latest great advance moved out across the present shore of New England to drop its load of debris in a terminal moraine now largely under water. Its irregular topography on the sea floor has been found by soundings across the Gulf of Maine from Nova Scotia to Cape Cod. South of the Gulf of Maine, where the moraine lies closer to shore, its top is exposed above the water in several places. In this section there are two prominent, nearly parallel moraines lying from one to twenty-five miles apart. The innermost one, also the youngest, is a conspicuous feature of Cape Cod. It stretches, an irregular lake-studded and hummocky band, across the upper arm of the Cape from Orleans Beach through Barnstable to Woods Hole. For the next sixteen miles it is a string of islands—Naushon, Pasque, Cuttyhunk, and several smaller ones. Between the islands and Narragansett Pier on the mainland it dips out of sight beneath the waters of Rhode Island Sound. It lies across southern Rhode Island and the east end of Long Island Sound, where it forms Fishers and Plum islands. As the Harbor Hill moraine, it extends across Long Island from the tip of the northern fishtail at Orient Point to central Brooklyn. In Rhode Island it is known as the Charlestown moraine, in the vicinity of Woods Hole as the Buzzards Bay moraine, and farther east on Cape Cod as the Sandwich.

South of Massachusetts and Rhode Island the outermost of the two moraines lies entirely off shore and makes the hilly and pitted northern parts of Nantucket and Martha's Vineyard islands. Block Island is another above-water part of this moraine. Here and there some of its typical features have been bulldozed off to make room for housing developments, but it can be traced, as the Ronkonkoma moraine, all the way from the easternmost tip of Long Island at Montauk Point across Suffolk and Nassau Counties to merge with (actually it passes beneath it) the Harbor Hill moraine south of Manhasset Bay. Lake Ronkonkoma, at the geographic center of Long Island, is a kettle-hole on this moraine, and Lake Success, near which the United Nations met while waiting for the completion of its present quarters, is another; it is at the point where the two great strings of glacial debris, Harbor Hill and Ronkonkoma, come together.

The Harbor Hill continues westward through Forest Park, past tennis-famous Forest Hills (named for the moraine). It crosses the entrance to New York Harbor at the Narrows, and from there it can be readily traced across Staten Island and northern New Jersey into Pennsylvania.

Immediately south of both the Harbor Hill and Ronkonkoma moraines, and of their counterparts farther east, the land is nearly flat and lakeless, contrasting sharply with the higher bumpy topography of the moraines themselves. These plains are very marked along the south shore of Cape Cod and in the southern halves of Nantucket and Martha's Vineyard, and they are especially striking on Long Island. Beneath their smooth surfaces is an extensive sheet of sand and gravel washed out from the melting ice sheet while the terminal moraine was accumulating. This glacial outwash is the reason for the near-absence of streams over much of Long Island. Most of the rain sinks into the porous and highly permeable sand and gravel and then percolates slowly southward in a subterranean course toward the ocean. This is the reason why homeowners south of the moraines on Long Island are assured of a water supply when they drill into the ground beneath their homes. Despite the huge number of septic tanks and other sources of pollution, most of this water is relatively pure, since to reach a well it must filter through a healthy volume of sand, regardless of the distance it moves.

The moraines and outwash of Long Island also control the character of the beaches. On the north shore where the waves are chewing into the rocky moraine, the beaches are bouldery. On the south shore where the only materials the waves have to work with are the sands and fine gravels in the outwash, they have sorted out the fine material and thrown it up into magnificent beaches.

It is on glacial outwash plains such as southern Long Island that housing developments and airports have their most ideal locations. The surface of the outwash is smooth and nearly flat; the material has good drainage properties and can be easily excavated. The airport constructors, however, sometimes forsake the outwash to put their runways on artificial fill dumped into swamps and bodies of water. Sometimes they do this to bring the airfield closer to the city, sometimes because the swampland is relatively cheap (but not after the word has got around), and for other reasons that perhaps only the politicians will ever understand.

The moraines just about get lost in some of the mountainous sections of northern Pennsylvania, and nowhere are they pronounced. But west of the mountains from central Ohio to North Dakota these glacier dumps, after several thousands of years' exposure to the elements, are still the most prominent landscape features.

As in the east, they are ridges pockmarked by innumerable kettles—now lakes, ponds, and bogs—and mounds. Most of the moraines are several hundred feet high and between one and ten miles wide. Their irregular topography has not been particularly suited to agriculture, so large sections are still wooded, another feature which adds to their contrast with the surrounding prairie. It would be difficult to single out any one of these moraines and say: "Here is the greatest of all." The Defiance moraine swings around the western end of Lake Erie in a great arc from near Ann Arbor, through Defiance, Ohio, then eastward between Akron and Cleveland to the northwest corner of Pennsylvania. The Ohio Turnpike cuts through the moraine in two places— just north of Akron and about twenty miles west of Toledo. Four or five other equally large moraines lie outside of this moraine in Ohio and Indiana.

Northern Illinois is covered with similar moraines. Between Peoria and Terre Haute the conspicuous Shelbyville moraine marks the farthest extension of the Wisconsin ice sheet.

The big Valparaiso moraine curves around the south end of Lake Michigan just outside of Chicago and Gary and extends north along the east shore of the lake.

One of the greatest of all Wisconsin moraines is the Bemis, which arcs in a great loop from the southeast corner of North Dakota southward to Des Moines, then northward beyond Minneapolis and St. Paul. Just north of Des Moines at the apex of its great bend, it is more than twenty-five miles wide. The Altamont moraine, just inside the Bemis, is equally extensive.

In Europe all the major Pleistocene ice sheets emanated from a principal center in Scandinavia and a lesser one in the highlands of the British Isles. During times of maximum glacierization sheets from these two centers merged to make one ice cover over the whole of northern and western Europe. The largest of these merged sheets extended as far south as a line connecting London, Amsterdam, Leipzig, and Krakow, and in the valley of the Dnieper a lobe pushed out to within 200 miles of the Black Sea, over 1,000 miles from the main center of ice dispersal in Scandinavia.

In later glacial stages the ice repeatedly advanced down across the Baltic Sea and onto the North German Plain. Some of the moraines made by the more recent advances have changed very little since they were deposited. One of the most prominent, the Brandenburg, extends from Denmark through Hamburg and Berlin and then on to the east. The Frankfurt-Poznan and the Pomeranian moraines lie from fifty to 100 miles farther north and together with the Brandenburg embrace the lake district of northern Germany and East Prussia.

Though these advances reached different destinations on the North German Plain, to the west they all terminated at about the same place along the east edge of the North Sea Basin. There, with each succeeding advance, one moraine was dumped upon another until they built up the backbone of a peninsula that now almost seals off the Baltic from the North Sea and makes most of the ground occupied by the nation of Denmark.

So, like the Long Islanders, the Danes are where they are largely because the big ice sheets piled up rocky debris, scraped from other lands, in a place which otherwise would now be mostly covered by the sea. Denmark's two contrasting shorelines, like those of Long Island, also owe their character directly to the activity of the ice sheets. The irregular east coast and its many bordering islands are in the heart of the moraine belt, while the other side of this tidy little peninsula is a flat outwash plain on the smooth surface of which the waves of the North Sea have built up the long, straight, sandy beaches of Jutland.

When the big North American ice sheets spread southward from Canada they gouged out the weak shales and limestones in the lowlands now occupied by the Great Lakes, grinding them into clay and pushing and spreading this tremendous load of debris toward the south. So great was this mass of drift that it clogged the under part of the ice, forcing the glacier to flow over it, thus at one fell swoop burying the hills and valleys of the preglacial landscape under a blanket of drift and protecting them from further gouging and scraping. This buried face of the Midwest we cannot see, but we know it is there because of countless wells that have been drilled down through the drift sheet to it. Today we can drive for hours across the fertile farmlands on the smooth surface of the drift that was plastered over a former landscape of hills and valleys, and not see a single trace of this preglacial topography.

This part of the drift sheet is known as the *ground moraine,* in contrast to the end moraines that here and there punctuate its gently rolling surface. Ground moraine covers much of the northern United States, southern Canada, and the western Canadian Plains. In Ohio it averages nearly 100 feet thick. In Iowa the glacier plastered it down nearly twice this thick.

The shales of the Midwest yielded much more readily to the ice than did the granite and other hard bedrock of New England's hills and mountains. Through thousands of years of scraping across these resistant rocks, the ice sheet naturally was able to break off a lot of fragments, but the quantity of this material was far less than that acquired by the ice where it crossed weaker, more easily erosible rock. So today both New England and Ohio are covered with ground moraine. Yet in Ohio one seldom sees a glacial boulder or cobble, and there probably isn't a single field bounded by a stone fence. In New England, on the other hand, where the drift may be only fifteen or twenty feet thick, the land is literally a sea of stones. Every field—and they

are much smaller than in Ohio—for miles in every direction is
outlined by fences of stone. Though these fences have grown
slowly through the years as farmers have picked and dug more
and more stones from the land, there still are many fields too
stony for the plow.

The North American and European drift sheets have striking similarities. Between the big end moraines on the North
German Plain and in eastern U.S.S.R., the drift is thick and contains a lot of clay scraped from the large area of weak rock
underlying the lowlands of Estonia, Latvia, and the Baltic Sea.
North of the Baltic Sea and also in Ireland, Scotland, and northern England where there are many outcroppings of more resistant rocks, the landscape—stone fences, scattered boulders, and
all—looks much like New England.

Glacier-transported rock fragments—boulders, cobbles, and
smaller pieces—whether embedded in till or lying loosely on the
surface are known as *erratics* if they are different from the bedrock on which they rest. It is largely from erratics that the stone
fences and walls of New England and the British Isles have
been made. Wherever erratics were abundant in Europe, men
began using them for construction thousands of years ago. Stone
rings and other religious or ceremonial structures are among
the oldest such things that still stand. Countless buildings in
northern Europe, including some of the oldest castles yet standing, were made from glacial erratics. Granite erratics from
Sweden have been used to build entire villages in North Germany.

Some erratics are too large to be handled, even by the
heaviest earth-moving machinery. There are countless erratics
weighing over 100 tons, and many are known which weigh
several thousand tons. There appears to be no limit to the size
of a rock a moving glacier can transport. One of the best-known
glacial boulders in the United States is the Madison erratic near
Conway, New Hampshire, measuring 88′ x 39′ x 37′. There are
even larger ones in the British Isles.

A lot of the large erratics are composed of granite and related resistant rocks, but there are places where incredibly large
slabs of limestone and other sedimentary rocks have been ripped
loose and transported by ice sheets. In Huntingdonshire, about

fifty miles north of London, an entire village has been built on top of one of these gigantic boulders. Single quarries have been operated for years in individual erratics. In Scandinavia and North Germany there are even larger erratics—up to several miles long.

The farther a boulder is transported, the smaller it becomes because of the shattering and grinding to which it is subjected. So obviously the colossal limestone erratics of Europe have not been transported for more than a few miles. Some of the big boulders of granite, however, now rest as much as fifty miles from the place where the ice ripped them loose from the bedrock.

Some of the smaller erratics—only those composed of resistant rocks—have been carried much farther. If these rocks are of distinctive types that can be distinguished readily from others, they can be traced back to their bedrock source. Thus they become *indicators* of the direction of former ice movement. It was by doing just this that geologists were able to determine the direction of flow of the former ice sheets and eventually to find the centers from which they spread.

In the moraines on Long Island are many granite fragments that the glacier tore loose from the high peaks in the Adirondacks. Maine and New Hampshire have contributed many of the rock fragments in the moraines on Cape Cod. Boulders containing native copper were carried from northern Michigan nearly 600 miles to southern Illinois. Somewhere between 700 and 800 miles seems to be the limit of long-distance glacier transportation, as no erratics have been found farther away from their source.

Where the ice sheet passed over elevated rock outcrops, the fragments torn from them were concentrated in their lee in long streaks or bands. Today these streaks of erratics are convincing indicators of the direction of former ice motion. Slight variations in the direction of ice flow over thousands of years caused most of these indicator streaks to fan out with increasing distance from the outcrop. Among the many prominent *indicator fans* within the North American drift sheet, most are in New England because of its abundance and variety of outcropping rock.

In northeastern Rhode Island, on the outskirts of Woonsocket, is a small, rather inconspicuous eminence known as Iron Hill. The dark, iron-filled igneous rock (named cumberlandite) of which it is composed fills the throat of an ancient volcano and is unlike almost every other rock in New England. Although barely 100 feet high, Iron Hill has found a lasting place in the annals of geology, because the ice sheet, in grinding over it, tore loose an uncountable number of fragments which now, spread out to the south, form a most remarkable indicator fan. From an apex at the hill, where the rock exposure is barely a quarter of a mile wide, this fan in an ever-widening band extends southward through Pawtucket and Providence, then down the length of Narragansett Bay, across Newport, where its width is seven miles, and finally out into the Atlantic Ocean forty miles from the outcrop.

Some of the other New England indicator fans are longer than the Iron Hill fan. In Europe several extend from central Sweden to the outer limits of the drift sheet in northern Germany. Norwegian erratics have been pushed across the floor of the North Sea all the way to England. Several fans with apexes in southern Finland reach across the Gulf of Finland into Estonia and Latvia.

Scattered through the drift in eastern Finland are many erratics bearing ore minerals of copper. Realizing that wherever they came from, there might be a valuable ore deposit, prospectors did some geologic sleuthing by plotting the positions of all the known copper-bearing rock fragments. Finally the plot took the form of a fan, at the apex of which they reasoned the bedrock deposit ought to be. Sure enough, after drilling a number of holes down through the cover of drift which mantled the site, the ore, later to become Finland's most important copper deposit, was discovered.

In several cases fans lead back to an apex where there is no source rock—the glacier has scraped all of it away. This is rare but it has happened where small remnants of a once-extensive, nearly horizontal bed of rock cap the tops of hills. The ice can uproot and tear away these slabs, just as it did the huge slabby limestone erratics in Great Britain, removing every trace of the former bedrock. Then the only relics of the former layer are the erratics scattered through the drift.

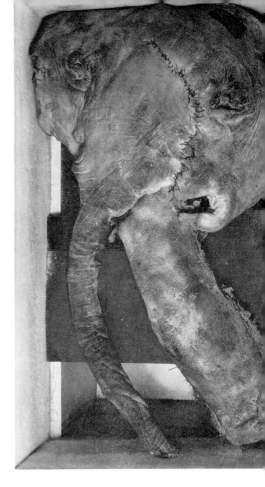

The 21,000-year-old Alaskan baby mammoth in its freezer at American Museum of Natural History. Only the trunk and the skin from the face and one foreleg were recovered from frozen ground near Fairbanks, Alaska.

An ice wedge in frozen ground exposed by placer mining. Wilbur Creek near Livegood, Alaska. Similar wedges probably connect to form a subterranean honeycomb of ice.

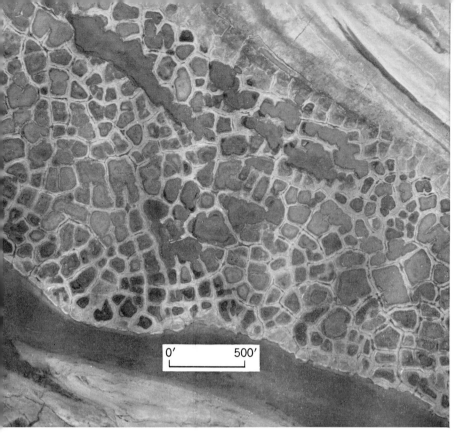

Vertical view of patterned ground in permafrost region on Ikpikpuk River delta, sixty miles southeast of Barrow, Alaska. Beneath lines are intersecting ice wedges made by freezing of water in ground which cracked because of intense cold.

Heat from furnace, located in basement beneath front of house, thaws ground ice, causing building to sink lower and lower. Bert and Mary's Roadhouse, Mile Post 275.8, Richardson Highway, Alaska.

A cluster of cryoconite holes (algae pits) on Greenland ice sheet. Heat from living algae melts ice and causes algae colonies to sink deeper into surface of ice sheet.

Cryoconite hole, more than four feet in diameter, formed by coalescence of smaller holes. Greenland.

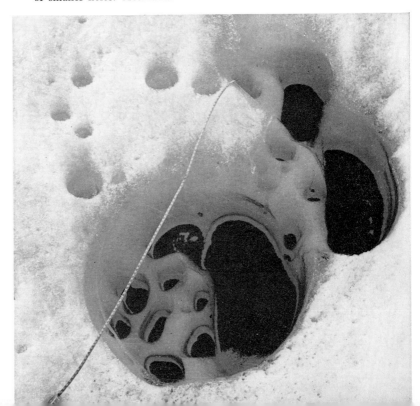

Recession of Columbia Glacier, Prince William Sound, Alaska. Plants have not yet begun to grow on the newly deposited jumble of moraine in foreground. 1931.

Twenty-six years later a new forest of willows and spruce has begun to clothe moraine, and vegetation in kettle hole in foreground is the first stage in formation of peat. Trimline between old and new forests on right. 1957.

Recession of Muir Glacier. In 1929 ice front lay on moraine in foreground; by 1941, when photo was taken, it had receded three and a half miles. McBride Glacier enters Muir from right.

By 1950 Muir had receded another three miles up Bay and had separated from McBride (just visible in center of view). After twenty-one years a few shrubs grow on moraine.

Emmons Glacier on Mount Rainier has left a conspicuous trimline where its edge has withdrawn from mature forest. Lower part of glacier is heavily covered with moraine on which a new forest will soon begin to grow.

The terminus of Warm Creek Glacier, British Columbia, lies well inside a pronounced forest trimline from which it has recently shrunk.

A sharp trimline is visible on far side of Great Aletsch Glacier, indicating height to which glacier extended before current recession. Marjelen Lake lies to right of big bend.

...ares Glacier advancing into ...ture forest. Crushed trees ...d much organic debris are ...xed with till on moraine in ...eground. Prince William ...und, Alaska.

Mendenhall Glacier terminates in Mendenhall Lake four miles from Juneau airport. Upper edge of barren zone on far side of glacier is trimline from which glacier has shrunk during this century. Dark line 500 feet above lake (arrow) is mid-eighteenth-century trimline. Below it 100-foot Sitka spruce have grown since ice retreated.

Trimlines in Lituya Bay, Alaska. Photo taken in 1953. Lowest trimline, made by giant wave of 1936, is very prominent. Much less striking trimline, from giant wave of 1853–4, is marked by arrow.

Aerial view taken one month after Lituya's giant wave of 1958, about five miles from its origin. Denuded zone is more than one-fourth mile wide. Dense spruce forest once extended nearly to shore. Trees stripped of branches litter washed area.

Nunatak Glacier, Yakutat Bay, Alaska in 1938. In 1908, glacier filled this fiord, was 2,000 feet thicker at terminus. It covered land around which glacier bends and distant mountain to height of hanging glaciers. So rapid has been recession, no vegetation has reached uncovered area in this view.

Coring a spruce pushed over by
advance of Hole-in-the-Wall Glac
Taku Inlet, Alaska. Surround
rubble is typical terminal mora
—clay and all sizes of rock fr
ments.

About 150 years was required
deposit of these varves—two lay
of sediment laid down during a s
gle year—in a former glacial l
near Puget Sound, Washington. M
varves are much thinner than th

LAKE HURON

0   ½

Mile

Aerial photo of high-level beaches along a former glacial lake that filled basin of Lake Huron several thousand years ago. Vegetation of sandy beaches differs from that on lower ground between them. Huron County, Michigan.

Highest terrace cut by waves of ancient Lake Bonneville on side of Wasatch Mountains is nearly 1,000 feet above Great Salt Lake. Lake Bonneville began to disappear when last big ice sheet was withdrawing from eastern North America.

NORTH

0 ½
Mile

Aerial photo of long narrow drumlins in Charlevoix County, Michigan. When former ice sheet moved across this country from northwest to southeast it dragged its till into long, narrow mounds.

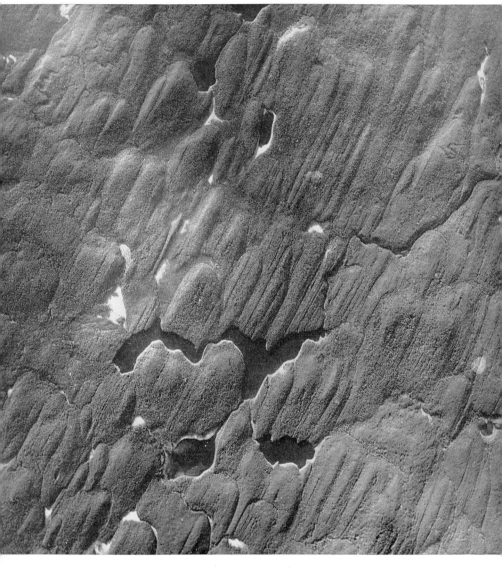

Aerial view of closely packed drumlins in Canada. Direction of former ice motion (upper right to lower left) is readily apparent.

Two drumlins in Wayne County, New York. Like most drumlins these two have their steepest end facing direction from which former ice sheet came—in this case from right (north).

A recessional terminal moraine north of Lake Ontario. This one was deposited between two lobes of former ice sheet.

An esker—a long, often winding, ridge of sand and gravel deposited by a melt-water stream on or under a stagnating ice sheet. This one near Fort Ripley,

Not all the unusual or even rare erratics are indicators. Sometimes they either lead nowhere or up a blind alley. One such quest had its beginning back in 1876 on a farm in southeastern Wisconsin. The farmer, in digging a well into glacial drift, found a peculiar glassy stone, which he saved as an oddity or possible thing of value. Finally, after displaying their curiosity for seven years, the farmer's wife sold it for one dollar to a jeweler in Milwaukee. Later when it was discovered that the thing was a sixteen-carat diamond, the new owner sold it to Tiffany's for a considerable sum of money. And as might be expected, the finder brought suit against the jeweler. The case was fought through the courts for a long time, finally all the way to the Supreme Court of the state of Wisconsin, which decided that the jeweler was entitled to the money he received for the stone, since he was ignorant of its value when he bought it.

The diamond find in Wisconsin, of course, set off a rush of searching for more of these elusive minerals in the drift sheet of the prairie states. As far as finding a diamond deposit is concerned, the search was fruitless, but it did result in the discovery, over a period of years, of more diamonds—all in the drift—five in Wisconsin, three in southern Indiana, and one each in Michigan and Ohio. One of these, found a few miles north of the original find, was a giant of twenty-one carats.

There undoubtedly are large numbers of diamonds in the drift of the states in which the eleven have been found, but they will be much more difficult to find than the proverbial needle in the haystack. As a last resort the haystack could be removed, piece by piece, until the needle is found.

Diamonds the world over occur in a special kind of igneous rock known as kimberlite, and it is almost always in the form of pipes—former volcanic conduits—that extend to great depths below the surface. In the fluid rock deep within these ancient volcanic throats, under pressure and heat greater than most other minerals can stand, diamonds are born. Geologists are almost certain that there is no such bedrock beneath the drift in or near the areas where the diamond erratics have been found.

Well, where, then, did they come from? Glacial grooves on the infrequent bedrock outcrops and indicator rocks in the drift point northward from the diamond localities in converging lines to a common area somewhere in the muskeg-choked and drift-covered part of Ontario that lies between Lake Huron and James Bay. In fact, an organized commercial exploration was made in this region in an effort to find the "mother lode." But again it was a case of looking for the needle in the haystack.

Yet geologists know that somewhere there is a bedrock source for the eleven glacier-borne diamonds. The possibility that the ice sheet has worn away all of the diamond-bearing bedrock, as it did some of the European limestone layers, is extremely remote. The deep vertical pipes in which diamonds occur have a better chance to outlive attacks by glaciers than almost any other type of rock formation on Earth. The source may be near the area where the unsuccessful exploration was conducted, or it might be even farther north. Diamonds, the hardest of all substances, can survive a long glacier ride. And there is some proof that these eleven have done just that, since the rock in which they were originally embedded has been completely worn away, leaving the diamonds as the only remnants of the source material still remaining in the drift. Someday we may find that they hold the long-distance record for glacial erratics.

So the rarest of all erratics—eleven diamonds scattered through the drift of an area larger than the state of Ohio—tell us that somewhere in the wilds of Canada there is a diamond deposit, but so far they have not told us where.

STREAMLINED DRIFT

It was late afternoon, the weather clear, the sun low in the west. The plane had just taken off from Syracuse and was gaining altitude for the run to Buffalo. Some of the passengers were talking, some dozing, some reading, and a few others, more interested in the outside vista, were straining at the windows eagerly watching the landscape slowly taking shape beneath them. Swiftly but subtly a new world passed below the plane. All the way to Lake Ontario and west as far as eyes pressed against the windows could see stretched a vast plain covered with hundreds—thousands—of streamlined mounds, all with an elliptical shape more pointed at the southern end than at the north, all with their long diameters lined up in a north-south direction. Dark crescent-shaped shadows, cast by the setting sun, blotted out the land on the east side of every mound, giving to the landscape an eerie, symmetrically splotched, out-of-this-world aspect. Some of those who saw this mounded, streamlined landscape quickly glanced at the other passengers to reassure themselves that they had not passed into the "Twilight Zone" and were now somewhere between the real and the unreal. Satisfied, they turned back to Earth again to watch mile after mile of this strange land pass beneath them.

The view that these people found so absorbing is indeed a rare though not unique piece of Earthly real estate. The stretched-out mounds, with a shape similar to the inverted bowl of a spoon, are part of the ground moraine. They are known by the Irish word, *drumlin,* and were molded or carved by the ice sheet as it passed over the thick drift building up beneath it. Some formed in the lee of bedrock hills, others formed where balling up of the clay-containing drift created mounds which were instantly molded into streamlined forms pointing in the direction of flow as the glacier continued to move over them.

Most of the drumlins are about a mile long, a third as wide, and from fifty to 200 feet high. In the area north of the Finger Lakes between Syracuse and Niagara Falls, there are approximately 10,000 of them. In this field there are few drumlins that lie more than half a mile from their nearest neighbor, and many are closer.

A similar but smaller cluster of drumlins covers more than 1,000 square miles in southeastern Wisconsin. There most of them are lined up in a northeast-southwest direction, since the ice that molded them moved down through the Green Bay lowland toward the southwest.

Another large cluster extends from central New Hampshire across Boston and Worcester into eastern Connecticut. In this field, because of the irregularity of the preglacial landscape onto which the moraine was plastered, the drumlins are not as noticeable as on the Lake Ontario plain and the prairie of southern Wisconsin. Some of the 200 drumlins in and around

Boston, however, are very prominent, and a few of them—
Bunker, Breed's, and Beacon Hills—are deeply rooted in United
States history. A number of the drumlins have been made even
more distinguished by being surmounted with hospitals and
soldiers' homes. All of the islands in Boston Harbor are partly
submerged drumlins, and, like Breed's and Bunker Hills, their
alignment shows that the ice which made them came from the
northwest.

The largest drumlin field in the world covers a vast area
of the plains of northwestern Canada. These drumlins differ
from most others in being narrow and much longer, and they
make the landscape even more streamlined than in the other
fields. Much of southern Finland is covered by a field of drumlins
like those in New York and Wisconsin.

LAKES, LAKES, EVERYWHERE

When the Minnesotans advertise their state as the "land of ten
thousand lakes," whether they know it or not, they are being very
conservative and are indirectly belittling the lake-making capacity of the last big ice sheet to cover their state. Almost all the
lakes in Minnesota—like those in Wisconsin, Michigan, New
England, and all other places inside the terminal moraines of
the last big ice sheets—owe their origin to the action of those
glaciers. The number of these lakes is astronomical. There are
vast expanses in Canada and Finland where there is more
water than land and where it is possible to go by canoe for
thousands of miles, across one glacial lake after another, with
infrequent, insignificant portages between.

Most of the very large fresh-water lakes in the Northern
Hemisphere were created by glaciers. Among these are the Great
Lakes, Great Bear and Great Slave Lakes, and Lake Winnipeg
in North America, and Lake Ladoga, straddling the boundary
between Finland and the U.S.S.R., and its neighbor, Lake Onega.

Some of the limitless number of glacial lakes, like the Great
Lakes, fill basins gouged out of bedrock by the grinding and
quarrying action of the ice. Others were created when the ice
made dams by dumping moraines across valleys, and count-

less numbers more, mostly small, fill depressions on the uneven surfaces of the moraines.

If lakes are now abundant in these formerly ice-covered lands, try to visualize what they must have been like just after the ice withdrew, when the myriads of peat bogs and the endless muskegs of Canada were also lakes. If all these bogs and muskegs could be reconverted to lakes, then the aspect over much of Canada and other parts of the glaciated world would certainly be one that could be described as an island-studded fresh-water sea.

The rarity of floods in Wisconsin, Michigan, Minnesota, and other glaciated areas where lakes and bogs are abundant is mainly due to the gift of the ice sheets. The thick drift itself absorbs a lot of water. The lakes are storage reservoirs, and the bogs and marshes are great sponges, trapping and holding quantities of water, letting it flow out evenly into the streams. This even flow is a peculiarity of streams in glaciated regions, especially if bogs are common. That we do not appreciate this wonderful gift of the ice sheets is quite evident in the frenzy with which we go about filling and draining our swamps and marshes to make them more "productive." Unfortunately, it will ever be thus; there are some lessons that man simply cannot learn.

Not only were there more lakes at those earlier times, but some of them, since vanished from the scene, were far larger than any lakes now in existence. These enormous lakes were all formed against the edge of the ice sheets themselves. The most ideal places for the formation of such bodies of water were in Canada and west-central Europe where large rivers flowed north into Hudson Bay and the Baltic.

The greatest of all these ice-dammed lakes was named for the founder of the glacial theory. Lake Agassiz was created when the last big ice sheet in its retreat reached what is now the northeast corner of South Dakota. From here on, the edge of the ice retreated across a land that sloped in the direction of retreat, all the way to Hudson Bay. The Nelson and Red Rivers, flowing down this slope, were blocked by the ice and, together with great volumes of melt water pouring from the glacier itself, created a great lake which became ever larger and larger as the ice front withdrew. This lake spilled out to the south through a giant stream known as the Warren River. The voluminous out-pouring of water, flowing across Minnesota into the Mississippi, scoured out a wide valley now occupied by Traverse and Big Stone Lakes, between Minnesota and South Dakota, and by the Minnesota River. This valley is far too large to have been carved by the Minnesota River of today.

After the edge of the ice had retreated north of the present site of Winnipeg, Lake Agassiz found a lower outlet that took its waters into Lake Superior. Finally, just before the outlet into Hudson Bay was uncovered, when Lake Agassiz attained its greatest size, it stretched northward from the northeast corner of South Dakota for 800 miles and covered parts of North Dakota, Minnesota, Saskatchewan, and fully half the province of Manitoba. The lake was then more extensive than the present-day Great Lakes combined.

Then, when the spruce forest was creeping across the abandoned bed of old Lake Chicago at Two Creeks, the ice re-treated far enough for Agassiz's waters to drain off into Hudson Bay, and the lake died. But it soon was reincarnated when the ice sheet moved forward in the Valders advance and the waters were blocked again, and another Lake Agassiz (Lake Agassiz II) was born.

Lake Agassiz II—and to some extent the earlier one, too —has bequeathed us much evidence of its existence. As soon as the lake came into being, silt and clay, washed from the sur-rounding moraine-covered land, began to fill it. All this material was spread over the moraine on the floor of the lake in slowly compacting thin layers, eventually to a thickness of forty or fifty feet. The top of this fill, one of the smoothest extensive plains in North America, is devoted largely to the growing of wheat. The smoothness of this plain seems especially striking when one enters it from the east, say, on U.S. Highway 52 or Interstate Highway 94 from Minneapolis. For more than 100 miles, from St. Cloud, past Sauk Center and Fergus Falls, one travels across hummocky lake-studded moraine. Then suddenly, about thirty miles from Fargo, the car emerges from the hills onto the smooth, lakeless, cleanly cultivated bed of old Lake Agassiz. To the north, to the south, and to the west the smooth, seemingly flat plain stretches to the horizon, every inch of its fertile soil covered with field after endless field of wheat and potatoes.

The former edge of the lake is marked by a beach—a long narrow ridge ten to fifteen feet high—where the waves rolling against the ancient shoreline piled up sand dragged from the shallow water. This strandline, known as Herman Beach— named for a small town in southwestern Minnesota located on it —can be traced for hundreds of miles across Minnesota, North Dakota, and Manitoba.

Even more prominent are similar beaches that lie out on the lake bed itself. These were created when the lake level was controlled by other, lower outlets uncovered by the retreat of the ice sheet. Traces of these beaches are present on many sections of the old lake bed, but if you were making a trip across the northern states and wanted to see the remnants of Lake Agassiz and its beaches with minimum effort and delay, you should travel on U.S. Highway No. 2 across eastern North Dakota. Whether viewed from the east or west, the beaches are conspicuous, but the westward traveler has a slight advantage. From Grand Forks travel westward for eighteen miles across the seemingly flat floor of the old lake bed. Then in the distance a slight but distinct and persistent rise, not more than fifteen feet high, appears on the horizon. In a few minutes this first beach ridge is past, but it is just one of five or six crossed by the highway within a distance of twelve to fifteen miles.

Though not as imposing as many of the features left us by the great ice sheets, the flat, treeless Agassiz plain and the low sandy ridges that stretch across it tell eloquently of a great event of bygone days—an event which might someday be repeated if Nature decides to reverse the cycle through which she is now taking us on our ride through time and space.

Agassiz was not the only ice-margin lake. There were many other great ones as well as thousands of small ones. Some of these persisted for no more than a few tens of years; others, like Agassiz, for several thousands.

An ice-margin lake about thirty miles long and ten miles wide was dammed between the edge of the ice sheet and the

Watchung Mountains in northern New Jersey. It was drained
when the retreating ice uncovered a low outlet through the
Passaic River at the present site of Paterson.

Ice-margin lakes probably were as common around the
edges of the European ice sheet as the North American. Large
northward-flowing rivers like the Oder, the Elbe, the Ob, and
the Yenesei must have been ponded against the ice for varying
periods of time. On several occasions when the ice sheet withdrew from the Baltic Basin but left its outlet temporarily blocked
by moraine, a tremendous ice-margin lake covered the present
area of the Baltic Sea and parts of southern Sweden and Finland.

Among the most interesting ice-marginal bodies of water
are the Glacial Great Lakes. The front of the latest ice sheet
moved back and forth across the Great Lakes basins for 9,000
years, pushing the lakes around and changing their levels as first
one outlet, then another, was alternately blocked and then uncovered. When Lake Chicago inundated the forest at Two Creeks
and overflowed through the Chicago River into the Mississippi,
Lake Erie, its outlet blocked by the ice sheet in the vicinity of
Niagara Falls, rose and overflowed across southern Michigan to
add its glacier-swelled water to Lake Chicago. At an earlier time
water from the Lake Erie Basin had flowed out across Indiana
through the Maumee and Wabash Rivers into the Ohio.

On several occasions water from Lake Erie, once including
all the lakes except Superior, flowed across New York state into
the Mohawk, thence down the Hudson to have the shortest
outlet to the sea in the history of the lakes. For a long period of
time Lake Duluth—the name given to ice-marginal Lake Superior—with its eastern end blocked by ice, flowed directly into the
Mississippi River through an outlet near the present site of
Duluth. Perhaps as late as 3,000 years ago the lakes had three
outlets at the same time—through the Chicago, St. Lawrence,
and Ottawa Rivers.

So the Great Lakes were born of the World of Ice, and
throughout their entire history they have been under its influence—destroyed by ice advances, re-created by retreats. At
one time they were small; at another, large. Their water has
found its way by three different routes into the Mississippi and
the Gulf of Mexico, by two routes into the Gulf of St. Lawrence,

through the Hudson into New York Harbor, and briefly into Chesapeake Bay when ice-dammed Lake Ontario spilled out through the Finger Lakes into the headwaters of the Susquehanna River.

Streams in and around the area blanketed by former ice sheets have undergone greater changes of complexion than the Great Lakes. All streams covered by the glaciers were obliterated. Many, after retreat of the ice, failed to be re-created, and many that did reappear could not follow their original courses because of the loads of debris the ice had dumped into their valleys.

Before the glaciers came, a large river, the preglacial Kanawha—known by geologists as the Teays—flowed in a deep valley from the Virginia Piedmont through the Blue Ridge and then across West Virginia, Ohio, Indiana, and Illinois into the Mississippi. This ancient river, about the same size as the present Ohio, was obliterated by the advance of the ice sheet. Beyond the edge of the ice the north-flowing tributaries of the Teays in West Virginia and Kentucky, as well as the Allegheny and Monongahela which flowed north across Pennsylvania into the Lake Erie Basin, were blocked by the ice and converted into lakes. One after the other of these ice-ponded streams overflowed through low places, some along the courses of tributaries, seeking new routes along the edge of the ice. Soon these new streams joined to create the present Ohio River. So this new great river, born while the land was in the throes of a great ice invasion, is made up of many short streams which prior to the coming of the ice were flowing in many diverse directions.

For a short part of its length—about fifty miles—where the Ohio flows in a northwest direction from Huntington, West Virginia to Portsmouth, Ohio, it follows the old Teays Valley. After retreat of the ice uncovered the valley of the Teays, the Ohio was so firmly intrenched that it had to remain in its new course. And the ice had so thoroughly filled and blocked Teays Valley with moraine that to this day long stretches of it contain no streams at all. The Scioto River follows it for a few miles south of Chillicothe, Ohio, and at several other places creeks and smaller streams, nearly lost in its spaciousness, follow it for short distances.

But Teays Valley and many of its tributary valleys, despite

the lack of surface streams, are not without water. Before Teays River was snuffed out by the ice sheet it deposited a thick accumulation of sand and gravel over the floor of its valley. It was from the minerals in this sediment, some of which could have come only from the rocks of the Virginia and North Carolina Piedmont, that geologists were able to find where the headwaters of this ancient stream lay.

What is more important, though, is that today this permeable sediment in the bottom of the valley forms a great winding subterranean reservoir through which pass, in a constant flow, great volumes of unpolluted ground water. Even where Teays Valley has been hidden from view by the moraine dumped into it—and this is the case throughout most of its course west of Columbus, Ohio—it has been located by the myriad wells that have been drilled into its fill and by seismic surveys that have been made in an effort to locate it. Nature, it seems, has found a way to protect her life-giving arteries from being befouled with human and industrial wastes.

The Missouri is another glacier-created stream with a history similar to that of the Ohio. One of the most striking features of the Missouri along the more than 900 miles of its course southward across the Dakotas and on down to where it swings east in the great bend at Kansas City is the lack of tributaries flowing into it from the east. On the west are the Platte and Niobrara in Nebraska, the White, Cheyenne, Moreau, and Grand in South Dakota, and a number of others in North Dakota.

All the evidence indicates that there was no preglacial counterpart of the lower Missouri. If there was anything that might be called a preglacial Missouri, it might have followed the present course of the upper Missouri across Montana, but instead of turning south after entering North Dakota it must have continued northeastward in or near the present course of the Assiniboine across southern Manitoba and into the preglacial Red near the present site of Winnipeg. At that time all the other east-flowing streams continued across the Dakotas or Nebraska to either the Red or the preglacial Mississippi, because even today this is the direction of the slope of the land.

But a lobe of the great glacier pushed south until its edge came to rest along an uneven line from northeastern Montana diagonally across the Dakotas and northeastern Nebraska into Missouri. The lower half of every east-flowing stream was covered with ice and plastered full of glacial debris. The upper Missouri, also blocked by the ice, was diverted toward the south along the edge of the glacier. Almost immediately the waters of these streams seeking out the lowest course joined into a single river, the present Missouri, which found its way around the southern end of the huge glacier lobe and into the Mississippi.

So the great glacier not only diverted one of America's main rivers from an outlet into Hudson Bay to one in the Gulf of Mexico, but created a new and even larger river and accomplished the remarkable feat of directing its course along the side of the vast central lowland valley of the United States rather than down into it where it ought to go. Not only that, but the ice laid the course of this new Big Muddy athwart the courses of a dozen other major streams. It is as though a river were picked up from its course and put down in another where it really doesn't belong. But there it stayed, and today in its one-sided valley it reminds us of the awesome power of the forces Nature can let loose upon the face of the Earth.

THE LANDS EMERGE

On the Replot skerry guard,* a group of islands off the Finnish shore at the narrowest part of the Gulf of Bothnia, lives a group of people who have been privileged to do something as part of their way of life that few people in the world—perhaps none outside of Finland—are able to do. Every fifty years for many generations the landowners have divided among themselves new land emerging from the sea.

The land on which these people live, not far from the center of the former Fennoscandian ice sheet, was depressed more than 1,000 feet by the weight of the now long-vanished ice. But since the glacier went away the surface has been rising —now at a rate of three feet a century—toward the level it had before the ice pressed it down.

* Skerry guard is the name used for groups (archipelagoes) of small rocky islands in places fringing the coasts of the Scandinavian countries.

Because the land is low-lying and the adjacent waters are shallow, a rise of only a few feet makes dry land of large sections of the neighboring sea floor. Seventeenth- and eighteenth-century maps of the Replot skerry guard are vastly different from those of today. Many new islands have emerged—there are hundreds now—and older ones have enlarged and joined with others. In 1760 there were three major islands, but about 1850 the channel between two of these dried up. In another 100 years the two remaining big islands will have joined to make one.

As the land emerges, though it means additional area for agriculture, the inhabitants, heavily dependent upon fishing, struggle to keep the channels open for boats and spawning fish as long as they can. But eventually they must give up, as the waterways are converted first to marshes and finally to meadows.

Probably nowhere else in the world is new land emerging so rapidly from the sea. While the ice sheet rested on Finland much of the land, like Antarctica today, was below sea level.

How far down will an ice sheet depress the crust? It depends upon several factors: density of the ice, thickness of the ice sheet, and the density of the rock underneath it. Sinking will continue until it compensates for the weight of the load. This distance apparently is equivalent to about one third the thickness of the ice. And after the load has been removed the land will slowly return to its original elevation.

Since the beginning of the last big ice retreat, roughly 10,000 years ago, the land along the west shore of the Gulf of Bothnia where the ice sheet was thickest seems to have risen more than 1,500 feet. And if the calculations are correct it has another 700 feet to go before it is again in equilibrium. Under parts of West Antarctica the land would rise nearly half a mile if all the ice were removed.

This moving up and down of the crust is possible because the material beneath it flows, under the high pressures prevailing there, and moves outward when the crust is pushed down into it, causing adjacent areas to rise. When the load is removed the displaced heavy rock moves back again, pushing the lighter crust up, like an iceberg in water, until it is again in balance with the heavier supporting rock.

Rising of a depressed area causes the rim regions to sink.

There is some evidence of this in both North America and Scandinavia, where lands outside those occupied by former ice sheets are slowly subsiding as subcrustal rock is drawn out from under them toward the rising sections. The effect on the land surface next to the ice sheets, however, is not pronounced, probably because the horizontal flow of material takes place at great depth.

The light crust cannot remain down in the denser sub-crust unless held there by a heavy weight. This plastic behavior of rock is similar to the flow of ice deep within a glacier, but is infinitely slower—hence the continuing rebound of Scandinavia and eastern North America today, several thousand years after the last remnants of the former ice sheets have disappeared.

This condition of balance in the outer part of the Earth is known as *isostasy*. The name was not coined until 1871, but the principle was proposed by T. F. Jamieson in 1865 as an explanation for marine sediments above sea level around the area earlier occupied by the British Isles ice sheet.

How large a load is necessary to bend the crust down? We know the big ice sheets can do it. What about smaller loads? The islands of Svalbard were covered several thousand years ago with a single ice sheet about the size of West Virginia. That it probably pushed the crust down is indicated by marine beaches, now at heights up to about sixty feet above the sea, to which the land has risen as the weight of the shrinking ice sheet decreased.

There are good grounds for believing that still smaller loads can depress the crust. The old shorelines of Lake Bonneville are about sixty feet higher on islands in the center of the lake bed than along its edges. Apparently the load of water was heavy enough to depress the crust at least sixty feet under the center of this ancient water body.

Man is a doer of big things. He has probed the depths of the Earth with his seismograph and has learned the secrets of outer space. Of course, he has not yet learned how to live with his fellow man, but he can turn missiles loose to do his bidding miles and miles away; he can control nuclear energy, and has made some progress in changing the weather. Thus we should not be surprised to learn that man, like Nature, is capable of

placing a load on the crust heavy enough to push it down. And
he does it, not by building skyscraping cities; it is easier than
that. He does it with water.

What man did, in effect, when he plugged the Colorado
River with Hoover Dam and created Lake Mead was to add—
rather suddenly, too—a 12,000,000,000-ton load of water to the
crust. About the time the reservoir became full, the section of
the crust on which it rested began to sink, and during the ensuing six years subsided a maximum distance of nearly five inches.
In the area affected—it has a diameter of about thirty miles—
the sinking was greatest near the center where the weight of
water was heaviest. Earthquakes always were frequent in this
area, but since creation of the lake they have been much more
common. Hundreds have been felt and thousands have been
recorded by local seismographs. These shocks emanate from
renewed movement along faults which apparently have been
inactive for many thousands of years.

Old marine shorelines now at varying distances above sea
level tell us how far the land has recoiled after release from its
load of ice. Each of these ancient strandlines is tilted—higher
the closer it is to the former ice center—thus revealing the
relative rate of uplift from place to place. Shorelines, marked by
recognizable beaches and sea cliffs that are hundreds of feet
above the sea near the head of the Gulf of Bothnia, are at or near
sea level in Denmark.

Tide gauges around Baltic shores show how fast this tilting
rise is going on. From three feet a century near the head of the
Gulf of Bothnia, it decreases southward to two feet in southern
Finland and four inches in southern Sweden. The city of Stockholm is being pushed up from one to two inches every ten years.
The line beyond which no uplift is currently taking place runs
through central Latvia, the southern part of the Baltic Sea, and
the city of Copenhagen.

Eventually—in another 5,000 years or so—as the water is
pushed southward out of the Gulf of Bothnia it will become dry
land, and Finland and Sweden will be connected throughout
their entire length. Though the uplift is slow at the southern
tip of Sweden, it wouldn't take much rise—little more than
thirty feet—to cut off the Baltic and convert it into a lake.

In North America, with a larger and perhaps thicker ice sheet, sinking of the crust under the ice load equaled or exceeded that in Europe. But we know less about this movement and the uplift following it, because very little field work has been done in the immense uninhabited area of Canada where the ice was thickest.

We know, however, that the land was depressed as far south as Long Island, Cleveland, and Milwaukee. And the clues are similar to those in Europe—mainly tilted shorelines now high above the sea or lake along which they were made. The tilting of some of the individual raised shorelines shows that uplift was not continuous. It seems to have slowed down or ceased altogether when the ice front paused in its retreat or made minor advances. Uplift was greatest when the glaciers were shrinking rapidly.

Nowhere is the uplift more clearly shown than along the former shores of old Lake Agassiz. At the southern outlet Herman Beach is 1,060 feet above the sea. One hundred and fifty miles to the north where U.S. Highway 2 crosses it west of Grand Forks this strand is 100 feet higher; in the seventy-five miles from here to the International Boundary it rises another 100 feet.

The shorelines made by the waves in Lake Chicago and the other Glacial Great Lakes are all warped in the same manner. So also are ancient high-level strands along the coasts of Newfoundland, Labrador, and the Canadian Arctic islands, where the highest ones are reported to be more than 1,400 feet above the sea.

So when the face of North America was pushed in by its massive load of ice—just like Antarctica today—the continental shelf from New England to northern Labrador was hundreds of feet lower than now, and long sections of the marginal parts of the continent were held far below the level of the sea. When the ice finally withdrew, the depressed land, its slow rise lagging behind the rapid retreat of the ice, was flooded by the sea. In coastal Maine great elongated bays filled the valleys of the Penobscot and Kennebec for seventy-five miles inland. For a while Hudson Bay was fully twice its present size.

When the edge of the ice rested against the Adirondacks

and the mountains of northern New England it blocked the sea from the St. Lawrence Valley, but as soon as the ice withdrew toward the north, the sea not only flooded the entire valley, but extended into the Lake Ontario basin and far up the Ottawa and Lake Champlain valleys, forming a bay which Jack L. Hough, who has made an exhaustive study of Great Lakes history, calls the St. Lawrence Sea. If the St. Lawrence Sea could be re-created today, the captain of the largest ocean liner afloat could take his ship safely over the tops of the highest buildings in Montreal and Ottawa because they would lie submerged under 500 feet of water.

How do we know that the St. Lawrence Sea existed? In places the beaches of the old shoreline, some now 700 feet above the sea, are still visible, and much of the land formerly beneath this long arm of water is covered with a blanket of clay and sand washed into it from the ground moraine on the adjoining uplands. These sediments contain the shells of marine clams and the skeletons of fish and seals.

Few, indeed, are those who would expect to find the skeleton of a whale on a Vermont hillside, but it has been done. Four hundred feet above Lake Champlain near the Quebec boundary the skeleton of a whale, which formerly sported in the waters of the St. Lawrence Sea, was dug from the clay. Bones of whales have been found at even higher elevations near Montreal and Quebec. How these aquatic giants succumbed is not known, but the discovery of their bones proves beyond the shadow of a doubt that there was a St. Lawrence Sea and that since it dried up the land has moved upward several hundred feet.

The St. Lawrence Sea probably existed for a long time— 2,000 years or so—because the rising of the sea, as melt water poured into it from the rapidly wasting ice sheets, was faster than the recoil of the land from the depression in which the ice had held it. But with further shrinking of the ice the rise of the sea slowed and the lands began to emerge. When the rising northeastern end of the Ontario basin rose to sea level the sea withdrew and a lake was created, which with only minor subsequent changes became modern Lake Ontario.

And the rise of the land still goes on, not quite as spectacular as in the Replot skerry guard, but fast enough to make significant visible changes in the span of a human lifetime. Seismologist Beno Gutenberg has calculated that in and around Hudson Bay, in the area where the former ice sheet was thickest and where the land is rising fastest, the land has another 800 or 900 feet to go—a total rebound of close to 2,000 feet—before it reaches equilibrium. Such a rise would create dry land out of almost the whole of Hudson Bay. The uplift of this area initially seems to have been at a rate of about twenty feet a century, as computed from a number of radiocarbon-dated shells at various places along the old tilted shorelines. The rate now may be as low as two feet in 100 years, but the rise is still going on.

The rebound, of course, diminishes progressively toward the south, but instrumental measurements show that it is affecting the crust as far as a line extending from Boston along the New York–Pennsylvania boundary, through Lake Erie, across Michigan just north of Detroit and Grand Rapids, and through the center of Lake Michigan. So, because the effect of an ice sheet, through the rebound of the area it depressed, continues long after the ice sheet itself is dead, the eventful glacial history of the Great Lakes has not yet been concluded. The current rise of the land in the upper St. Lawrence Valley is well over a foot per 100 years; at Niagara Falls it is between seven and ten inches. If this southward tilting should continue for several thousands of years—and the experts say it will—there is some possibility that the St. Lawrence outlet of the lakes will be cut off and Lakes Ontario and Erie will have to find other outlets, perhaps along routes they temporarily used in earlier periods of their glacial history.

As the land emerges along the north shores of the Great Lakes—and along the north shore of Lake Superior it is rising at twenty inches per 100 years—it submerges along the south shores, because the water is literally pushed from north to south as the land tilts in that direction. So as time goes on a greater and greater proportion of the water from the upper lakes will leave through the Chicago Canal. If the Straits of Mackinac, now rising nearly ten inches each 100 years, are cut off, all or most of the water from Lake Michigan will reach the sea through the Mississippi River, as it did more than once in the last several thousand years.

SEAS COME AND GO

Ever since fishermen began to drag their trawls along the bottom over the Dogger Bank in the middle of the North Sea, they
have been pulling in, along with their fish, one of the strangest
assortments of material ever yielded by the sea. This unwanted
debris is hauled off by the fishermen and dumped in deeper
water where it will not again foul their nets. Among it are masses
of peat, remains of trees, and the bones of large land mammals
including those of mammoth, woolly rhinoceros, musk ox, reindeer, and others. Even a harpoon of Stone Age man has been
hauled in.

Though most of the recovered treasure has been thrown
away, enough of it has been saved for scientists to re-create the
scene long since buried by the waters. During the last main
glacial stage of Wisconsin-Würm time, there was sufficient
water tied up in the world's glaciers to drop sea level at least
250 feet lower than it is now, exposing the floors of the English
Channel and the southern half of the North Sea.

At this stage of glaciation neither the Scandinavian ice
sheet nor the smaller one over the northern part of the British
Isles extended more than a few miles beyond the present shorelines. Thus much of the North Sea floor was free of both ice and
water. As this new land emerged, plants were not far behind the
retreating shoreline. It was a cool land, a land of birch and willow and peat bogs, and on it for some thousands of years Stone
Age man survived by outwitting the mammoth, the reindeer, the
bison, and the musk ox.

Soundings have revealed the valleys of streams which
crossed this now-submerged land. The Rhine flowed northward
through a boggy coastal plain for another 250 miles before entering the sea at the latitude of the southern tip of Norway. On
the way it was joined by the Thames and other minor tributaries
from the west. The Seine flowed through the center of the present English Channel and into the sea far beyond Lands End
and the tip of the Brittany peninsula.

The southern parts of England and Ireland were connected,
and through the lowland between them flowed a river draining

melt water from the icecap that covered all the rest of the islands. There was no Irish Sea then; its northern part was under the icecap and its southern part was dry land. But like the emergent North Sea bottom, it was a cool land of tundra, bogs, and birches and willows. Except for the big mammals, now extinct, it must have been a land much like northern Canada today.

Of course, the drop in sea level which joined the British Isles to the mainland did the same thing to many other islands throughout the entire world. Sumatra, Borneo, and Java were connected, and together they formed a big-headed peninsula connected to the mainland of Asia by Malaya. The Timor and Arafura Seas dried up, joining New Guinea with Australia, to increase tremendously the area of that southern continent. And Ceylon was part of India.

Bones and teeth of extinct musk ox, moose, and mastodon have been dredged from the sea bottom between the Delaware and Hudson rivers nearly as far out as the edge of the continental shelf. At the time they lived, withdrawal of the sea had exposed a strip of land forty to fifty miles wide all the way from Cape Cod to Cape Canaveral. Along the Gulf coast it was even wider.

Today Bering Strait, the fifty-mile strip of water separating Alaska and Siberia, is nowhere 150 feet deep. For 400 miles north of the Strait the Chuckchi Sea is less than 250 feet deep. The shallow character of this sea has been known for many years, but never was it so much in evidence as when Commander Anderson took the submarine *Nautilus* from Bering Strait to the Pole. With difficulty, and only after he had tried more than one route, was he able to take his ship on a submerged route into the Arctic Basin at all. The *Nautilus's* fathometer revealed the average water depth to be only 120 feet, barely room enough to maneuver the ship between the base of the pack ice—over fifty feet thick in places where storms had piled it up—and the bottom of the sea.

At the height of the Wisconsin ice age the bottom of this shallow sea, known as the Bering-Chuckchi Platform, was a low, nearly flat plain forming a 600-mile-wide land connection between the two continents. Over this bridge, during the many thousands of years of its existence, perhaps most of the 70,000 years of the Wisconsin-Würm glacial interval, animals migrated back and forth between the Eastern and Western Worlds, and by it a number of animal species, including man, made their first entry into North America.

What kind of land was this bridge between Eurasia and North America, this isthmus that was ten or more times as broad as Panama? It probably wasn't a great deal different from the lands on either side of the Strait today. The climate was colder when the bridge was there, since a glacial stage was in progress, but, like the great central valley of Alaska, there were no glaciers on it. So there was no ice to act as a deterrent to trans-isthmian traffic.

Trees—pine, spruce, fir, and others—are pushing out from east and west toward Bering Strait, but none reaches it. Almost the entire Seward Peninsula is treeless. The westernmost spruce in Alaska fail by more than 150 miles to reach the Strait. In Siberia the spruceless zone is an impressive 1,400 miles wide. Though a few other tree genera have worked their way a little closer to the Strait, the treeless tundra straddling the meeting points of the Eastern and Western Worlds is a good 900 miles wide. And during the glacial intervals when the Bering-Chuckchi province was above water the two treelines—one in Asia and one in North America—must have gone back even farther from the Bering Isthmus. The proof lies in the Pleistocene bogs on the Seward Peninsula. In these wastebaskets of ancient times only the plants of the tundra are represented. There is no pollen from trees. The tundra plants from the Eastern and Western Worlds met and mixed on this Bering-Chuckchi plain and both groups extended their ranges around the world in circumpolar lands. But the forests from east and west did not make contact.

In the opinion of geologist David M. Hopkins of the United States Geological Survey, who has spent a lot of time in the lands bordering the Bering-Chuckchi Platform, it is likely that the forests of Alaska and the Chukotski Peninsula on the other side of Bering Strait have not been in contact since Pleistocene time began. Though the pines, the spruces, and the firs on the Alaskan side differ very little from the pines, the spruces, and the firs on the Siberian side, no single species of tree occurs in both

Siberia and Alaska. Hopkins believes that this in itself is strong though indirect evidence that the two forests have not merged for a very long time.

Man didn't use this isthmus simply as a passageway from the old world to the new; he lived on it in an environment which, though harsh, was favorable for his existence. Sharing it with him were the mammoth, the reindeer, the bison, the musk ox, and the carnivores that fed on them.

Early man couldn't travel very fast, but like the English sparrow, he got around. While he lived on the Bering-Chuckchi Platform others of his species slowly but surely spread out to the south—at times there was an overpopulation problem then, too —to occupy all the ice-free part of a vast empty continent.

But the ice sheets began to wane, and the waters of the Pacific and Arctic Oceans encroached farther and farther onto the Bering-Chuckchi plain. Inch by inch, man had to yield this happy hunting ground to the sea. Finally, about 11,000 years ago when sea level had risen to within about 140 feet of its present level, the Alaska-Siberia land bridge was covered by water. Some men were living on one side of it, some on the other.

But at this stage of history men were still inhabiting the Dogger Bank and the forest lands of the English Channel. Most of the plants and animals that had lived in Great Britain and Ireland in the preceding interglacial time were destroyed or driven out by the ice in Würm time. But with the waning of the icecap, plants and animals from the mainland began to move into the new lands bared of ice. Many reached England. Fewer got as far as Ireland, which had been almost completely covered by ice before return of melt water to the sea re-created the Irish Sea and put a stop to further migration of plants and animals from Britain and the mainland. And so to this day there are no snakes on the Emerald Isle because the British Isles icecap—not St. Patrick—drove them out, and the big ice sheets, by returning melt water to the sea, prevented their return. And yet one species each of lizard, salamander, and toad were able to make the trip from the mainland before the sea closed in behind them.

The return of many species of plants as well as animals to Ireland was also prevented by the rising sea; there are far fewer plant species in Ireland than in Britain. Among the trees, the linden (*Tilia*) and beech (*Fagus*) are two that never got back. This difference in plant populations can be explained in part by the much greater variety of climates in Britain, from the arctic-alpine cold of the Scottish bens to the mildness of the South Downs and the coast of Sussex, but the difference in numbers is too great to be explained without the aid of the water barrier that has isolated Ireland for the past 8,000 or more years.

Anyhow, England remained connected to the rest of the continent for a while longer. Eight thousand years ago the Dogger Bank was still a peninsula in the North Sea, and England was made part of the mainland by a strip fully 300 miles wide. Ireland had already been isolated. Not until another 1,000 years went by did the North Sea and the English Channel finally unite to sever England from the mainland and effectively put an end to all further invasions—plants, animals, and men—by land. In the meantime not only snakes but many other animals and hosts of plants crossed the intervening lowlands under their own steam and established themselves on this island-to-be.

Where Will the World of Ice Go From Here?

WHAT WILL the glaciers do next? What will the consequences be? They exert such a tremendous effect now on the world's life and are capable of making such radical changes on this old planet that we have good reason for being interested in what in the World of Ice they will do next!

We certainly know a lot about their past performances, and because of far-flung observations all over the world—wherever there are glaciers, sea ice, and ice underground—we are fairly familiar with what is happening to the world's ice. We know that the climate has changed in the past and that it is changing now, and we know of nothing that will keep it from changing in the future.

But the fact remains that the time in which we are living—an age of ice—is a most unusual period in the Earth's history. If the present were a normal period, the inhabitants of central Europe and the northern United States would probably be enjoying a subtropical climate. So the inquisitive ones among us would like to know what brings on these colder times which have been so infrequent in the Earth's long history.

Some people hold steadfastly to the view that the major climatic changes initiating ice ages are the same as but on a larger scale than those responsible for the minor variations known to have taken place throughout the Pleistocene Epoch and still in progress. Thus changes in the composition of the atmosphere—principally involving carbon dioxide, water vapor, and volcanic ash—and changes in the amount of solar radiation have been called upon to do the job.

But changes in the amount of atmospheric carbon dioxide and water vapor, though they may be responsible for minor climatic variations, are not generally regarded as capable of cooling the atmosphere enough to start an ice age from scratch. In order to bring about the necessary reduced temperature the atmosphere would have to lose over half its moisture, and no one can figure out why or how this might occur. And as for carbon dioxide, calculations have shown that its enormous recent increase from the burning of fossil fuels has been too small to account for the warming of the Earth's surface that seems to have occurred during the same period. And, too, the concentration of carbon dioxide may never become very high because of absorption by sea water.

So it appears that carbon dioxide and water vapor in themselves cannot be the cause of an ice age. Volcanic ash may be no more able to do the job either, since in order to create the proper climatic conditions its concentration would have to be high for many hundreds if not thousands of years. The best that Katmai, Krakatoa, and other observed great eruptions could do was depress world temperatures for two or three years.

That brings us to variations in the amount of solar radiation as a means of starting an ice age. And here we may be getting close to pay dirt because we know that recent climatic variations have been tied closely to fluctuations in the number of sunspots and hence to changes in the amount of solar radiation. And energy received from the sun is virtually the sole driving force behind all atmospheric processes. Still this theory is not without its weaknesses. At the beginning of Pleistocene time, for example, had there been as few mountain ranges and had the average elevation of the continents been as low as throughout most of geologic time, lowering of the snowline because of reduced solar radiation could not have started an ice age. Except in Antarctica, the snowline would not have encompassed enough land to cause widespread glacierization.

But we know that, just before Pleistocene time and continuing into it, the Earth underwent a major crustal revolution. Mountains and other continental areas were raised high. The snowline enveloped many mountain ranges and high plateaus. Ice from the high places spread out across the plains, and the ice age was in full swing. This is the cause that Professor Flint believes got the Pleistocene and probably all other major ice ages off to a start.

The rising of the continents and the creation of mountain ranges might well be the reason for the ice ages, but it certainly cannot explain the alternation of glacial and interglacial stages which we know took place throughout the Pleistocene and supposedly in earlier ice ages. The mountain ranges thrown up at the beginning of the Pleistocene are still with us. Most of them are about as high now as they were at the height of the Wisconsin-Würm glacial stage. A few are even higher. So Professor Flint starts his ice ages by combining mountain-building with a drop in solar radiation and calls for subsequent minor variations in solar radiation to force the snowline up and down and thus cause glacial and interglacial stages and minor fluctuations in the world's load of ice. According to this view, variations in the amount of solar radiation have always occurred, but only during times when extensive mountain-building took place could they initiate an ice age.

Some people have gone so far as to suggest that ice ages are actually started by warming up of the climate rather than cooling. Behind this theory is the belief that a great increase in snowfall is necessary to start an ice age and that the increased precipitation and storminess in northern latitudes must come from increased evaporation, a process that requires greater amounts of heat. This theory may be valid, but higher temperature would cause more and more of the precipitation to be in the form of rain, rather than snow, and it is likely that a very rainy interglacial rather than a glacial stage would develop. And all the geological evidence points to dry rather than wet interglacials. Too, the snowline during glacial stages was more than 3,000 feet lower than in interglacial times, a situation that hardly seems feasible if the climate were warming up. Tropical seas, too, as shown by oxygen-isotope ratios in Foram shells, were distinctly cooler during glacial stages.

Professors Maurice Ewing and William Donn of Columbia University, in an appealing theory widely disseminated in several large-circulation magazines, have presented what they consider are good reasons for the climatic fluctuations and the comings and goings of glaciers during an ice age. They believe that because the maximum temperature of each interglacial stage of the Pleistocene was about the same—which is also about the same as the present temperature—the climatic variations of the Pleistocene are controlled by an "internal, self-regulating mechanism" and not by any external forces such as variation in solar radiation.

There are many complicating factors involved in any theory dealing with the causes of ice ages, but in essence the Ewing-Donn view maintains that Arctic and Subarctic glaciers are shrinking today because the Arctic Ocean is frozen over. If this seems strange, let us look further into their reasoning. They say the Arctic Ocean is cold—and thus frozen over—because today's relatively low sea level greatly reduces the entry of warm Atlantic water into the Arctic through the rather shallow passages around Iceland and Svalbard. But they maintain that because the Arctic Ocean is frozen over it furnishes very little moisture for the nourishment of the Greenland ice sheet and other glaciers in high latitudes. So these glaciers are shrinking. But as they shrink and return water to the oceans, sea level rises and the waters of the Arctic and North Atlantic Oceans begin to interchange through the Iceland and Svalbard passages. This will cool the North Atlantic and warm the Arctic, and the Polar ice pack will melt away.

But as a consequence of more evaporation from an unfrozen Arctic Ocean, precipitation on adjacent lands will increase and glaciers will again begin to grow. Their expansion will reduce sea level, and when the passages between the North

Atlantic and Arctic reach a critical low level, greatly reducing interchange between the two oceans, the Arctic will again freeze over. The ice sheets, having attained their maximum size, will then, with much of their moisture supply cut off, begin to shrink again. Thus glacial and interglacial stages will go on and on, with no end in view for perhaps another 500,000 or so years. Ewing and Donn account for the lowered snowline and consequent growth of glaciers in other parts of the world, especially in mountain ranges far distant from the Arctic, by changes in atmospheric circulation resulting from the open Arctic Ocean, the cooler Atlantic waters, and the growth of ice sheets in northern latitudes.

The self-regulating mechanism of an alternately open and frozen Arctic Ocean may be the cause of alternating glacial and interglacial intervals in an ice age, but it cannot account for the initiation of the Pleistocene or any other ice age. Since the ice age has not been with us forever, Ewing and Donn have adopted a theory proposed many years ago to bring on an ice age—wandering of the Poles relative to the lands. They believe that if the North Pole were in the North Pacific and the South Pole antipodal to it in the South Atlantic, there could be no ice age because ocean currents would readily mix warm Equatorial water with that in the Polar regions. World climate would be much more uniform than now and a lot milder. Ewing and Donn say the present ice age began when the Pole migrated from the North Pacific to a position within the enclosed Arctic Basin, and that the world will continue to experience alternate invasions and retreats of large ice sheets as long as the North Pole remains within this enclosure. And a mass of rapidly accumulating data indicates that neither the continents nor the Poles have always been in the locations they now occupy.

Within a congealing lava flow are many iron-bearing mineral particles magnetized by the Earth's magnetic field. As these particles, each a small magnet with positive and negative pole, move about in the fluid rock they orient themselves in line with the Earth's magnetic field. Similar magnetized mineral grains in the sediment carried by a river and dumped in the sea also line up in the Earth's magnetic field when they settle in quiet water. Long after the lava has congealed into rock and the sediment has been consolidated, the orientation of these micro-scopic magnetized particles remains to tell us the location of the magnetic poles at the time the rocks formed. If, as many scientists believe, the magnetic poles and the geographic poles have always been relatively close together, the *paleomagnetism* of these tiny magnetized minerals holds the answer to the former wandering of the Poles.

Those who have made a profession out of studying the wandering of the Poles see in the evidence a migration of the North Pole along a path starting near the west coast of North America and crossing the central Pacific near the Hawaiian Islands to Japan and the Asiatic mainland. All this happened in Precambrian and Paleozoic time. In the Mesozoic the North Pole swung toward the northeast across Siberia and entered the Arctic Ocean about the beginning of the Cenozoic Era. But there seems to be no evidence for appreciable changes in its position during the past 20,000,000 years or so. If this is the case, Ewing and Donn's ice age was some millions of years behind schedule.

Obviously, there is universal lack of agreement on Polar wandering and continental drift and even on the causes of ice ages. But there is no doubt about the existence of the Pleistocene ice age and that it is still upon us. We know where the ice sheets got their start and where they spread. We know what happened to the plants and animals as the ice came forward and then withdrew. We can see what the ice did to the Earth's crust, to the face of the land, and to the seas—and we have timed these events.

It now remains for the scientists to clear up the uncertain-ties and resolve their lack of agreement about some of the more difficult problems. And because of the army of dedicated men at work on these problems the solutions can't be long in com-ing. Few will be surprised if a number of factors—solar radia-tion, Polar wandering, mountain-building, a freezing and un-freezing Arctic Ocean, and others—constitute the answer to the question: What makes an ice age and what keeps it going?

Can we use this knowledge of what happened in the past to predict what will happen in the future?

Most geologists believe that we are still in the ice age and many of them are of the opinion that vast sheets of ice will again spread over North America and Europe. There are some data to support this view, very few against it. It is futile to argue that the climate today is not under the same controls that have regulated it for thousands of years, perhaps for the entire Pleistocene Epoch. The span of time since the ice sheet retreated beyond the Great Lakes is far less than the length of any of the main interglacial stages of the Pleistocene. If the present is an interglacial stage comparable in length to several of the earlier ones, we are now somewhat less than halfway through it. If this be so, in another 10,000 to 15,000 years ice sheets will be on the move again. We know what they will do to the land—exactly what they have done in the past—but how they will treat mankind is an unanswered question and will depend a great deal upon man himself.

Will the ice sheets bury Berlin, New York, and Chicago, as some persons predict? Or when they advance that far, will they pass over a peaceful land, marred only by the roots of former cities—scenes of destruction and decay of an ancient, short-lived civilization? Or at the time of the next ice invasion will New York, Cleveland, and Chicago be one vast city, a colossal anthill inhabited by human troglodytes, ignorant of the world beyond their limited horizon and under the iron control of men and forces they know nothing about? Will it be into this place, where the Earth's countenance has been annihilated by the hand of man, that the ice will advance, giving Nature a chance to renew the land and make her impression upon it again?

Let's assume, perhaps wishfully, that man will learn to plan his future and to balance his numbers against his environment, so that he will have a future, and that 10,000 to 15,000 years hence there will be cities, not differing greatly in size from existing ones, where now are Berlin, New York, and Chicago.

What will happen? To say, as some have done, that these cities will be buried or overwhelmed by the ice is putting it too briefly and certainly is misleading. Let's paint a more realistic picture.

First of all, before northern North America and Europe are engulfed by ice again, the extrapolation into the future of known climatic curves of the past few thousands of years indicates it's likely there will be a lot more melting of existing ice. Should we have another period similar to the Hypsithermal (6,000 to 500 B.C.) when temperatures were several degrees higher than now, sea level might rise from three to six feet. Although over a period of hundreds of years this would slowly inundate some of the low marshy lands along the shores, its effect on coastal cities and the human occupancy of adjacent lands would be negligible.

Of greater concern is what might happen in the drier parts of the world—those in which the supply of water today is barely adequate to meet the demands put upon it. Surely these places would become drier still; deserts would expand.

If the snowline should rise much higher above the mountains of our own West, the resulting decrease in spring and summer run-off from melting snow and glaciers would fall below the amount needed for irrigation and municipal use. A lot of land now cultivated would revert to grassland and much land now used for grazing would be converted to desert. Under these conditions it is not difficult to visualize shifts of population toward more moist lands, even as in the days of the Okies, though probably on a larger scale.

Of course, salt-water conversion by that time may be able to alleviate or eliminate this problem, but many of the potentially arid lands are far inland. Put five, ten, or a hundred times as many people on the land and then consider the problems involved in desalinizing sea water and transporting it all over the face of the land.

Yet when the ice sheets themselves finally do come, what can we expect for our distant progeny? As the ice spreads out across central North America, Lake Agassiz will be reborn, just as it has been on several occasions in the past. But the cooling of the climate as the glacier approaches will have so shortened the growing season on the Manitoba prairies that many of the farmers and those who depend upon the land-tillers for a living will have abandoned their land and migrated before the encroaching waters of the lake come in view. To extend the lives of the emaciated cities still in existence when the waters arrive, dikes will be thrown up around them and the lake outlet will be dredged deeper and deeper to hold down as long as possible the rising level of the lake.

There will be nothing catastrophic about the advance of the lake and the ice across the prairies—the battle might go on for several thousand years. There will be places where large-scale agriculture will finally give way to small-scale subsistence farming, which in turn may yield to nomadism, and this perhaps eventually to the glaciers themselves. In his slow retreat before the glaciers and rising waters, man would fight them all the way. But against the ice it would be a losing battle until the glacier finally stopped its advance. Though northern men would have been defeated in the generations-long battle, in the army of people wresting their livelihood from the land south of the ice there will be the germ of an advance guard which someday, generation by generation, will move back to the north in the wake of the retreating glacier to take over the land once buried beneath the ice. Immigration into these virgin lands made habitable by climatic change might be no more pronounced than it is now into Alaska, northern Canada, northern Siberia—here perhaps not always by choice—and into Greenland.

What can we say about Chicago or whatever metropolis is sprawled around the southern rim of Lake Michigan at the time of the next ice invasion? The die has already been cast. When the ice again cuts off the Straits of Mackinac and isolates Michigan from the other lakes, all its water will go out through the Chicago outlet and into the Mississippi, if tilting of the Earth's crust has not already caused it to do so. Unlike the former forest at Two Creeks, Chicago and other lakeside cities will not be submerged under rising waters. If the volume of outflowing water becomes too large for the channel to accommodate, it will simply be enlarged by dredging. By that time earthmoving equipment will have been developed to the point where deepening of river channels and the making of new ones will be mere child's play—or the channel will be made larger by an army of troglodytes wielding picks and shovels! In any event the water would cause few problems. An occasional iceberg that had floated down from the edge of the glacier might get stuck in the channel and cause local flooding, but these trouble spots would quickly be eliminated.

There will, however, be some other events that will have much greater impact on the citizenry of the times. Generations of people will come and go while the ice front advances the length of Lake Michigan. For each one of these generations the changes, because of their slowness, may scarcely be apparent, but during this time Chicago, without moving an inch, will become a city of the Subarctic, as first one climatic zone and then another retreats from around it. A shorter and shorter growing season will drive the land of tall corn to the south, and even the dairy herds of Wisconsin—if the people of those times are still using so inefficient a machine as a cow to manufacture their milk—will be inching their way into Illinois and Kentucky.

Long before the ice reaches the Straits of Mackinac much of the lake traffic will have disappeared because of the exhaustion of the iron mines, but now, with the glacier in Lake Michigan itself, all shipping on the lake will have vanished. The shifting sands of shore dunes may be moving again, this time through the ruins of vast steel mills. Slowly but surely the city will be strangled by the destruction of its hinterland.

Not everywhere, on the other hand, will Nature be unkind to man. The southward migration of the Polar Front and Prevailing Westerlies will bring more water to wet the world's arid lands. Each generation of ranchers and farmers in the western desert basins will have a little more irrigation water than the one before it. There will be more snow in the mountains and more rain in the basins. Lakes will begin to expand and playas and salt flats will slowly be covered with permanent water as new lakes are born. The plains east of the mountains, too, will benefit from the new pluvial age.

In the Sahara, in the great deserts of interior Asia, and in other vast dry regions the same changes will take place—more snow in the mountains, more rain in the lowlands. Lakes will expand and new ones will be born.

Past events tell us that in some arid regions there may be more water than men will want. Lakes Bonneville and Lahonton will be re-created, and lands previously made productive by increased rain and by water from the mountains will be claimed by the rising lake waters.

When the new pluvial age starts, so also will begin the slow creep of Bonneville's waters up toward the wave-cut benches of the old Provo and Bonneville shorelines and the level of the ancient outlet into the headwaters of the Snake River at Red

Rock Pass. But it is unlikely that many generations of the valley inhabitants will watch these waters rise over fertile fields without doing something about it. This time the water will not rise until it is 800 feet deep at the site of the Mormon Temple in Salt Lake City, as it was when old Lake Bonneville flowed out through Red Rock Pass. Regional planners will have determined a critical elevation above which they will not allow the lake to rise. When the water reaches this level the excess waters will be pumped through huge aqueducts for sixty miles along the route of the old outflow and dumped into the headwaters of the Portneuf River to continue their journey through the Snake and Columbia rivers to the Pacific. Other giant pumping stations might force water over the Wasatch Range to the Colorado in order to help hold this future Lake Bonneville in check.

It might be interesting to speculate on what may happen to our largest metropolis in a glacial stage 10,000 years hence, assuming, of course, that there will be at that time a city where New York now stands. Long before the ice reaches the city, the sea, with its sustenance cut off by growing ice sheets, will have begun to fall, but routine dredging from year to year will keep the harbor navigable. But as the water level slowly sinks, the area of best port facilities will move closer to the sea. And the city, too, without being aware of it, will spread out toward the retreating shore.

By the time the ice reaches the St. Lawrence Valley, sea level will have fallen more than fifty feet, and the Port of New York will be situated on what is now the continental shelf, miles beyond the present entrance into the lower harbor. At this same time the opposite shores of Bering Strait will be slowly approaching each other as the sea withdraws from the Bering-Chuckchi Platform, and submarines will have to use a canal to get from the Pacific Ocean to the Arctic. Men and other animals will again wander over swampland now at the bottom of the North Sea and the English Channel.

But who can predict anything about the condition of civilization when the next ice invasion comes? Too much time is involved. Even if an ice invasion should begin now or, better still, if it were well under way—with an actively expanding ice sheet in the heights of Labrador and northern Quebec—who could say what the ice would encounter when it reached New York and Chicago? That wouldn't be for at least another 1,000 years; 5,000 is more likely. And in that space of time much can happen to man at his own hand.

There are reasons for believing that the ice will never reach New York City, that it will never again extend into the Great Lakes region as it did in Valders time, and that each succeeding advance will be less widespread than the one before it. Every glacial invasion leaves the elevation of the land lower than it was before. We need only look at the deeply scoured cirques and U-valleys and the residual horn peaks to be impressed by the amount of down-cutting. Some ranges, after one or two major glacial episodes, consist only of scattered horn peaks. No longer do they have extensive upland areas on which glacier-making snow can pile up. In succeeding cool periods lowering of the snowline, except on those ranges which keep on growing in height faster than erosion cuts them down, will produce less and less ice. Finally, the world will return again to the balmy days of the early Cenozoic—perhaps even if the Poles remain in their present positions.

But this we can't expect for another 100,000 or more years, and the condition of man then, should he still be around, is impossible to predict. Certainly, many civilizations will have risen and fallen before then. Man doesn't know what his fate will be fifty years hence. Through the best leaders he can put in office now, he is hardly capable of determining his future from one year to the next.

There is also a possibility that a major ice invasion would have less effect upon the human population than some of the operations which man himself is presently conducting. You could get people to argue on both sides of the question: "Would a glacier invasion of New England have as much effect on the United States as the ripping and slashing now being done to the face of the land to make room for the network of multiple-lane highways?" It's a good question, but the argument, if applied to Canada, might be overwhelmingly one-sided.

Perhaps man can do something about the weather and climate and thus be able to exercise some control over the world's store of ice. If complaints about the weather and climate are serious, perhaps a majority of people would rather change the climate than adjust to it.

Scientists need to know much more about the consequences before they undertake major or even minor experiments on changing weather and climate. Just whom would such changes favor? Look at the results already obtained by minor attempts to tinker with the weather.

In Utah and Nevada nearly all the precipitation reaching the land is extracted by high mountains from moisture-bearing west winds—none too wet at best, because the Sierra Nevada has just about wrung them dry. Soon after 1946, the year when Vincent J. Schaefer and Irving Langmuir made snow by dropping dry ice into clouds over western Massachusetts, Nevada resorted to the dry-ice treatment to produce snow for ski meets. Utah, which had already made a big thing out of ski resorts, immediately threatened to go to the Supreme Court to prevent Nevada from milking snow from Utah-bound clouds. New York's cloud-seeding operations over its watersheds were brought under the fire of Boston, whose water-supply people feared that such artificially induced rain would rob their own watershed.

At the moment interest in rain-making has subsided from its peak in 1952 when fifteen per cent of the total land area of the United States was under contract to the rain-makers. The fact remains, however, that under certain conditions rain and snow can be induced by seeding clouds with dry ice or silver iodide crystals. But, too, we need to know much more about how Nature makes precipitation before we can get accurately controlled results. Silver iodide crystals, for example, can be used to prevent as well as create precipitation. Experiments in dispersing rain with silver iodide crystals have been made on the west coast of Norway in an attempt to keep rain from falling until moisture-bearing winds could reach mountains farther inland where more rain would be advantageous, especially to the many hydroelectric plants located there. To date, it's been well-nigh impossible to determine the critical amount of silver iodide which will either cause or prevent precipitation.

But these are all minor operations. What might happen if large-scale weather (and thus climate) changes are attempted? Perhaps the world's glaciers can be controlled in this way! A number of schemes have already been proposed and there will be others. Some relatively small structures might actually be able to make rather significant alterations in world climate.

A dam across the outlet of the Mediterranean at Gibraltar, which has appealed to some engineers as a possible source of hydroelectric power, might eventually make the Atlantic less salty by preventing the deep current of very salty water from passing out of the Mediterranean into the Atlantic. It has been postulated that this would put a stop to cold water sinking near the Arctic and thus would cause changes in water and wind circulation that would affect the climate of the whole world. But, as oceanographer Henry Stommel wrote in the July 1958 *Scientific American,* one can construct from this scheme two equally plausible arguments, one holding that the world would grow colder, the other that it would grow warmer.

A number of people at various times have advocated the construction of a dam across Bering Strait as a means of warming up the Arctic. But the mere presence of the dam, to Ewing and Donn's way of thinking, would cause the Arctic to be even more enclosed and thus colder than it is now; so the Alaskan and Siberian shores of the Arctic Ocean would become more, not less, frigid.

A Russian engineer proposed that pumps be installed at the dam to pump cold Arctic water over the barrier into Bering Sea, supposedly in the belief that this outflow of cold water would suck greater volumes of warmer Gulf Stream water into the other side of the Arctic Ocean, eventually through the pumps and out into the Pacific. The pack ice and the permafrost, according to this theory, would melt away and vast new lands would be opened to agriculture. Obviously the proponents of this idea do not subscribe to the Ewing-Donn theory, and they also visualize pumps of considerably larger size than most people, including pump-makers, have dreamed about. R. A. McCormick of the U.S. Weather Bureau has calculated that at least 100 years of pumping, as visualized by the Russians, would be required to melt the ice in the Arctic Ocean. But, as in the case of a Gibraltar dam, until we know far more about what Nature is doing now, no one really knows what the results of such a scheme might be.

A man long associated with meteorological research, Dr. H. Wexler of the U.S. Weather Bureau, has advanced the possibility of reducing the return of infrared radiation to space as a means of warming the Earth's atmosphere. He suggests that this might be done by the creation of a huge ice cloud. That such a cloud would decrease surface cooling, he maintains, has been demonstrated by the ice fogs that form at very low temperatures when sources of moisture are available, such as where there are many chimneys or steam vents or at openings in ice covering bodies of water. They have even been formed over herds of caribou and other animals. Since we are in the atomic age Dr. Wexler says:

> The cheapest and most effective way of producing an ice cloud would be by application of nuclear energy. Let us imagine the explosion of ten really "clean" hydrogen bombs, of 10 megatons each, at optimum depth in the Arctic Ocean to produce steam, which would then gush into the atmosphere, condense into water droplets, and freeze.*

Of course, the bombs would have to be properly spaced so that winds would spread the ice particles all over the Arctic Ocean but not beyond it. And, too, the great bulk of the steam would have to be converted into ice particles of a size which would remain in the air for the longest time and be most effective in sealing off the radiation from the surface. According to Dr. Wexler, if everything worked out all right, this scheme might cause the Arctic pack to disappear in less than ten years, but, like Ewing and Donn, he believes that this would cause increased glacier growth and bring on a new ice age.

Like other authorities in the fields of meteorology and climatology, Dr. Wexler urges that when serious proposals for weather modification are made, all available knowledge be put to use ". . . in predicting the results so as to avoid the unhappy situation of the cure being worse than the ailment."

Warming up Hudson Bay by atomic-powered heaters is another elaborate scheme that has been proposed for altering the climate. The proponents hold that winter Arctic winds blowing southward over the unfrozen waters of the Bay would lose much of their cold. Thus southern Canada and the northern

* *Science,* Vol. CXXVIII, No. 3,331 (October 31, 1958), p. 1061.

states would have a much milder climate. But is this really what would happen? George H. T. Kimble in his entertaining and informative book, *Our American Weather,* says:

Assuming that the Bay could be heated up (and it is nine times the size of Alabama to begin with), what would follow? One possibility seems to have been given little attention, and it is this. As the cold air traveled southward across the open waters of the Bay, it would not only be warmed up, it would also absorb a great deal of moisture vapor, for the capacity of cold, dry air for water vapor increases rapidly with the temperature. (Thus air at 32°F. can hold about twice as much moisture as air at 10°F., and about four times as much as air at 0°F.) On reaching the height of land to the south of the Bay, part of this newly acquired load of moisture would be discharged in the form of snow, for not even the superoptimists believe that such a device could warm up the whole Bay to the point where the winter precipitation would all occur as rain. If the snowfall were increased by, say, 20 to 30 inches, it is conceivable that the annual deposit of snow would be greater than the annual loss by melting and evaporation. Were this to happen, then a new ice age would be slowly, but surely, initiated—the very last thing the sponsors of the suggestion have in mind.

All in all, there is something to be said for doing nothing much about the weather.*

This is just by way of emphasizing how delicate the balance may be between an icy and an iceless world.

There is no doubt that scientists will make a lot of progress during the next few decades in weather modification, at least on a local scale. It will almost certainly be possible to reduce drought damage by increasing precipitation when and where it is most needed and by desired amounts. Frost damage to citrus crops by that time may be a thing of the past. It may even be possible to weaken the strength of hurricanes and typhoons or deflect them into paths where they won't be as destructive.

But when it comes to the world's load of ice, what can we predict? Maybe we will control the climate to hold the ice where it is now. Some people would be favored if the ice were eradicated, but a lot of others would have an insurmountable water problem on their hands. Unless we can level the mountains, the human race will just have to expect to be pushed around once in a while by the World of Ice.

BIBLIOGRAPHY

OBSERVATION and study during many years of field work and the teaching of geology to college students have gone into the writing of this book. This has involved the reading of countless articles and books about ice—many hundreds about glaciers alone. Obviously it would be pointless, even impossible, to tabulate all of these publications which have contributed so much.

At the beginning of the following list are several books which the general reader may consult if he desires further, more detailed information. The remainder of the references, listed chapter by chapter, though they be but a few of those which have been consulted in writing this book, have been helpful in its preparation.

About the Pleistocene

Charlesworth, J. K.: *The Quarternary Era with Special Reference to Its Glaciation.* In two volumes. London: Edward Arnold, Ltd.; 1957. An exhaustive work on all phases of the Pleistocene Epoch. Most suitable as a reference work.

Flint, R. F.: *Glacial and Pleistocene Geology.* New York: John Wiley and Sons; 1957. A comprehensive and authoritative work designed primarily as a textbook and reference, but highly readable.

Zeuner, F. E.: *The Pleistocene Period.* London: Hutchinson and Co., Ltd.; 1959. A detailed account of chronology, environments, and faunal evolution primarily for serious students of the Pleistocene.

About Glaciers

Matthes, F. E.: "Glaciers." Chapter v in *Hydrology* (*Physics of the Earth,* Vol. IX). New York: McGraw-Hill Book Co.; 1942. A lucid and brief (66 pages) article dealing with the origin, structure, motion, and variations of glaciers.

Sharp, R. P.: *Glaciers*. Eugene, Ore.: The University of Oregon Press; 1960. A brief and excellent account in which the technical approach is made easily understandable for the general reader.

About Climatic Change

Brooks, C. E. P.: *Climate through the Ages*. New York: McGraw-Hill Book Co.; 1949. A comprehensive treatise dealing with climate and its causes and effects throughout all of geologic time.
Shapley, Harlow (ed.): *Climatic Change*. Cambridge: Harvard University Press; 1953. Twenty-two distinguished scientists discuss as many aspects of climatic change.

Chapters 1 and 2

Field, W. O.: *Geographic Study of Mountain Glaciation, Part I*. Contract No. DA 19-129-QM-409. U.S. Army Quartermaster Research and Engineering Center, Natick, Mass.; 1958.
Muller, E. H., and Coulter, H. W.: "Incipient Glacier Development within Katmai Caldera, Alaska." *Journal of Glaciology*, Vol. III, No. 21 (March 1957), pp. 13–17.
U.S. Weather Bureau: "General Summary of Weather Conditions." *Climatological Data, National Summary, United States Department of Commerce*, Vol. VII, No. 13 (1956), compiled by L. H. Seamon.
Visher, S. S.: *Climatic Atlas of the United States*. Cambridge: Harvard University Press; 1954.
Williams, Howel: *The Geology of Crater Lake National Park, Oregon*. Washington, D.C.: Carnegie Institution; 1942.

Chapters 3 and 4

Beatty, M. E.: "Mountain Sheep Found in Lyell Glacier." *Yosemite Nature Notes*, Vol. XII, No. 12 (December 1933), pp. 110–12.
Desio, Ardito: "An Exceptional Glacier Advance in the Karakoram-Ladakh Region." *Journal of Glaciology*, Vol. II, No. 16 (October 1954), pp. 383–5.
Gutenberg, B., Buwalda, J. P., and Sharp, R. P.: "Seismic Explorations on the Floor of Yosemite Valley, California." *Geological Society of America Bulletin*, Vol. LXVII (1956), pp. 1051–78.
Longman, William: "Modern Mountaineering and the History of the Alpine Club." *The Alpine Journal* (1878), Supplement to Vol. VIII (August 1876 to May 1878).
Miller, Don J.: "Giant Waves in Lituya Bay, Alaska." *United States Geological Survey Professional Paper* 354-C (1960), pp. 51–86.
Moffit, F. H.: "Geology of the Gerstle River District, Alaska, with a Report on the Black Rapids Glacier." *United States Geological Survey Bulletin* 926-B (1942), pp. 146–60.

Chapters 5 to 7

Field, W. O.: "Atlas of Mountain Glaciers in the Northern Hemisphere." Part 10 of *Geographic Study of Mountain Glaciation in the Northern Hemisphere.* Technical Report EP-92; Contract No. DA 19-129-QM-409. U.S. Army Quartermaster Research and Engineering Center, Natick, Mass.; 1958.

Mason, Kenneth: "The Study of Threatening Glaciers." *Geographical Journal,* Vol. LXXXV, No. 1 (1935), pp. 24-41.

Morrison, C. C.: "Glaciers and Human Activities." Chapter i, Part 9 in *Geographic Study of Mountain Glaciation in the Northern Hemisphere.* Contract No. DA 19-129-QM-409. U.S. Army Quartermaster Research and Engineering Center, Natick, Mass.; 1958.

Nichols, R. L., and Miller, M. M.: "The Moreno Glacier, Lago Argentino, Patagonia." *Journal of Glaciology,* Vol. II (1952), pp. 41-6.

Nielsen, L. E.: "The Valdez and Klutina Glaciers, Alaska." *Appalachia,* Vol. XXXIII, No. 1 (June 1960), pp. 31-6.

Schrader, F. C.: "A Reconnaissance of a Part of Prince William Sound and the Copper River District, Alaska, in 1898." In *Twentieth Annual Report, United States Geological Survey,* Vol. VII (1899), pp. 347-69.

Stone, Kirk: *Alaskan Ice-dammed Lakes.* Final Report to Arctic Institute of North America on Project ONR 67. Madison, Wisc.; 1955.

Thorarinsson, Sigurdur: "The Thousand Years Struggle against Ice and Fire." *Museum of Natural History, Department of Geology and Geography, Miscellaneous Papers,* No. 14. Reykjavik; 1956.

Chapters 8 and 9

Bentley, C. R., Crary, A. P., Ostenso, N. A., and Thiel, E. C.: "Structure of West Antarctica." *Science,* Vol. CXXXI, No. 3394 (January 15, 1960), pp. 131-6.

Carder, D. J.: "Level Divergences, Seismic Activity, and Reservoir Loading in the Lake Mead Area, Nevada and Arizona." *Transactions, American Geophysical Union,* Vol. XXIX, No. 6 (December 1948), pp. 767-71.

Cook, John: "An Electrical Crevasse Detector." *Geophysics,* Vol. XXI, No. 4 (October 1956), pp. 1055-70.

Hydrographic Office, U.S. Navy: "Ice Atlas of the Northern Hemisphere." *H. O. Publication,* No. 550. Washington, D.C.; 1946.

National Academy of Sciences: *IGY Bulletin,* No. 23: "Antarctic Snow Stratigraphy." *Transactions, American Geophysical Union,* Vol. XL, No. 2 (May 1959), pp. 181-4.

Odishaw, Hugh: "International Geophysical Year—A Report on the United States Program." *Science,* Vol. CXXVII, No. 3290 (January 17, 1958), pp. 123-4.

Patenaude, R. W., Marshall, E. W., and Gow, A.: "Deep Core Drilling in Ice, Byrd Station, Antarctica." *United States Army Snow, Ice, and*

Permafrost Research Establishment, Technical Report, No. 60 (July 1959).

Ragle, R. H., Hansen, B. L., Gow, A., and Patenaude, R. W.: "Deep Core Drilling in the Ross Ice Shelf, Little America V, Antarctica." *United States Army Snow, Ice, and Permafrost Research Establishment, Technical Report,* No. 70 (June 1960).

Smith, E. H.: "Recent Movements of North Atlantic Ice and a Proposed Coast Guard Expedition to the West Greenland Glaciers." *Transactions, American Geophysical Union,* Vol. XXI (1940), pp. 668–71.

Smith, P. M.: "An Electrical Crevasse Detector." *Journal of Glaciology,* Vol. III, No. 23 (1958), pp. 224–5.

Chapter 10

Armstrong, Terence: *The Russians in the Arctic.* Fairlawn, N.J.: Essential Books; 1958.

Herdman, H. F. P.: "The Antarctic Pack Ice." *Journal of Glaciology,* Vol. I, No. 4 (October 1948), pp. 156–63.

Hydrographic Office, U.S. Navy: "Oceanographic Atlas of the Polar Seas, Part I, Antarctic." *H. O. Publication,* No. 705. Washington, D.C.; 1957.

———: "Oceanographic Atlas of the Polar Seas, Part II, Arctic." *H. O. Publication,* No. 705. Washington, D.C.; 1958.

Nansen, Fridtjof: *Farthest North,* Vols. I and II. New York: Harper and Brothers; 1898.

Papanin, Ivan: *Life on an Ice Floe.* New York: Julian Messner; 1939.

Shackleton, Sir Ernest: *South!* New York: The Macmillan Co.; 1920.

Stefansson, Vilhjalmur: *The Friendly Arctic.* New York: The Macmillan Co.; 1939.

Chapter 11

Crary, A. P.: "Arctic Ice Island and Ice Shelf Studies, Part II." *Arctic,* Vol. XIII, No. 1 (March 1960), pp. 32–50.

———: "Bathymetric Chart of the Arctic Ocean along the Route of T-3, April 1952 to October 1953." *Geological Society of America Bulletin,* Vol. LXV (1954), pp. 709–12.

Debenham, Frank: "The Ice Islands of the Arctic: A Hypothesis." *Geographical Review,* Vol. XLIV, No. 4 (1954), pp. 495–507.

Hunkins, K. L., Ewing, M., Heezen, B. C., and Menzies, R. J.: "Biological and Geological Observations on the First Photographs of the Arctic Ocean Deep-sea Floor." *Limnology and Oceanography,* Vol. V, No. 2 (April 1960), pp. 154–61.

IGY World Data Center A: Glaciology: American Geographical Society: "Navy Establishes New Ice Island Research Station." *Glaciological Notes,* No. 7 (July 1961), pp. 6–9.

Koenig, L. S., Greenaway, K. R., Dunbar, M., and Hattersley-Smith, G.: "Arctic Ice Islands." *Arctic,* Vol. V, No. 2 (July 1952), pp. 65–103.

Polunin, Nicholas: "Attempted Dendrochronological Dating of the Ice Island T-3." *Science,* Vol. cxxii, No. 3181 (December 16, 1955), pp. 1184–6.

Rodahl, Kaare: "Ice Islands in the Arctic." *Scientific American,* Vol. cxci, No. 6 (December 1954), p. 41.

Stefansson, Vilhjalmur: See Chapter 10.

Webster, Clifford: "The Soviet Expedition to the Central Arctic, 1954." *Arctic,* Vol. vii, No. 2 (1954), pp. 59–80.

Chapter 12

Gurney, A. B.: "Grasshopper Glacier of Montana and Its Relation to Long-distance Flights of Grasshoppers." *Smithsonian Institution Annual Report* (1952), pp. 305–26.

Milne, Lorus, and Milne, Margery: "Temperature and Life." *Scientific American,* Vol. clxxx, No. 2 (February 1949), pp. 46–9.

Nobles, L. H.: "Glaciological Investigations, Nunatarssuaq Ice Ramp, Northwestern Greenland." *United States Army Snow, Ice, and Permafrost Technical Report,* No. 66 (May 1960).

Péwé, T. L.: "Mummified Seal Carcasses in the McMurdo Sound Region, Antarctica." *Science,* Vol. cxxx, No. 3377 (September 18, 1959), p. 716.

Rivolier, Jean: "Polar Realm of the Emperors." *Natural History,* Vol. lxviii, No. 2 (February 1959), pp. 67–81.

Steinböck, Otto: "Die Tierwelt des Ewigschneegebietes." *Zeitschrift für Deutscher und österreichischer Alpenverein.* Vol. lxii (1931), pp. 29–46.

Stephenson, J.: *The Oligochaeta.* Oxford: Clarendon Press; 1930. Pp. 618–20.

Chapter 13

Anthony, H. E.: "Nature's Deep Freeze," *Natural History,* Vol. lviii, No. 7 (September 1949), pp. 296–301.

Black, R. E.: "Permafrost." Chapter xiv in *Applied Sedimentation* (ed. by Parker D. Trask). New York: John Wiley and Sons; 1950.

———: "Permafrost—A Review." *Geological Society of America Bulletin,* Vol. lxv (1954), pp. 839–56.

Cedarstrom, D. J., Johnson, P. M., and Subitsky, S.: "Occurrence and Development of Groundwater in Permafrost Regions." *United States Geological Survey Circular,* No. 275 (1953).

Herz, O. F.: "Frozen Mammoth in Siberia." In *Annual Report of the Smithsonian Institution* (Washington, D.C.; 1903), pp. 611–25.

Leffingwell, E. deK.: "The Canning River Region, Northern Alaska." *United States Geological Survey Professional Paper,* No. 109 (1919).

Muller, S. W.: "Permafrost or Permanently Frozen Ground and Related

Engineering Problems." *United States Geological Survey Special Report, Strategic Engineering Study 62.* Second Edition. Military Intelligence Division, Office of the Chief of Engineers, U.S. Army; 1945. Also lithographed by Edwards Brothers, Ann Arbor, Mich.; 1947.

Péwé, T. L.: "Permafrost and Its Effect on Life in the North." *Arctic Biology, Proceedings, 18th Biology Colloquium* (Oregon State College; 1957), pp. 12–25.

Taber, Stephen: "Perennially Frozen Ground in Alaska—Its Origin and History." *Geological Society of America Bulletin,* Vol. LIV (1943), pp. 1433–1548.

Tolmachoff, I. P.: "The Carcasses of the Mammoth and Rhinoceros Found in the Frozen Ground of Siberia." *Transactions of the American Philosophical Society,* Vol. XXIII (Washington D.C.; 1929).

Washburn, A. L.: "Classification of Patterned Ground and Review of Suggested Origins." *Geological Society of America Bulletin,* Vol. LXVII (1956), pp. 823–65.

Wimmler, N. L.: "Placer-mining Methods and Costs in Alaska." *United States Bureau of Mines Bulletin,* No. 259 (1927), pp. 37–40.

Chapter 14

Abbot, C. G., and Fowle, F. E.: "Volcanoes and Climate." *Smithsonian Miscellaneous Collections,* Vol. LX, No. 29 (1913), pp. 1–24.

Ahlmann, H. W.: *Glacier Variations and Climatic Fluctuations.* Bowman Memorial Lectures, Series Three. New York: American Geographical Society; 1953.

————: *Glaciological Research on the North Atlantic Coasts.* Royal Geographical Society Research Series, No. 1. London: Royal Geographical Society; 1948.

Field, W. O., Jr.: "Glacier Recession in Muir Inlet, Glacier Bay, Alaska." *Geographical Review,* Vol. XXXVII (1947), pp. 369–99.

Hovgaard, William: "The Norsemen in Greenland: Recent Discoveries at Herjolfsnes." *Geographical Review,* Vol. XV (1925), pp. 605–16.

Lawrence, D. B.: "Glacier Fluctuation for Six Centuries in Southeastern Alaska and Its Relation to Solar Activity." *Geographical Review,* Vol. XL (1950), pp. 191–223.

Marett, C.: "On the Retreat of the Swiss Glaciers; and On the Legal Rights to Glaciers and to the Soil Beneath Them." *The Alpine Journal* (1878), Vol. VIII (August 1876 to May 1878), pp. 275–8.

Rabot, Charles: "Récent travaux glaciaires dans les Alpes françaises." *La Géographie,* Vol. XXX (1915), pp. 257–68.

Reid, H. F.: "Glacier Bay and Its Glaciers." *United States Geological Survey, 16th Annual Report, 1894–95,* Part I (1896).

Russell, R. J.: "Climate through the Ages." In *Yearbook of Agriculture (Climate and Man).* Washington, D.C.: U.S. Government Printing Office; 1941.

Symons, G. J. (ed.): *Eruption of Krakatoa and Subsequent Phenomena. Report of the Krakatoa Committee of the Royal Society.* London: Trübner and Company; 1888.

Tarr, R. S., and Martin, L.: *Alaskan Glacier Studies.* Washington, D.C.: National Geographic Society; 1914.

Wexler, H.: "Meteorology in the International Geophysical Year." *Scientific Monthly,* Vol. LXXXIV, No. 3 (March 1957), pp. 141–5.

Chapter 15

American Journal of Science. Radiocarbon Supplement 1 (1959); *Supplement 2* (1960).

Antevs, Ernst: "Retreat of the Last Ice-Sheet in Eastern Canada." *Geological Survey of Canada, Memoir,* No. 146 (1948).

Broecker, W. S., Turekian, K. K., and Heezen, B.: "The Relation of Deep Sea Sedimentation Rates to Variations in Climate." *American Journal of Science,* Vol. CCLVI (1958), pp. 503–17.

Cooper, W. S.: "Terminology of Post-Valders Time." *Geological Society of America Bulletin,* Vol. LXIX (1958), pp. 941–5.

———: "The Problem of Glacier Bay, Alaska." *Geographical Review,* Vol. XXVII (1937), pp. 37–62.

Deevey, E. S., and Flint, R. F.: "Postglacial Hypsithermal Interval." *Science,* Vol. CXXV, No. 3240 (February 1, 1957), pp. 182–4.

Emiliani, C., Mayeda, T., and Selli, R.: "Paleotemperature Analysis of the Plio-Pleistocene Section at Le Castella, Calabria, Southern Italy." *Geological Society of America Bulletin,* Vol. LXXII (1961), p. 679–88.

Flint, R. F.: "Rates of Advance and Retreat of the Margin of the Late Wisconsin Ice Sheet." *American Journal of Science,* Vol. CCLIII (1955), pp. 249–55.

Koenigswald, G. H. R. von, Gentner, W., and Lippolt, H. J.: "Age of the Basalt Flow at Olduvai, East Africa." *Nature,* Vol. CLXXXII, No. 4804 (November 25, 1961), pp. 720–1.

Lawrence, D. B.: "Glaciers and Vegetation in Southeastern Alaska." *American Scientist,* Vol. XLVI, No. 2 (June 1958), pp. 89–122.

———: "Estimating Dates of Recent Glacier Advances and Recession Rates by Studying Tree Growth Layers." *Transactions, American Geophysical Union,* Vol. XXXI (1950), pp. 243–8.

———: See reference for Chapter 14.

Leakey, L. S. B.: "New Finds at Olduvai Gorge." *Nature,* Vol. CLXXXIX, No. 4765 (February 25, 1961), pp. 649–50.

———, Evernden, J. F., and Curtis, G. H.: "Age of Bed I, Olduvai Gorge, Tanganyika." *Nature,* Vol. CXCI, No. 4787 (July 29, 1961), pp. 478–9.

Libby, W. F.: "Radiocarbon Dating." *Science,* Vol. CXXXIII, No. 3453 (March 3, 1961), pp. 621–9.

———: *Radiocarbon Dating.* Second Edition. Chicago: University of Chicago Press; 1959.

Rosholt, J. N., Emiliani, C., Geiss, J., Koczy, F. F., and Wangersky, P. J.:

"Absolute Dating of Deep-sea Cores by the Pa^{231}/Th^{230} Method." *Journal of Geology*, Vol. LXIX, No. 2 (March 1961), pp. 162–85.
Wilson, L. R.: "Two Creeks Forest Bed, Manitowoc County, Wisconsin." *Wisconsin Academy of Science Transactions*, Vol. XXVII (1932), pp. 31–46.

Chapter 16

Cross, A. T., and Schemel, M. P.: *Geology and Economic Resources of the Ohio River Valley in West Virginia; Part I, Geology of the Ohio River in West Virginia.* West Virginia Geological Survey, Vol. XXII (1956).
Elson, J. A.: "Lake Agassiz and the Mankato-Valders Problem." *Science*, Vol. CXXVI, No. 3281 (November 15, 1957), pp. 999–1002.
Flint, R. F., and Brandtner, F.: "Climatic Changes Since the Last Interglacial." *American Journal of Science*, Vol. CCLIX (1961), pp. 321–8.
Geological Society of America: *Glacial Map of the United States East of the Rocky Mountains.* New York; 1959.
———: *Glacial Map of North America.* New York; 1945.
Godwin, H.: *The History of the British Flora.* Cambridge, England: Cambridge University Press; 1956.
Hopkins, D. M.: "Cenozoic History of the Bering Land Bridge." *Science*, Vol. CXXIX, No. 3362 (June 5, 1959), pp. 1519–27.
Hough, J. L.: *Geology of the Great Lakes.* Urbana, Ill.: University of Illinois Press; 1958.
Hustich, Ilmari: "The Boreal Limits of Conifers." *Arctic*, Vol. VI, No. 2 (July 1953), pp. 149–62.
Lee, Hulbert: "Late Glacial and Postglacial Hudson Bay Sea Episode." *Science*, Vol. CXXXI, No. 3413 (May 27, 1960), p. 1609.
Smeds, Helmer: "The Replot Skerry Guard: Emerging Islands in the Northern Baltic." *Geographical Review*, Vol. XL (1950), pp. 103–33.

Chapter 17

Cox, A., and Doell, R. R.: "Review of Paleomagnetism." *Geological Society of America Bulletin*, Vol. LXXI (1960), pp. 654–768.
Droessler, E. G.: "The Present Status and Promise of Weather Modification." *Transactions, American Geophysical Union*, Vol. XLI, No. 1 (March 1960), pp. 26–31.
Ewing, M., and Donn, W. L.: "A Theory of Ice Ages." *Science*, Vol. CXXIII, No. 3207 (June 15, 1956), pp. 1061–6.
———: "A Theory of Ice Ages II." *Science*, Vol. CXXVII, No. 3301 (May 16, 1958), pp. 1159–62.
Stommel, Henry: "The Circulation of the Abyss." *Scientific American*, Vol. CIC, No. 1 (July 1958), p. 85.
Wexler, H.: "Modifying Weather on a Large Scale." *Science*, Vol. CXXVIII, No. 3331 (October 31, 1958), pp. 1059–63.

GLOSSARY

TECHNICAL TERMS have been used sparingly in the book and each one when it first appears has been defined. But because it might be inconvenient to try to find the definition when the word is encountered later, this glossary is included. A few words, though they have not been used in the book, appear in this list because you may encounter them from time to time in other reading.

ABLATION. The removal of ice from a glacier by melting and evaporation.

ACTIVE LAYER. This is the name of the layer of ground above the permafrost which freezes in winter and thaws in summer. In the Far North it extends from the surface down to the top of the permafrost. Farther south in many places it extends only part way down to permafrost, so that there always is in such places a permanently unfrozen layer between the base of the active layer and the top of the permafrost.

AFTONIAN. The name of the earliest major interglacial stage of the Pleistocene Epoch. It followed the Nebraskan and preceded the Kansan glacial stages. In Western Europe the equivalent stage is known as the GÜNZ-MINDEL INTERGLACIAL.

ANTARCTIC. The region around the South Pole which includes the continent of Antarctica and the seas extending several hundred miles northward to the ANTARCTIC CONVERGENCE, the northern limit of cold Antarctic waters.

ARCTIC. Means different things to different people, but in the most general sense it comprises the area of the Arctic Ocean and a narrow but irregular band of land surrounding it. More technically, Arctic lands are those in which the mean temperature of the warmest month is below 50°F. The location of this isotherm corresponds roughly with the northern limit of trees. The SUBARCTIC includes those lands where the mean temperature is not higher than 50°F. for more than four months of the year. Some regard as Subarctic all those lands between the southern limit of the Arctic and the southernmost known limits of permafrost. At sea the Arctic includes all areas where Arctic water is at the surface. Arctic water originates in the Arctic Ocean and is much colder and has much lower salinity than non-Arctic water. According to these definitions the Arctic embraces a narrow strip of coastal Alaska north of the mouth of the Yukon, the Canadian Arctic islands, the Northwest Territories, and northern Quebec. It includes all of Greenland, most of Iceland, the extreme northern tip of Norway, and a strip averaging 300 miles wide along the northern edge of Siberia.

ARÊTE. A narrow, serrate ridge with high and very precipitous sides which separates the heads of opposing valleys presently or formerly occupied by glaciers. As glaciers erode more deeply into the arête, it narrows and eventually may be cut through in a number of places. After the glaciers disappear these low places become COLS; the intervening remnants of the arête are HORNS.

AVALANCHE. A sliding mass of snow moving rapidly down a precipitous mountain slope. Avalanches may consist of ice as well as snow, and masses of rocks broken loose on the way down. Some mountain glaciers are nourished mainly by avalanches.

BEDROCK. The solid rock present everywhere on Earth beneath the cover of soil and the sediments on the ocean floor. On slopes too steep for soil and weathered rock debris to accumulate and in quarries and other excavations bedrock is exposed.

BERGSCHRUND. This is the name of a crevasse or group of closely spaced crevasses at the head of a glacier where movement of the glacier pulls the ice away from the mountain wall (cirque headwall) or away from masses of ice still adhering to the wall.

CALVING. The breaking away of blocks of ice, usually along crevasses, from the end of a glacier. The most spectacular calving occurs at the ends of tidewater glaciers, where the calved blocks immediately become ICEBERGS.

CIRQUE. The large amphitheater-like head of a formerly glaciated valley. Its head (the HEADWALL) and sides, very precipitous and frequently nearly vertical, were carved and quarried by the former glacier ice.

COL. See ARÊTE.

CONTINENTAL SHELF. The sea-covered, gently sloping marginal zone of a continent. Around most continents the average depth of the sea on the outer edge of the shelves (where they join the more steeply sloping CONTINENTAL SLOPE) is about 500 feet, except around Greenland and Antarctica where the weight of the ice sheets depresses the shelves to much greater depth.

CONTINENTAL SLOPE. The sloping border of a continent between the outer edge of the continental shelf and the ocean abyss.

COULEE. In the tier of states from North Dakota to Washington the term is applied to any steep-sided gulch or stream channel. Some of the largest coulees, including Grand Coulee, are in eastern Washington and were carved by former glacier melt-water streams.

CREVASSES. Open cracks or fractures in glaciers. They may be several yards wide at the top and 200 feet deep.

DENDROCHRONOLOGY. The science of determining time by counting the annual rings in trees and correlating the rings from one tree to another. Many of the glacier fluctuations and climatic changes for the past 3,000 or 4,000 years have been reconstructed in this way.

DRIFT (GLACIAL DRIFT). Rock debris carried by glaciers and deposited either by the ice itself or by streams of melt water flowing from the glaciers.

DRUMLIN. An elongated hill of glacial drift streamlined by the passage of the glacier over it. A drumlin's long axis is parallel to the direction of flow of the ice and the end facing in the direction whence the ice came is the steeper of the two.

ERRATIC. A glacier-transported rock fragment resting on bedrock unlike that from which the fragment was derived.

ESKER. A low, narrow ridge—often winding—of crudely stratified sand and gravel deposited in a tunnel within a glacier.

FAST ICE. Sea ice which freezes out from shore and remains attached to the land.

FAULT. A fracture or zone of closely spaced fractures in bedrock along which there has been displacement (movement of rock on one or both sides of the fracture and parallel to it). Faults also develop in glaciers.

FIORD (FJORD). A glacier-carved valley with its lower end inundated by the sea.

FIRN. Granular snow one year or more old. It is permeable to air and water and has a density greater than 0.55. The FIRN AREA is the accumulation zone of a glacier. NÉVÉ is equivalent to firn.

FIRN LINE (FIRN LIMIT). The lower edge of the snow blanket on a glacier in late summer just before the snow blanket begins its winter expansion. It marks the boundary between the zone of accumulation and the zone of wastage on the glacier.

FLOE. A large slab of sea ice—part of the PACK ICE—which is normally composed of many smaller pieces that have frozen together. Scientific stations have been established on floes measuring several miles across.

FLOODPLAIN. The relatively smooth lower part of some valleys over which the stream periodically floods and deposits a thin layer of sediment. The lower Nile Valley is a classic example.

FOLIATION. Closely spaced layering in a glacier made by deformation of the ice, probably involving some recrystallization, as a result of flow. On the surface of the ice foliation resembles banding. Foliation, probably caused in the same way, is a feature of metamorphic rocks and originated when the rocks were under great pressure deep below the surface.

FORAMINIFERA. The name of a large and diverse group of single-celled shelled animals, which individually are known as Foraminifers or Forams. They have lived in abundance in the seas for millions of years, and by determining the ratio of oxygen–18 to oxygen–16 in their shells which have collected in the ooze on the sea floor, scientists have been able to ascertain the temperature of the seas when these animals lived.

GLACIAL DRIFT. See DRIFT.

GLACIAL GEOLOGY. The study of the origin and development of all features resulting from the action of glaciers.

GLACIAL LAKES. Lie in basins (depressions) created by direct action of glaciers. Such lakes include:

(1) *Rock basin lakes:* they fill basins gouged out of bedrock.

(2) *Cirque lakes:* rock basins in cirques.

(3) *Moraine lakes:* formed where debris dumped by a glacier has dammed a stream.

(4) *Kettle lakes:* lie in kettle holes, the depressions on moraines and outwash caused by collapse of the surface after blocks of buried ice melt away.

(5) *Ice-dammed lakes (proglacial lakes):* form against the ice where the glacier itself blocks a stream.

GLACIATION. See GLACIERIZATION.

GLACIER. A mass of moving (flowing) land ice derived from snow. The principal types of glaciers are:

(1) *Ice sheet:* a large sheetlike glacier in which the ice moves outward in all directions.

(2) *Continental glacier:* an ice sheet covering all or much of an entire continent. Today the only true example is the Antarctic ice sheet. In earlier periods of the Pleistocene Epoch there were others.

(3) *Icecap:* a small ice sheet, although the Greenland ice sheet is often called an icecap.

(4) *Valley glacier:* an ice stream confined to a valley and originating in one or more cirques.

(5) *Cirque glacier:* a small glacier confined to a cirque.

(6) *Mountain glacier:* a general term including valley and cirque glaciers.

(7) *Outlet glacier:* an ice stream draining an ice sheet, usually through a fiord.

(8) *Piedmont glacier:* the expanded terminal part of a valley or outlet glacier where it emerges from the mouth of a valley.

GLACIER ICE. A mass of interlocking ice crystals derived from snow. Although the mass may contain some trapped air it is relatively impermeable and has a density greater than 0.84 (compared with 1.0 for water).

GLACIERIZATION. A term used mostly by the British, it is the inundation of land by ice. According to this usage Antarctica and Greenland are being glacierized at the present time. The equivalent American term is GLACIATION which, as now generally used, means the covering of the land by glacier ice, as well as the alteration of the land surface by the ice resting on or passing over it. In this sense Greenland and Antarctica are being glaciated now; northern New England was glaciated some thousands of years ago.

GLACIOLOGY. In its narrowest sense means the study of existing glacial ice. The British Glaciological Society, however, holds the word to mean the study of ice in all its forms.

GRAVIMETER (GRAVITY METER). An instrument for measuring variations in the Earth's gravitational field.

GROUND ICE. Grains and masses of clear ice in permanently frozen ground.

GROUND MORAINE. See MORAINE.

GÜNZ. See NEBRASKAN.

HANGING VALLEY. A valley the floor of which is considerably higher than the valley into which it leads. They are common in glaciated mountain ranges and result from the failure of tributary glaciers to cut their valleys down as fast as do the larger glaciers in the main valleys.

HEADWALL. See CIRQUE.

HORN (HORN PEAK). A pyramidal peak the faces of which are the headwalls of three or more cirques.

HYPSITHERMAL. The name of the geologic time interval which extended from about 7,000 B.C. to 500 B.C. It is the long middle part of the period since the former large ice sheets withdrew from middle latitudes.

ICECAP. See GLACIER.

ICEFALL. A badly crevassed and broken section of a glacier where it flows down a very steep slope or plunges over a cliff.

ICE FIELD. A small mountain icecap.

ICE ISLAND. A large slab of ice, fifty to more than 150 feet thick and several square miles in extent, floating in the sea. Ice islands form by the breaking off of large sections from Arctic ice shelves.

ICE SHEET. See GLACIER.

ICE SHELF. A thick tabular mass of floating ice attached to land. Some ice shelves are the seaward extension of coalesced glaciers. Most, however, are nourished both by glaciers and by snow falling directly on the shelf.

ICE STREAM. A valley or outlet glacier.

IGNEOUS ROCK. Rock formed by the solidification of molten material either beneath or on the Earth's surface. Molten rock below the surface is called magma; when it flows out it becomes lava.

IGY. The abbreviation of International Geophysical Year, a great international scientific undertaking during 1957 and 1958 to improve our knowledge and understanding of the changes taking place in the solid Earth and in its enclosing blankets of water and air. It included studies and investigations in a great diversity of fields, including airglow and ionospheric physics, the aurora, cosmic rays, the Earth's magnetic and gravity fields and its volcanic activity, glaciology, meteorology and nuclear radiation, oceanography, rockets and satellites, and solar activity.

ILLINOIAN. The name of the third major glacial stage of the Pleistocene in North America. It is the equivalent of the RISS glacial stage in Western Europe.

INDICATOR. A glacier-transported rock which can be traced back to the outcrop of bedrock where the glacier picked it up. Strings or bands of indicators (INDICATOR FANS) have enabled geologists to determine the source and the direction of flow of former ice sheets.

INTERGLACIAL. A term designating the time intervals between major glacial advances of the Pleistocene.

ISOSTASY. A condition of approximate equilibrium in the outer portion of the Earth which causes light parts of the crust, whether they be mountain ranges or the continents themselves, to be counterbalanced by lower more dense parts. According to this concept the continental rock is less dense than the rock beneath ocean basins, and both these segments rest on a still more dense subcrust. When a load such as an ice sheet is added to a part of the crust, that part will sink until it is again in balance with the rock beneath and surrounding it. When the load is removed by melting, the crust will rise to its original position of equilibrium.

ISOTHERM. A line connecting points with the same mean temperature at a given time.

KAME. A term applied most frequently to mounds and conical shaped hills of sand and gravel deposited along the edge of a glacier by streams flowing from its surface or from beneath it. Kames are usually associated with moraines and may be parts of moraines.

KANSAN. The second great glacial stage of the Pleistocene in North America. The equivalent stage in Western Europe is the MINDEL.

KETTLE HOLES (KETTLES). Depressions, frequently water-filled, on moraines and outwash which were formed by the melting of buried chunks of glacier ice.

LEAD (pronounced LEED). A long narrow section of open water in the pack ice wide enough to give passage to boats. A lead usually starts as a crack through a floe. It may eventually attain a width of hundreds of yards and a length of several miles.

LOESS. A deposit of wind-transported silt and clay. It covers thousands of square miles in the central parts of the United States and Europe in a blanket in places fifty or more feet thick. Much loess originates from the blowing of soil from desert and semiarid regions, but a great deal

also has come from the fine sediments in the extensive plains of outwash associated with former large ice sheets.

MAMMOTH. An elephant with a hair-covered hide. It ranged throughout
northern North America and Eurasia during much of Pleistocene
time. Though it became extinct several thousand years ago we know
much about it from well-preserved frozen carcasses recovered from
frozen ground in Arctic regions.

MELT WATER. Water from the melting of ice and snow.

MINDEL. See KANSAN.

MORAINE. An accumulation of glacial drift (mostly till) deposited by a
glacier in sheets, mounds, ridges, and other forms. There are several
types of moraines:

Terminal (end) moraine: a ridge or connected string of ridges and
mounds deposited at the end of a glacier.

Lateral moraine: a ridge of debris on or along the edge of a valley
glacier. This material has fallen from or been scraped off the valley
sides.

Medial moraine: long ridges of debris on a glacier formed where two
lateral moraines come together at the junction of two valley glaciers. Usually part of a medial moraine lies beneath the ice in a
vertical sheet, squeezed between the two converging ice streams.

Ground moraine: the sheet of debris which glaciers, mainly ice
sheets, spread over the surface.

NEBRASKAN. The North American name for the oldest (first) of the major
glacial stages of the Pleistocene Epoch. Its equivalent in Western
Europe is the GÜNZ.

NEOTHERMAL. A name applied to the time interval embracing the last
10,000 to 11,000 years of geologic time. A more frequently used term
is RECENT.

NÉVÉ. See FIRN.

NUNATAK. A part of the land, usually a hill or peak, projecting through the
surface of a glacier.

OGIVES. Curved dark bands, convex in the down-glacier direction, that
form below icefalls on some glaciers.

OUTLET GLACIER. See GLACIER.

OUTWASH. Drift (layers of sand and gravel) carried from glaciers and deposited by melt-water streams.

OXYGEN ISOTOPES. The two forms of oxygen (oxygen–16 and oxygen–18)
present in water and ice. See FORAMINIFERA.

PACK ICE. A large area of floating sea ice consisting of pieces and floes held
closely together. In the Arctic during the summer the pack ice has
many open areas, both narrow leads and larger, irregularly shaped
areas of open water. In winter many of the open areas freeze shut,
and openings form mainly when storms rip the large floes apart. The
Arctic pack averages five to seven feet thick in summer, ten to twelve
in winter.

PALEOMAGNETISM. Magnetism induced in tiny mineral particles during the
geologic past by the Earth's magnetic field. The present orientation of
these magnetized particles, now enclosed within solid rock, yields
clues to the former wandering of the Earth's Poles.

PALYNOLOGY. The study of pollen and spores, and the individual who does
the studying is a PALYNOLOGIST. These are terms used by persons who
are not satisfied with the adequate terms "pollen analysis" and "pollen
analyst."

PATTERNED GROUND. Confined almost entirely to present or former areas
of permafrost or intensive frost action and marked by symmetrically
arranged stripes, polygons, nets, etc.

PERMAFROST (PERENNIALLY FROZEN GROUND). Ground, including bedrock,
soil, and many other materials, in which the temperature has been
continuously below freezing for at least two years.

PIEDMONT GLACIER. See GLACIER.

PLEISTOCENE. The latest epoch in geologic time. It is sometimes called
the Ice Age and includes the interval during which, because of
climatic fluctuations, large ice sheets repeatedly spread over the lands.
Its exact time span is not known but is generally regarded as about
1,000,000 years. Though some persons hold to the view that the
Pleistocene ended about 10,000 years ago, in this book it is regarded
as including the present.

PLUVIAL. The term is used to describe former periods of heavy rainfall in
previously dry regions while other areas were subjected to glaciation.
While northern North America was being glaciated, the southwestern
United States and Mexico experienced pronounced pluvial climates.
These were the times when Lake Bonneville and other extensive
bodies of water were present in now-dry regions.

POLYNYA. A Russian term for an area of open water surrounded by sea ice.
It is not linear like a lead, but is more equidimensional.

PRESSURE RIDGE. A long ridge on the surface of sea ice caused by horizontal
pressure.

RADIOCARBON DATING. The determination of the age of organic material by
the proportion of carbon–14 (radiocarbon) in the carbon it contains.
This method has been used to obtain reliable ages up to about 70,000
years.

REGIONAL SNOWLINE (SNOWLINE). The altitude above which more snow
accumulates than can be dissipated by melting and evaporation. Thus
it is the altitude above which glaciers form.

RISS. See ILLINOIAN.

SANGAMON. The name used in North America for the last major interglacial stage (between the Illinoian and Wisconsin glacial stages) of the
Pleistocene. Its European equivalent is the RISS-WÜRM interglacial.

SEA ICE. Ice formed on the surface of the sea by the freezing of sea water.

SEASONAL SNOWLINE. A temporary line or zone which at any time separates a snow-covered area from a snowless one. It rises and falls from

day to day and week to week but generally moves downward in early winter and upward in spring and summer, finally disappearing to return again the following winter.

SEISMIC SOUNDING. A method of determining the thickness of glaciers and other ice masses and the depths of various types of rock below the surface. It is done by the reflection of elastic waves (seismic waves) generated by setting off explosive charges.

SERAC. A jagged pinnacle of ice on the surface of a glacier, usually formed by the intersection of several crevasses.

SIPRE. The U.S. Army's Snow, Ice, and Permafrost Research Establishment which for several years had headquarters at Wilmette, Illinois. In 1961 it was replaced by the Army's Cold Regions Research and Engineering Laboratory (CRREL) at Hanover, New Hampshire.

SNOW BRIDGE. An arch of snow across a crevasse.

SNOW FIELD. A large patch of snow which persists from year to year but never becomes thick enough to form a glacier.

SNOWLINE. See REGIONAL SNOWLINE.

SOLAR RADIATION. Radiation (mostly in the short-wave part of the spectrum) received directly from the sun.

STRIATIONS (STRIAE). Scratches and grooves on bedrock and rock fragments made by the scraping and grinding action of rock fragments held in the base of a glacier.

SUBARCTIC. See ARCTIC.

SUNSPOTS. Great electrical and magnetic storms (or perhaps areas of calm) on the sun which appear as dark spots because they are not as hot as the surrounding surface. They vary in number but reach a maximum about every twenty-two years. They influence our weather and climate because the Earth's average temperature is higher when sunspots are at a minimum. For this reason sunspot activity is thought to be related to variations in glaciers.

TAIGA. Russian name for the cold, forest-covered region immediately south of the tundra in North America and Eurasia.

TILL. The heterogeneous mixture of drift carried and deposited directly by glaciers.

TREELINE. The elevation on mountains above which trees are not present. It varies from range to range and even from one side of a mountain to the other. A similar treeline surrounds the North Polar regions and corresponds generally with the border between tundra and taiga.

TRIMLINE. The line marking the recent former extent of the edges of a glacier. Where the line occurs within a forest it is called a FOREST TRIMLINE and can be readily distinguished because the trees on one side of it are larger (and older) than those on the other side. Forest trimlines also mark the upper limits of giant waves along wooded shores.

TUNDRA. The vast treeless area of northern North America and Eurasia bordered on the north by the Arctic Ocean.

VALDERS. The 2,000-year-long glacial stage of the Pleistocene culminating just short of 11,000 years ago in an advance of the North American ice sheet from southern Canada across the Great Lakes States to the present sites of Milwaukee and Buffalo.

VARVE. A pair of contrasting layers of sediment deposited in one year's time. They are very pronounced in lakes receiving glacier melt water. The summer layer is light and the winter one dark. The counting and correlating of varves has revealed how long a time was required for the last ice sheet to disappear from northern Europe.

WISCONSIN. The North American name for the last major glacial stage of the Pleistocene Epoch. Its European equivalent is the WÜRM. The length of the WISCONSIN-WÜRM stage was about 70,000 years.

WÜRM. See WISCONSIN.

YARMOUTH is the second major warm interglacial stage of the Pleistocene. It followed the Kansan and preceded the Illinoian stages. Its European equivalent is the MINDEL-RISS interglacial.

INDEX

A NOTE ON THE TYPE

THE TEXT of this book was set on the Linotype in a new face called PRIMER, designed by RUDOLPH RUZICKA, earlier responsible for the design of Fairfield and Fairfield Medium, Linotype faces whose virtues have for some time now been accorded wide recognition. The complete range of sizes of Primer was first made available in 1954, although the pilot size of 12 point was ready as early as 1951. The design of the face makes general reference to Linotype Century (long a serviceable type, totally lacking in manner or frills of any kind) but brilliantly corrects the characterless quality of that face.

Composed, printed, and bound by
Kingsport Press, Inc., Kingsport, Tennessee.
Typography and binding design by
VINCENT TORRE

A NOTE ABOUT THE AUTHOR

JAMES LINDSAY DYSON was born in 1912, in Lancaster, Pennsylvania. He earned his B.S. at Lafayette College in 1933, his M.A. and Ph.D. at Cornell University in 1935 and 1938 respectively. After some years of teaching, at Cornell (1935–8) and Colgate (1938–41), the war took him into the armed forces where he saw active service in Australia, New Guinea, and Luzon, ending with the rank of Colonel. He was awarded the Legion of Merit in 1944. After the war, Mr. Dyson went to Hofstra College as Associate Professor (1946–7) and on to Lafayette College as full Professor and Head of the Department of Geology and Geography (1947 to the present). He has been a consulting geologist (since 1947); a geologist with the Pennsylvania Geological Survey (since 1952); a member of the Research Committee on Glaciers of the American Geophysical Union (1946–52); Chairman of the Mission 66 Committee of the American Geological Institute (1957–62); Chairman of the Geology Selection Committee on Fulbright Awards of the National Academy of Sciences–National Research Council (1960–1); President of the Pennsylvania Academy of Science (1961–2). Mr. Dyson has twice won Lafayette's Thomas L. Jones Award for Superior Teaching (1956, 1957), and has lectured widely on glaciers, geology, natural history. He lives in Easton, Pennsylvania, with his artist wife and two daughters.

January 1962